GCSE Electronics

Also by Tom Duncan

Physics for Today and Tomorrow

Science for Today and Tomorrow
    (with M A Atherton and D G Mackean)

Exploring Physics, Books 1 to 5

Electronics and Nuclear Physics

Advanced Physics: Materials and Mechanics

Advanced Physics: Fields, Waves and Atoms

Physics: A Textbook for Advanced Level Students

Adventures with Physics

Adventures with Electronics

Adventures with Microelectronics

Adventures with Digital Electronics

Success in Electronics

Success in Physics

Physics for the Caribbean
    (with Deniz Önaç)

GCSE Physics

Basic Skills: Electronics

GCSE Electronics

Tom Duncan

John Murray

© Tom Duncan 1989

First published 1989
by John Murray (Publishers) Ltd
50 Albemarle Street London W1X 4BD

Typeset by Chapterhouse, Formby
Printed and bound in Great Britain by
The Alden Press, Oxford

British Library Cataloguing in Publication Data

Duncan, Tom, *1922–*
  GCSE electronics
  1. Electronics – For schools
  I. Title
  537.5

ISBN 0-7195-4633-8

Preface

This book covers the material required for examinations in electronics set by the main GCSE examining groups. The 50 chapters are organized and treated so as to allow some flexibility in the order in which they are studied. Four aspects have received special attention:

◆ Electronics systems and the systems approach
◆ Electronics and society
◆ Applications of electronics
◆ Dangers of electricity and safety precautions.

The **Questions** (totalling 180) at the end of every chapter are intended to test basic knowledge and understanding. The **Additional questions** (totalling 70) after each group of related chapters are arranged in two levels: **'Core' level** (for all students for whom the material is relevant) and **'Further' level** (for those seeking higher grades). Answers are given to all questions, often with some explanation.

The **Check lists** of specific objectives should help students to monitor their progress and aid revision.

Practical work must play a major part in any course on electronics if the skills and abilities stated in the *National Criteria for Science and Technology* (i.e. observing, investigating, searching for patterns, interpreting, applying and communicating) are to be encouraged. This will generally take the form of
(i) investigations into the behaviour of systems, sub-systems and components
(ii) projects involving the design and construction of simple electronic systems.

Practical Electronics for GCSE by **Owen Bishop** is intended to complement this book by providing step-by-step practical work grouped in topics. The contents list refers to these at the appropriate point, so that theoretical knowledge and practical skills can be developed side-by-side.

Thanks are due to John Allen for his painstaking analysis of GCSE syllabus requirements and other helpful comments.

T.D.

Contents

Preface

Basic principles

Practical work*

Components

Meters, measurements and safety

Electronic systems and society

* See *Practical Electronics for GCSE* by Owen Bishop (Published by John Murray, 1989)

Digital sub-systems

Analogue sub-systems

Communication systems

Computers and microprocessors

Basic principles

1 Electric current

◆ Circuit symbols

Electronic circuits consist of *components* (parts) such as lamps, resistors and transistors connected to an *electrical supply*, e.g. a battery. The connnections are wire or strips of a good *electrical conductor* such as copper. The connections and components must make a *complete path*, i.e. a circuit.

Circuits are represented by diagrams in which each part is shown by a *symbol*. Some are given in Fig. 1.1.

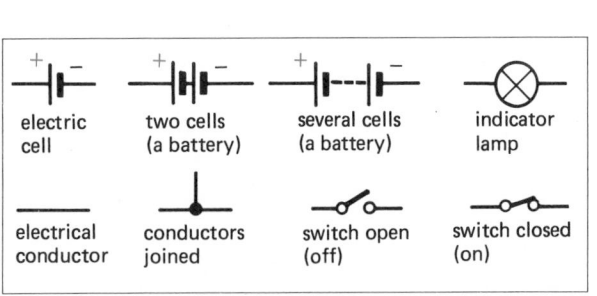

Fig. 1.1

◆ Current

(a) What is it? An atom consists of a tiny core or *nucleus* with a positive (+) electric charge, surrounded by *electrons* which have an equal negative (−) charge, Fig. 1.2. In a conductor, some electrons are loosely

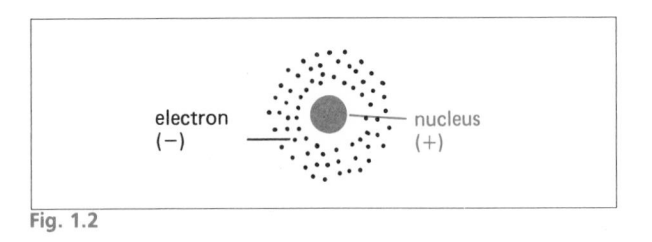

Fig. 1.2

attached to their atoms. When the conductor is part of a circuit connected to a battery, the battery forces these electrons to move through the conductor from its negative (−) terminal towards its positive (+) terminal, Fig. 1.3. This *flow of electrons* is an electric current.

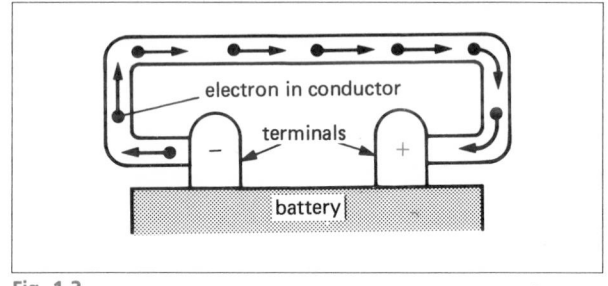

Fig. 1.3

(b) Direction. Before the electron was discovered, scientists thought of current as positive charges moving from a battery's + terminal round the circuit to its — terminal. So arrows on circuit diagrams show the direction of what is called the *conventional current*, Fig. 1.4. It is the direction in which + charges would move.

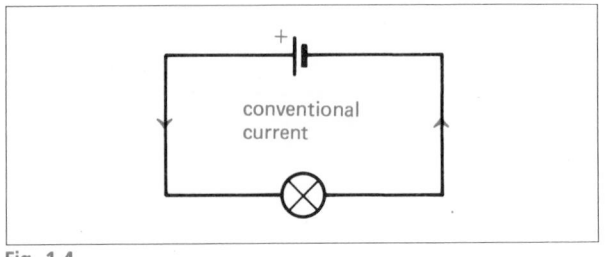

Fig. 1.4

(c) Effects. The presence of current in a conductor can be detected by its *heating* effect (i.e. it warms the conductor) and by its *magnetic* effect (i.e. a nearby compass is deflected).

1

◆ The ampere and ammeters

Current (symbol I) is measured in amperes (shortened to A) by an *ammeter*. The current through a large flash-lamp bulb is about 0.5 A and through a car headlamp 3 A to 4 A.

An ammeter is shown in Fig. 1.5a, b with its symbol. One terminal is marked + (or coloured red) and this is the one the conventional current must enter, that is, *it must lead to the + terminal of the battery*. Otherwise the pointer on the ammeter is deflected in the wrong direction and the ammeter may be damaged.

(b)

(a)

Fig. 1.5

Two smaller units of current used in electronics are the *milliampere* (mA) and the *microampere* (μA; pronounced mu A).

$$1 \text{ mA} = 1/1000 \text{ A or } 1000 \text{ mA} = 1 \text{ A}$$

$$1 \,\mu\text{A} = 1/1\,000\,000 \text{ A} = 1/1000 \text{ mA or}$$

$$1\,000\,000 \,\mu\text{A} = 1 \text{ A and } 1000 \,\mu\text{A} = 1 \text{ mA}$$

◆ Current is not used up

To measure a current, the circuit has to be broken and the ammeter connected in the gap.

(a) Series circuit. In Fig. 1.6 lamps L_1 and L_2 are in series, i.e. one after the other. The readings on ammeters (A₁), (A₂) and (A₃) are equal and show that the current is the *same* at all parts of the circuit.

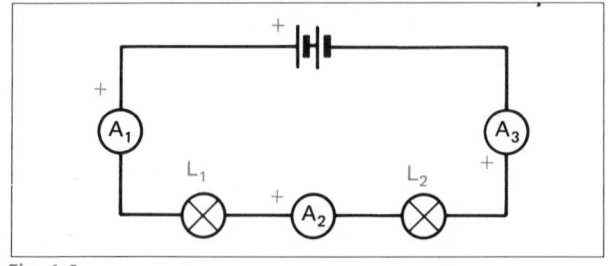

Fig. 1.6

(b) Parallel circuit. In Fig. 1.7 L_1 and L_2 are in parallel, i.e. side by side, and there are alternative paths for the main current I which splits into I_1 and I_2. The readings on ammeters (A₁), (A₂) and (A₃) show that

$$I = I_1 + I_2$$

For example, if $I_1 = 0.1$ A and $I_2 = 0.3$ A then $I = 0.4$ A. In words, the *sum of the currents entering a junction*, such as X in Fig. 1.7, *equals the sum of the currents leaving it*. In neither circuit is current used up.

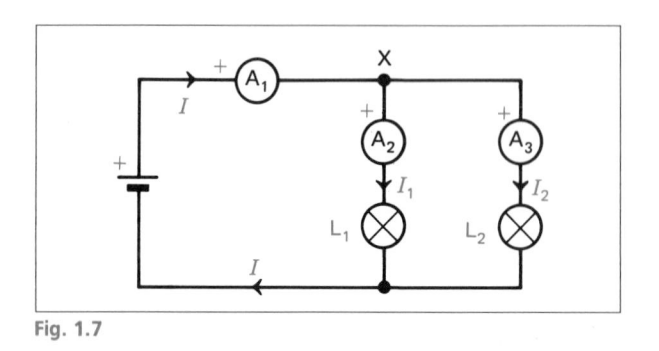

Fig. 1.7

◆ Conductors, insulators and semiconductors

The best *conductors* are the metals silver, copper and gold because they contain electrons that are free to move.

In *insulators* such as polythene and PVC (polyvinyl chloride) all electrons are firmly bound to their atoms and electron flow, i.e. current production, is difficult. However, *static electric charges* can be obtained on insulators. For example, when polythene is rubbed with a cloth, electrons pass from the cloth to the polythene. The cloth is left with a + charge because its atoms have lost electrons, while the polythene gets a − charge since it gains electrons (which have a − charge), Fig. 1.8.

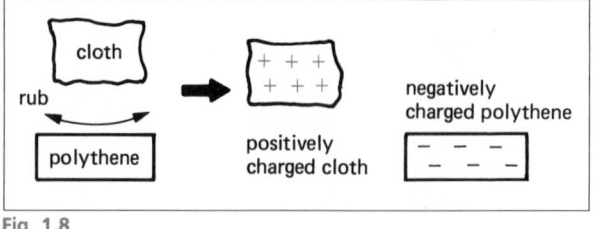

Fig. 1.8

Static charges cause sparks and crackles when a nylon garment is 'rubbed' and becomes charged when it is taken off. It can be shown that

like charges (+ and +, − and −) *repel*, and
unlike charges (+ and −) *attract*.

Semiconductors like silicon and germanium conduct to a certain extent.

◇ **Questions**

Q1
In Fig. 1.9, if one lamp fails, in which of the circuits A,B,C will the total number of lamps going out be **(a)** one, **(b)** two, **(c)** four?

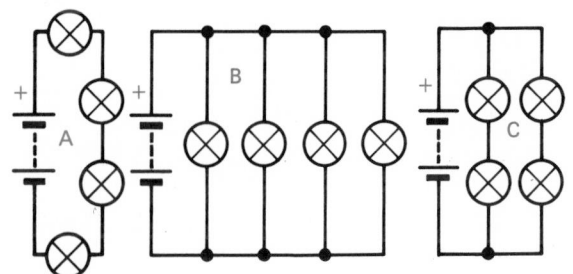

Fig. 1.9

Q2
(a) In Fig. 1.6, if Ⓐ₁ reads 0.2 A what are the readings on Ⓐ₂ and Ⓐ₃?
(b) In Fig. 1.7, if Ⓐ₂ reads 0.3 A and Ⓐ₃ reads 0.2 A, what does Ⓐ₁ read?

Q3
If the lamps are exactly the same as each other in Fig. 1.7, what do Ⓐ₂ and Ⓐ₃ read if Ⓐ₁ reads 0.4 A?

Q4
(a) In Fig. 1.10 if Ⓐ₂ reads 0.3 A, what do Ⓐ₁ and Ⓐ₃ read?
(b) Copy Fig. 1.10 and mark the +terminal of Ⓐ₁, Ⓐ₂ and Ⓐ₃ for correct connection.

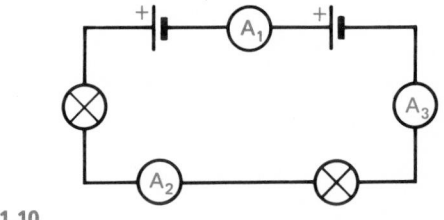

Fig. 1.10

Q5
(a) What are the following in mA: **(i)** 1 A, **(ii)** 0.5 A, **(iii)** 0.02 A?
(b) What are the following in A: **(i)** 1500 mA, **(ii)** 300 mA, **(iii)** 60 mA?
(c) What are the following in μA: **(i)** 2 mA, **(ii)** 0.4 mA, **(iii)** 0.005 mA?

2 Potential difference

◆ **About potential difference**

Potential difference or p.d. (symbol *V*) *causes current* and is produced by a cell, a battery or a generator. It is also called *voltage* and is measured in *volts* (shortened to V) by a *voltmeter*. A smaller unit of p.d. is the *millivolt* (mV) where

$1\,mV = 1/1000\,V$ or $1000\,mV = 1\,V$

There will be a current in a conductor only when there is a p.d. across it.

The voltage of a carbon–zinc or dry cell, Fig. 2.1*a*, is 1.5 V. Two cells connected in series, that is the +terminal of one to the −terminal of the other, Fig. 2.1*b*, have a voltage of $2 \times 1.5\,V = 3\,V$. In a 9 V battery six 1.5 V cells are connected in series.

If a supply has a voltage of, say, 6 V, you will often find on circuit diagrams that the negative of the supply is marked as 0 V and the positive as +6 V.

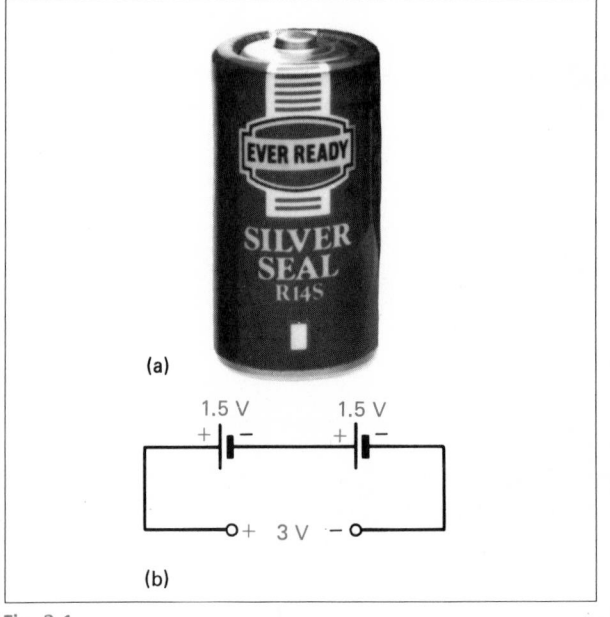

Fig. 2.1

◆ Voltmeters

A voltmeter with its symbol is shown in Fig. 2.2a, b. Like an ammeter, its +terminal (often coloured red) must lead to the +terminal of the voltage supply being measured, as in Fig. 2.2c. Otherwise the voltmeter may be damaged.

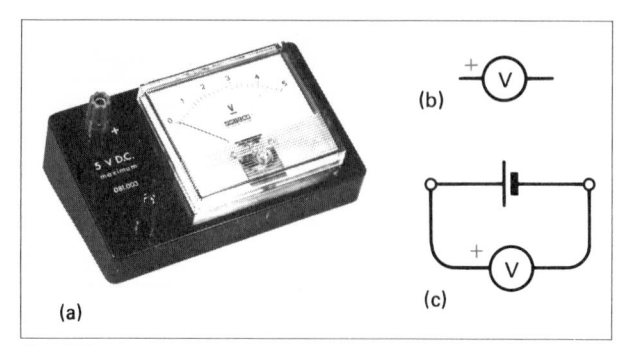

Fig. 2.2

◆ Voltage is used up in a circuit

If there is current in any part of a circuit, there must be a *voltage drop* or *p.d.* across that part. The drop is measured by connecting a voltmeter across that part, i.e. in *parallel* with it (by contrast an ammeter is connected in *series* to measure current).

(a) Series circuits. In Fig. 2.3, Ⓥ measures the voltage drop in

A, across L_1, which equals the supply voltage of 1.5 V,
B, across L_2, i.e. 1.5 V if L_2 and L_3 are identical lamps,
C, across L_3, i.e. 1.5 V if L_2 and L_3 are identical lamps, and
D, across L_2 and L_3 in series, which is the supply voltage of 3 V.

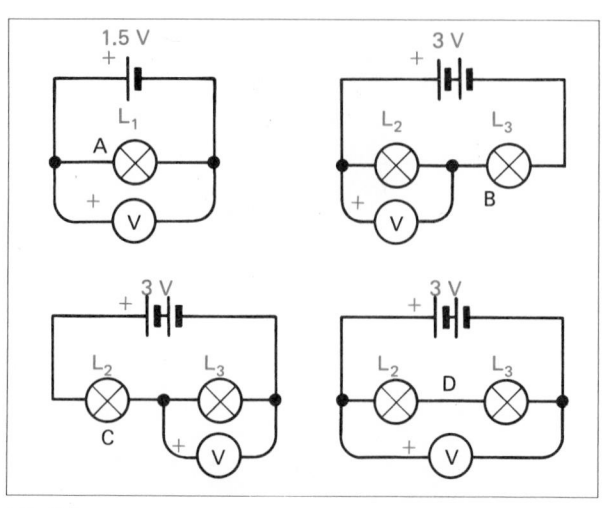

Fig. 2.3

The supply voltage is used up round a circuit and measurements show that

supply voltage = sum of all the voltage drops round the circuit

For example, in Fig. 2.4, if Ⓥ₁ = 2 V, Ⓥ₂ = 3 V and Ⓥ₃ = 4 V, then

supply voltage $= (2 + 3 + 4)V = 9V$
$=$ all voltage drops added

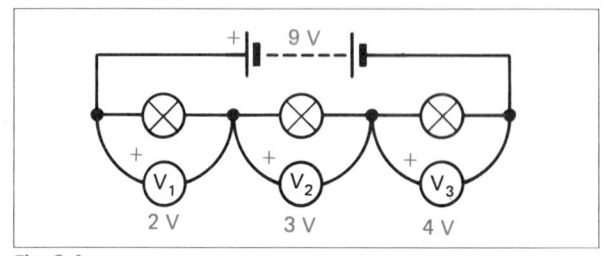

Fig. 2.4

(b) Parallel circuits. In Fig. 2.5, L_1 and L_2 are in parallel across the supply and the voltage drop across each is the *same* and equal to the supply voltage. That is Ⓥ₁ = Ⓥ₂ = 1.5 V.

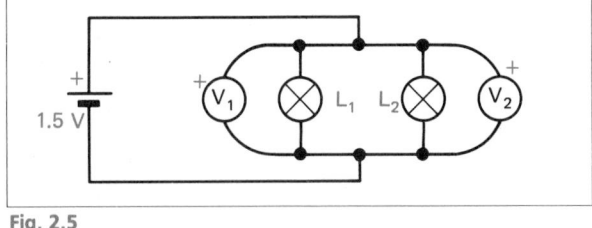

Fig. 2.5

◆ Principle of electronic switching circuits

Switching circuits are at the heart of modern electronic systems such as calculators and computers. The principle on which these circuits work can be understood from the simple electrical circuits in Figs. 2.6 and 2.7 and requires a knowledge of *p.d.* and *current*.

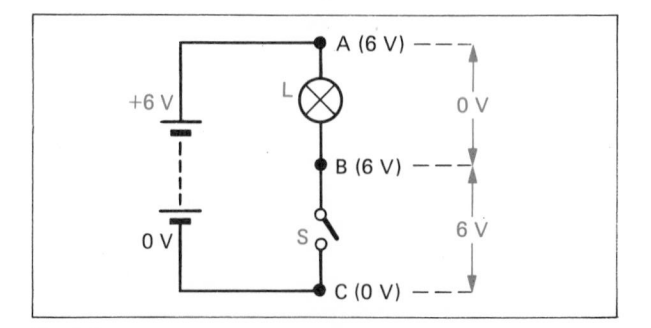

Fig. 2.6

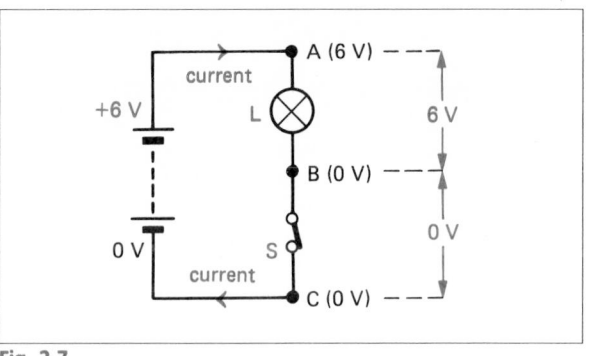

Fig. 2.7

In Fig. 2.6, *S is open* (OFF) and no current can pass through L. Therefore the p.d. across L, i.e. between A and B, is 0 V, but that across S, i.e. between B and C, is 6 V.

In Fig. 2.7, *S is closed* (ON) and current passes round the circuit through L. Therefore (since L is a 6 V lamp) the p.d. across L, i.e. between A and B, is 6 V, but the p.d. across S, i.e. between B and C, is now 0 V.

◇ Questions

Q1
What are the voltages of the batteries of 1.5 V cells connected as in Fig. 2.8*a, b*?

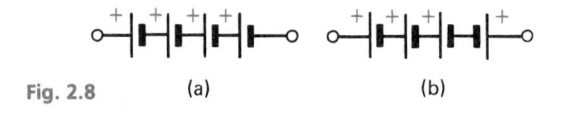

Fig. 2.8 (a) (b)

Q2
Three voltmeters ⓥ, ⓥ₁, ⓥ₂ are connected as in Fig. 2.9.
(a) if ⓥ reads 9 V and ⓥ₁ reads 6 V, what does ⓥ₂ read?
(b) Copy Fig. 2.9 and mark the + terminals of the voltmeters for correct connection.

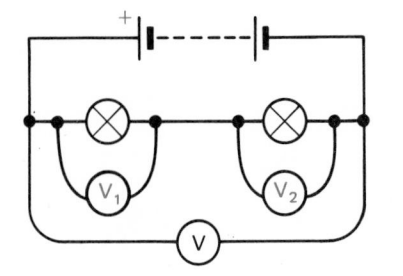

Fig. 2.9

Q3
The table below gives the voltmeter readings that were obtained with the circuit of Fig. 2.9 when different batteries were used. What are the values of *x*, *y* and *z*?

Reading in volts		
V	V_1	V_2
x	12	6
6	4	*y*
12	*z*	4

Q4
In Fig. 2.10 what is the voltage drop across **(a)** AB, **(b)** CD?

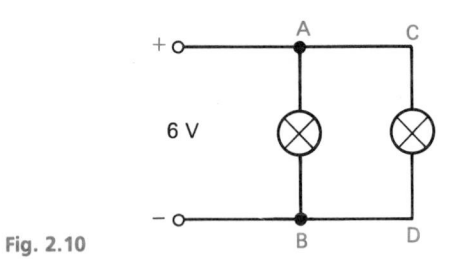

Fig. 2.10

Q5
In Fig. 2.11 what is the p.d. across L when S is **(a)** open, **(b)** closed?

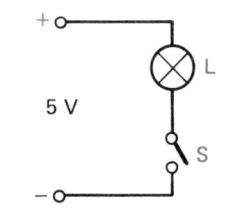

Fig. 2.11

Q6
(a) Express in mV: **(i)** 1 V, **(ii)** 0.7 V, **(iii)** 0.02 V.
(b) Express in V: **(i)** 1600 mV, **(ii)** 400 mV, **(iii)** 50 mV.

3 Resistance and Ohm's law

♦ About resistance

Electrons move more easily through some conductors than others. Opposition to current is called *resistance*. The current caused by a certain p.d. is greater in a good conductor than in a poor one. We use this fact to measure resistance.

If the current through a conductor is I when the p.d. across it is V, its resistance R is given by the equation

$$R = \frac{V}{I}$$

This is a reasonable way to measure R since the smaller I is for a certain V, the greater is R. If V is in volts and I in amperes, then R is in *ohms* (symbol Ω, pronounced omega).

For example, if $I = 2$ A when $V = 6$ V, then

$$R = \frac{6\,\text{V}}{2\,\text{A}} = 3\,\Omega$$

But if $I = 1$ A when $V = 6$ V, then

$$R = \frac{6\,\text{V}}{1\,\text{A}} = 6\,\Omega$$

That is, R is greater in the second case because I is smaller.

♦ Circuit calculations

Sometimes R is known and we have to calculate V or I. The above equation for R can be rearranged so that

(i) V can be found when R and I are known using the equation

$$V = I \times R$$

(ii) I can be found when R and V are known using the equation

$$I = \frac{V}{R}$$

The triangle in Fig. 3.1a is an aid to remembering the three equations. To use it, cover the quantity you want with your finger, then what you still see is what the quantity equals. For instance, covering I leaves V/R (Fig. 3.1b), and covering V gives $I \times R$ (Fig. 3.1c).

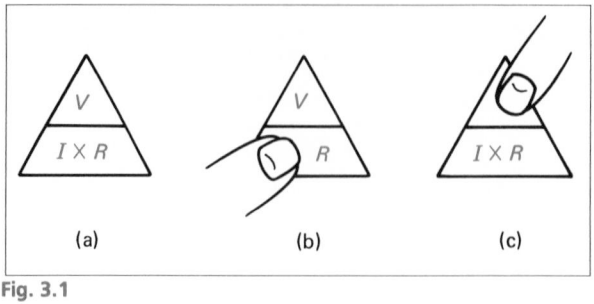

Fig. 3.1

◇ Worked examples

1 Find the p.d. across a wire of resistance 10 Ω carrying a current of 0.5 A.

$R = 10\,\Omega,\ I = 0.5\,\text{A},\ V = ?$
$V = I \times R = 0.5\,\text{A} \times 10\,\Omega = 5\,\text{V}$

2 Calculate the current through a wire of resistance 3 Ω when there is a p.d. of 9 V across it.

$R = 3\,\Omega,\ V = 9\,\text{V},\ I = ?$
$I = \dfrac{V}{R} = \dfrac{9\,\text{V}}{3\,\Omega} = 3\,\text{A}$

♦ Two points about units

1 Two larger units of resistance are the *kilohm* (kΩ) and the *megohm* (MΩ).

$1\,\text{k}\Omega = 1000\,\Omega \qquad 1\,\text{M}\Omega = 1\,000\,000\,\Omega$

2 In electronics I is often in mA and R in kΩ. Using these units, V is still in volts. For example, if

(a) $I = 2$ mA and $R = 10$ kΩ, then
$V = I \times R = 2\,\text{mA} \times 10\,\text{k}\Omega = 20\,\text{V}$
(b) $I = 2$ mA and $V = 4$ V, then
$R = V/I = 4\,\text{V}/2\,\text{mA} = 2\,\text{k}\Omega$
(c) $R = 2$ kΩ and $V = 6$ V, then
$I = V/R = 6\,\text{V}/2\,\text{k}\Omega = 3\,\text{mA}$

♦ Ohm's law

For conductors (e.g. wires) made from metals, some alloys and carbon, V/I is constant whatever the value of V, if their temperature does not change. Since $R = V/I$ it follows that the resistance of such conductors is constant for different p.ds. We can write

$$\frac{V}{I} = \text{constant or } I \propto V$$

This is Ohm's law and states that *the current through a conductor is directly proportional to the p.d. across it if the temperature is constant.* Doubling or trebling *V* therefore doubles or trebles *I* so that the ratio *V/I* stays the same.

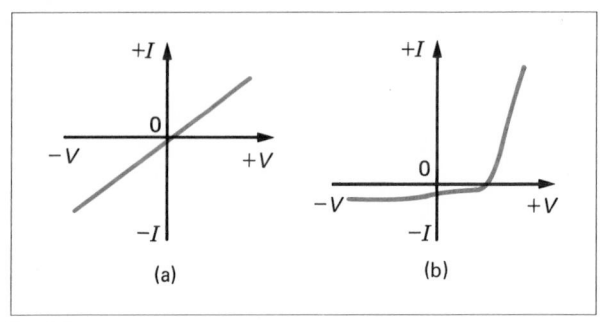

Fig. 3.2

Ohmic or *linear* conductors obey Ohm's law, and a graph of *I* against *V*, called a *characteristic curve*, is a straight line through the origin 0, Fig. 3.2a.

The resistance of a *non-ohmic* or *non-linear* conductor varies with the p.d. across it and its *I–V* graph is curved. The one in Fig. 3.2b is for a semiconductor diode (Chapter 13).

◆ Resistors

Resistors are conductors that are specially made to have resistance. They limit the current to a desired value when connected in series in a circuit (see Chapter 14).

Fixed resistors have fixed values and one is shown in Fig. 3.3a, b with its symbol.

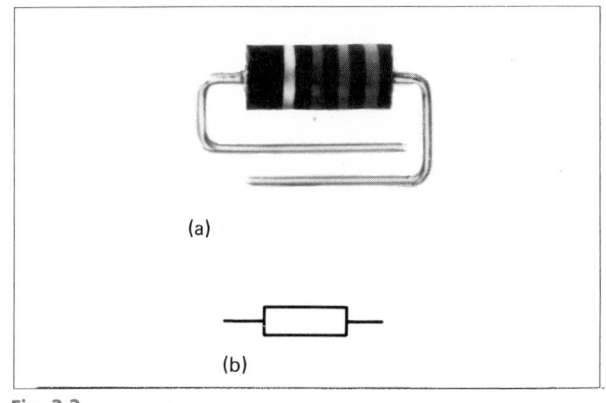

Fig. 3.3

Variable resistors can have their values changed and allow the current to be varied. One is shown in Fig. 3.4a, b with its symbol.

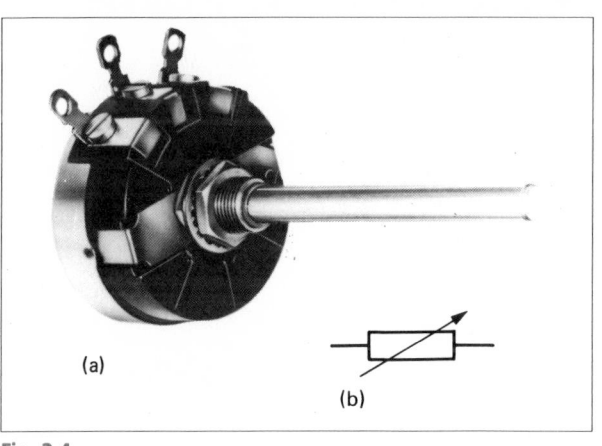

Fig. 3.4

◇ Questions

Q1
(a) What will the ammeter Ⓐ read in Fig. 3.5?

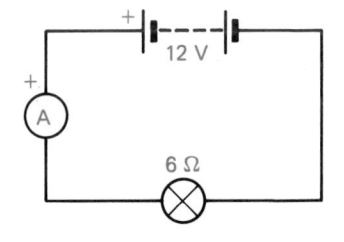

Fig. 3.5

(b) What is the p.d. (voltage drop) across the lamp of resistance 6 Ω?
(c) Redraw the circuit with a voltmeter Ⓥ connected to measure the p.d. across the lamp; mark its + terminal.

Q2
(a) What is the resistance of a wire when a voltage of 6 V across it causes a current of 1.5 A?
(b) Calculate the p.d. across a wire of resistance 10 Ω carrying a current of 2 A.

Q3
In the circuit of Fig. 3.6 calculate:
(a) *V* if *I* = 5 mA and *R* = 2 kΩ,
(b) *R* if *V* = 12 V and *I* = 3 mA,
(c) *I* if *V* = 10 V and *R* = 5 kΩ.

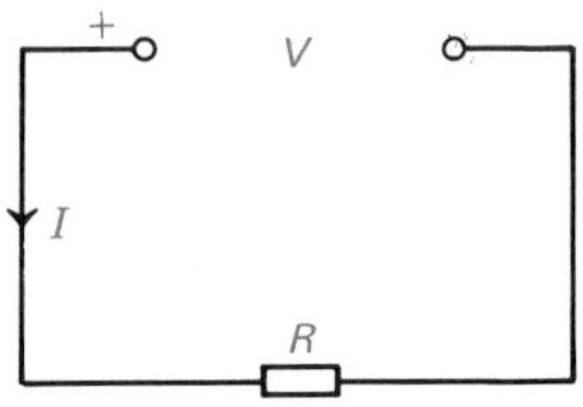

Fig. 3.6

4 Resistor networks

◆ Resistors in series

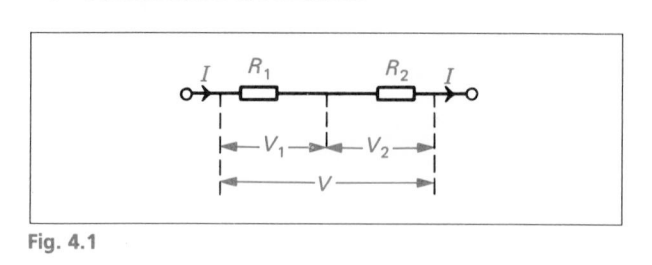

Fig. 4.1

In Fig. 4.1 we can say that

(i) the current I is the same in resistors R_1 and R_2 because they are in series,

(ii) $V = V_1 + V_2$ since the voltages V_1 and V_2 across resistors R_1 and R_2 in series are added to give the total voltage V where $V_1 = I R_1$ and $V_2 = I R_2$.

From these two facts it can be shown that the total or effective resistance R of two resistors R_1 and R_2 in series is given by the equation

$$R = R_1 + R_2$$

Therefore if $R_1 = 1\ \Omega$ and $R_2 = 2\ \Omega$, then $R = 1 + 2 = 3\ \Omega$.

From these two facts it can be shown that the total or effective resistance R of two resistors R_1 and R_2 in parallel is given by the equation

$$\frac{1}{R} = \frac{1}{R_1} + \frac{1}{R_2}$$

or

$$R = \frac{R_1 \times R_2}{R_1 + R_2}$$

For example, if $R_1 = R_2 = 2\ \Omega$, then

$$R = \frac{2 \times 2}{2 + 2} = \frac{4}{4} = 1\ \Omega$$

If $R_1 = 3\ \Omega$ and $R_2 = 6\ \Omega$, then

$$R = \frac{3 \times 6}{3 + 6} = \frac{18}{9} = 2\ \Omega$$

Note that the total resistance of the network is *less* than either R_1 or R_2, because alternative paths are provided for the current I, making electron flow easier. When $R_1 = R_2$, R is *half* either R_1 or R_2.

◆ Resistors in parallel

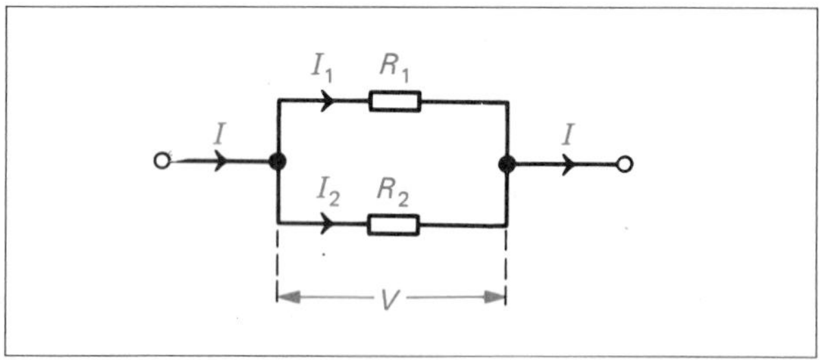

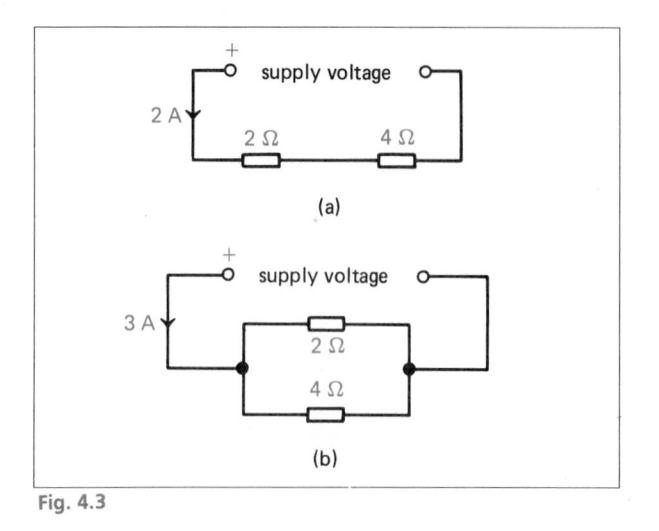

Fig. 4.2

For Fig. 4.2 we can say that

(i) $I = I_1 + I_2$ since the sum of the currents going into a junction in a circuit is the same as the sum of the currents coming out of the junction.

If $R_1 = R_2$ then I splits so that $I_1 = I_2 = \frac{1}{2}I$.
If R_1 is *twice* R_2, then I_1 is *half* I_2. For example, if $I = 3$ A, $R_1 = 2\ \Omega$ and $R_2 = 1\ \Omega$ then $I_1 = 1$ A and $I_2 = 2$ A (since $I = I_1 + I_2 = 1 + 2 = 3$ A).

(ii) V is the same across R_1 and R_2 since the voltages across resistors in parallel are equal, i.e. $V = I_1 R_1 = I_2 R_2$.

◇ Worked examples

1 For the circuits in Fig. 4.3a, b what is
(i) the current in the 2 Ω resistor,
(ii) the current in the 4 Ω resistor,
(iii) the voltage across the 2 Ω resistor,
(iv) the voltage across the 4 Ω resistor, and
(v) the supply voltage?

Fig. 4.3

(a)
(i) 2 A
(ii) 2 A
(iii) $2\,A \times 2\,\Omega = 4\,V$
(iv) $2\,A \times 4\,\Omega = 8\,V$
(v) $4\,V + 8\,V = 12\,V$

(b)
(i) 2 A since the current in the 2 Ω resistor will be *twice* that in the 4 Ω resistor
(ii) 1 A since 3 A enters the network
(iii) $2\,A \times 2\,\Omega = 4\,V$
(iv) $1\,A \times 4\,\Omega = 4\,V$
(v) 4 V

2 For the network in Fig. 4.4 calculate
(i) the combined resistance R_p of R_1 and R_2 in parallel,
(ii) the total resistance R of the network,
(iii) I,
(iv) V_p and V_3, and
(v) I_1 and I_2.

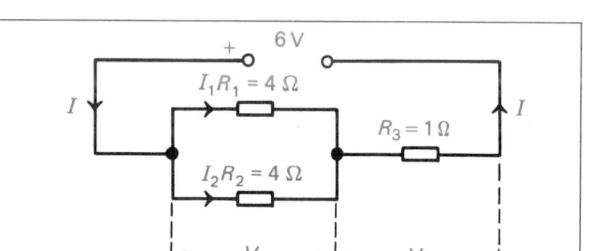

Fig. 4.4

(i) $R_p = \dfrac{R_1 \times R_2}{R_1 + R_2} = \dfrac{4 \times 4}{4 + 4} = \dfrac{16}{8} = 2\,\Omega$

(ii) $R = R_p + R_3 = 2 + 1 = 3\,\Omega$

(iii) The p.d. *V* across the *whole* network is 6 V and its total resistance *R* is 3 Ω therefore

$$I = \frac{V}{R} = \frac{6\,V}{3\,\Omega} = 2\,A$$

(iv) $V_p = I \times R_p = 2\,A \times 2\,\Omega = 4\,V$
But $V = V_p + V_3$
therefore $V_3 = V - V_p = 6 - 4 = 2\,V$

(v) $I_1 = I_2 = \tfrac{1}{2}\,I$ (since $R_1 = R_2$)
therefore $I_1 = \tfrac{1}{2} \times 2\,A = 1\,A$

◇ **Questions**

Q1
Draw a diagram to show how you would connect two 10 Ω resistors to give a total resistance of **(a)** 20 Ω, **(b)** 5 Ω.

Q2
In the circuit of Fig. 4.5 what is
(a) the current in the 3 Ω resistor,
(b) the current in the 6 Ω resistor,
(c) the p.d. across the 3 Ω resistor,
(d) the p.d. across the 6 Ω resistor, and
(e) the supply voltage?

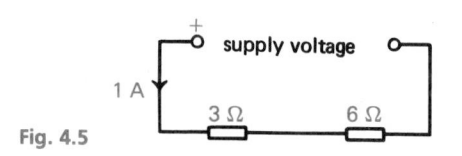

Fig. 4.5

Q3
Repeat question 2 for the circuit in Fig. 4.6

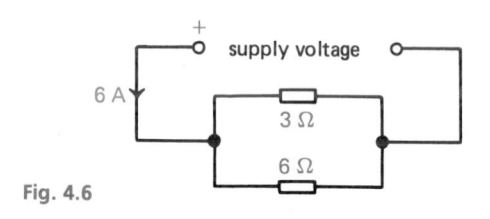

Fig. 4.6

Q4
For the network in Fig. 4.7 calculate the total resistance between **(a)** X and Y, **(b)** Y and Z, **(c)** X and Z.

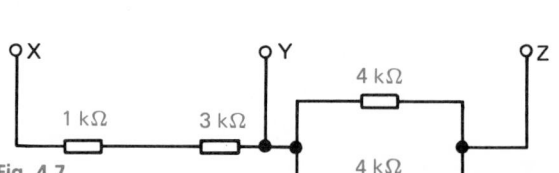

Fig. 4.7

5 Potential divider

In its simplest form, a potential divider consists of two resistors in series. It divides the *input voltage* applied across it into a number of equal parts so that the *output voltage* it supplies is a certain fraction of the input voltage.

◆ Using two fixed resistors

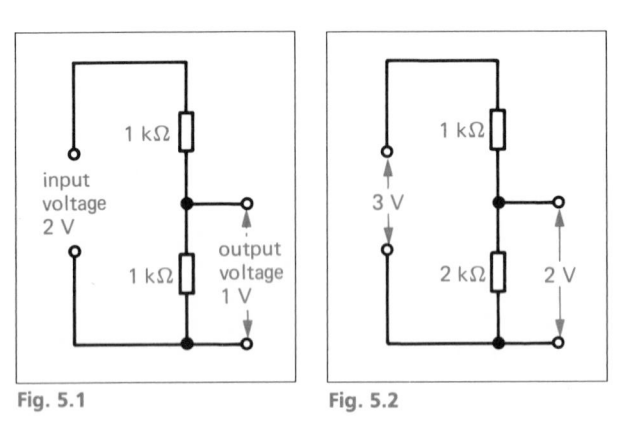

Fig. 5.1   Fig. 5.2

In Fig. 5.1 the potential divider consists of two 1 kΩ resistors in series with a voltage of 2 V applied across them as the input. This voltage is divided by the resistors into *two* equal parts (since the resistors are equal), each of 1 V. One of these parts, i.e. half the input voltage, is tapped off from the lower resistor as the output voltage to be applied to another circuit.

In Fig. 5.2, the 1 kΩ and 2 kΩ resistors split the input p.d. of 3 V into *three* equal parts of 1 V each. Two of these, i.e. ⅔ of the input p.d., are taken off across the 2 kΩ resistor as the output voltage of 2 V.

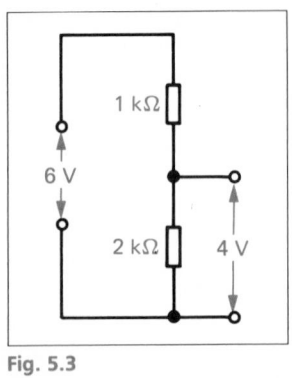
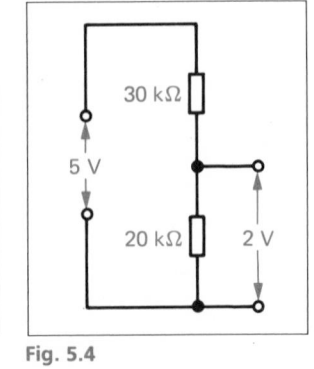

Fig. 5.3   Fig. 5.4

In Fig. 5.3, 6 V is split into *three* equal parts of 2 V, two of which, i.e. 4 V, are tapped off as the output voltage.

In Fig. 5.4, the input p.d. of 5 V is divided into *five* equal parts. Two of these, i.e. 2 V, are taken off across the 20 kΩ resistor as the output p.d.

◆ General circuit

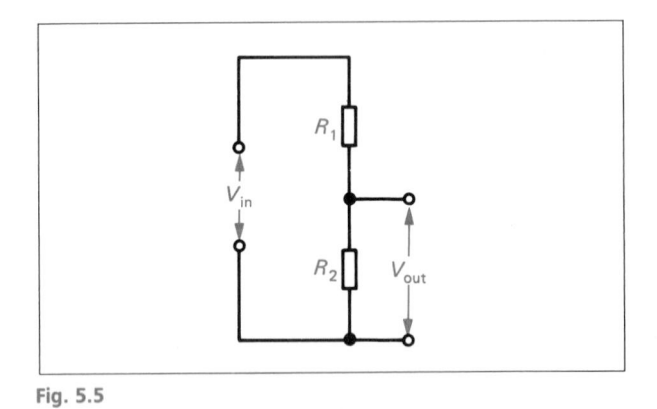

Fig. 5.5

In Fig. 5.5, R_1 and R_2 form the potential divider to the input voltage V_{in}. The output voltage V_{out} is taken off across R_2 and can be shown to be given by (see question 3)

$$V_{out} = \left(\frac{R_2}{R_1 + R_2}\right) V_{in} \qquad (1)$$

For example, if $V_{in} = 5$ V, $R_1 = 30$ kΩ and $R_2 = 20$ kΩ (Fig. 5.4), then

$$V_{out} = \left(\frac{20}{20 + 30}\right) 5 = \frac{20 \times 5}{50} = \frac{100}{50} = 2 \text{ V}$$

In general, V_{out} depends on the ratio R_1/R_2.

◆ Using a variable resistor

If all three connections are used on a variable resistor (Chapter 9) as in Fig. 5.6, it acts as a potential divider in which the ratio of R_1 to R_2 is readily changed.

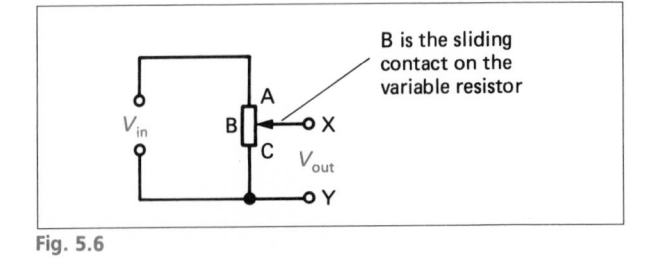

Fig. 5.6

The resistance between A and B represents R_1 and that between B and C represents R_2. A continuously variable output voltage V_{out}, from 0 to V_{in}, is available between X and Y, depending on the position of the sliding contact. $V_{out} = \frac{1}{2}V_{in}$ when $R_1 = R_2$, which, in a *linear* variable resistor (Chapter 9), occurs when AB = BC.

◆ Effect of load on output voltage

When the output voltage from a potential divider drives current through another circuit, this current 'loads' the potential divider. As a result the output voltage is less than the calculated value.

However, the difference is small if the current drawn by the 'load' from the potential divider is small compared with the current through the potential divider. In practice the 'load' current should not exceed $\frac{1}{10}$ of the potential divider current.

◇ Questions

Q1
For the potential divider in Fig. 5.5, calculate the output voltage V_{out} across R_2 when the values of the input voltage V_{in}, R_1 and R_2 are those in the table below.

	(a)	(b)	(c)	(d)
V_{in}	4 V	6 V	9 V	10 V
R_1	2 kΩ	10 kΩ	2 kΩ	3 kΩ
R_2	2 kΩ	20 kΩ	1 kΩ	2 kΩ

Q2
In Fig. 5.6, if BC = $\frac{2}{3}$ AC and $V_{in} = 9$ V what is V_{out}?

Q3
Using the circuit in Fig. 5.5 work out equation (1) for V_{out}. (*Hint.* Let I be the potential divider current through R_1 and R_2, then $V_{out} = IR_2$ and $V_{in} = I(R_1 + R_2)$. Now divide one equation by the other to get V_{out}/V_{in}.)

6 Electric power

◆ Power of a device

(a) Meaning. Current passing through a device which has resistance causes electrical energy to be changed into other forms of energy. For example, in a lamp, heat and light are produced. The *rate* at which this occurs is called the *power* of the device and is measured in *watts* (W).

In a 100 W lamp, four times as much electrical energy is changed into heat and light every second as in a 25 W lamp.

(b) Calculating power. It can be shown that the power P of a device carrying a current I when there is a p.d. of V across it is given by

$$P = V \times I \qquad (1)$$

where P is in *watts*, if V is in *volts* and I is in *amperes*.

For example, if $V = 12$ V and $I = 2$ A, then

$$P = 12\,V \times 2\,A = 24\,W$$

In units

$$\text{WATTS} = \text{VOLTS} \times \text{AMPERES}$$

If the device has resistance R in *ohms*, then since $V = I \times R$, we also have

$$P = (I \times R) \times I = I^2R \qquad (2)$$

For example, if $R = 10\,\Omega$ and $I = 1$ A, then

$$P = 1^2 \times 10 = 10\,W$$

But if $I = 2$ A, then

$$P = 2^2 \times 10 = 40\,W$$

Therefore doubling I quadruples P.

A third expression for P is obtained by substituting $I = V/R$ in (1) to get

$$P = V \times \left(\frac{V}{R}\right) = \frac{V^2}{R} \qquad (3)$$

(c) Other units. Larger units of power are the *kilowatt* (kW) and the *megawatt* (MW) where

$$1\,kW = 1000\,W \text{ and } 1\,MW = 1\,000\,000\,W$$

A smaller unit is the *milliwatt* (mW) where

$$1000\,mW = 1\,W$$

For example, the power P of a device carrying a current $I = 5$ mA when the p.d. V across it is 10 V, is

$$P = 5\,mA \times 10\,V = 50\,mW$$

◆ Power rating of a resistor

Heat is produced in a resistor when current passes through it and the greater the current, the hotter the resistor becomes. Overheating causes damage so for every resistor there is a limit to the amount of heat that can be generated (dissipated) in it per second. This maximum safe rate of heat production is called the *power rating* of the resistor and should not be exceeded. In general the larger the physical size of a resistor the greater is its rating.

In most electronic circuits resistors with 0.25 (¼) or 0.5 (½) W ratings are adequate.

◇ Worked example

Find the maximum safe current which can be passed through a 10 kΩ, 0.25 W resistor.

We have

$R = 10\,\text{k}\Omega = 10\,000\,\Omega = 10^4\,\Omega$ and
$P = 0.25\,\text{W}$

But from equation (2) above,

$P = I^2 R$ or

$I^2 = \dfrac{P}{R}$

Taking the square roots of both sides, we get

$I = \sqrt{\dfrac{P}{R}}$

Substituting for P and R gives

$I = \sqrt{\dfrac{0.25}{10^4}}$

Multiplying numerator and denominator under the square root sign by 100 does not alter the equation.

Therefore

$I = \sqrt{\dfrac{0.25 \times 100}{10^4 \times 100}} = \sqrt{\dfrac{25}{10^6}} = \sqrt{\dfrac{5 \times 5}{10^3 \times 10^3}}$

$= \dfrac{5}{10^3}\,\text{A} = 5\,\text{mA}$

◇ Questions

Q1
What is the power of a lamp rated at **(a)** 6 V 1 A, **(b)** 240 V 0.25 A?

Q2
What is the maximum power in kilowatts of the appliance(s) that can be connected safely to a 240 V 13 A mains supply?

Q3
The largest number of 100 W bulbs which can be safely run from a 240 V, 5 A supply is
A 2 **B** 5 **C** 10 **D** 12 **E** 20

Q4
Calculate the power of a 4 Ω resistor carrying a current of 2 A.

Q5
Calculate the maximum safe current through a resistor of
(a) 100 Ω 1 W,
(b) 100 Ω 4 W,
(c) 1.8 kΩ 0.5 W.

Q6
Calculate the power dissipated by a resistor having a p.d. of 9 V across it and a current of 3 mA through it.

7 Alternating current

◆ Direct and alternating currents

In a *direct current* (d.c.) electrons flow in one direction only. A battery produces d.c. The *waveform* of a current is a graph whose shape shows how the value of the current changes with time. Those in Fig. 7.1*a*, *b* are for steady and varying d.c.

In an *alternating current* (a.c.) the direction of electron flow reverses regularly. An alternator (in a car or power

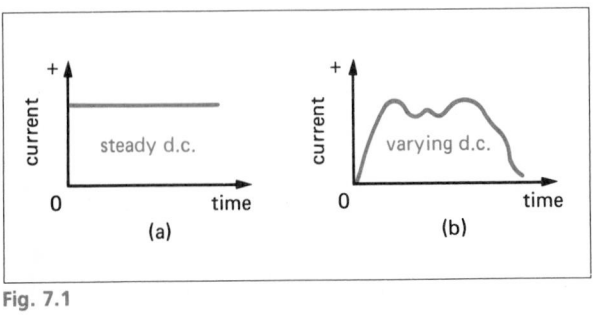

Fig. 7.1

station) produces a.c. In the a.c. waveform of Fig. 7.2, which is a sine wave, the current rises from zero to a maximum value in one direction (+), and falls to zero again before becoming a maximum in the opposite direction (−). It then rises to zero once more, and so on. The circuit symbol for an a.c. power supply is ~ .

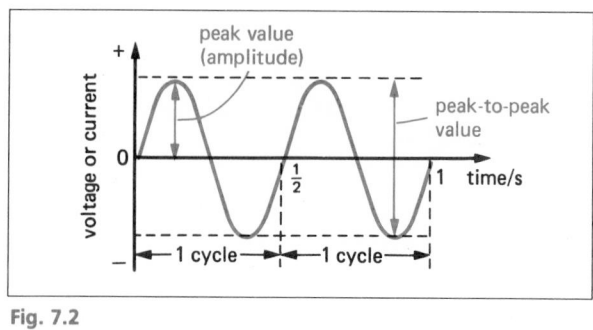

Fig. 7.2

The pointer of an ammeter for measuring d.c. is deflected one way by d.c., Fig. 7.3*a*. A.c. makes it move to and fro on either side of the scale zero if the direction changes are slow enough, Fig. 7.3*b*. If they are too fast, no deflection occurs.

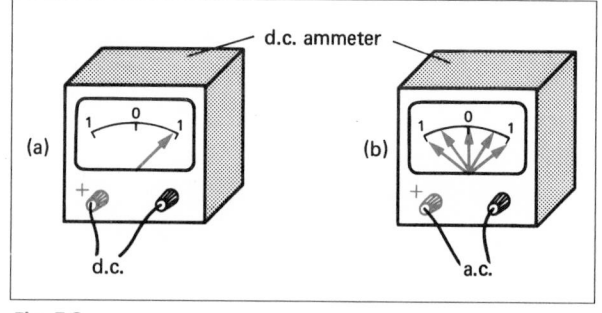

Fig. 7.3

Like d.c., heating and magnetic effects are caused by a.c. Electric heaters and lamps work off either a.c. or d.c. but most electronic systems require a d.c. power supply.

◆ Frequency of a.c.

The *frequency* (*f*) of a.c. is the number of complete alternations or cycles made in 1 second. The unit of frequency is the *hertz* (Hz). The a.c. in Fig. 7.2 makes two cycles in 1 second, that is, its frequency is 2 Hz. The frequency of the mains supply in many countries (including the UK) is 50 Hz.

Larger units are the *kilohertz* (kHz) and the *megahertz* (MHz).

$$1\,\text{kHz} = 1000\,\text{Hz} = 10^3\,\text{Hz}$$
$$1\,\text{MHz} = 1\,000\,000\,\text{Hz} = 10^6\,\text{Hz}$$

The *period* (*T*) is the time for which one cycle of the a.c. lasts. If *f* = 2 Hz, there are two cycles per second, so *T* = ½ s. In general

$$T = \frac{1}{f}$$

where *T* is in seconds and *f* in hertz.

If *f* = 1 kHz = 1000 Hz then

$$T = \frac{1}{1000}\,\text{s} = 1\,\text{millisecond (ms)}$$

If *f* = 1 MHz = 1 000 000 Hz then

$$T = \frac{1}{1\,000\,000}\,\text{s} = 1\,\text{microsecond} \ (\mu s)$$

Audio frequency (AF) currents have frequencies from 20 Hz or so to about 20 kHz. They produce an audible sound in a loudspeaker.

Radio frequency (RF) currents have frequencies above 20 kHz and produce radio waves from an aerial.

Electronic circuits called *oscillators* can generate AF and RF currents.

◆ Root-mean-square values

Since the value of an alternating quantity changes, the problem arises of what value to take to measure it. The average value of a sine wave over a complete cycle is zero; the peak value (or amplitude) might be used. However, the *root-mean-square* (r.m.s.) value is chosen because many calculations can then be done as they would be for d.c.

The r.m.s. (or effective) value of an alternating current (or voltage) is the steady direct current (or voltage) which would give the same heating effect.

For example, if the lamp in the circuit of Fig. 7.4 is lit first by a.c. (by moving the 2-way switch to the left) and its brightness noted, then if 0.3 A d.c. produces the same brightness (when the switch is moved to the right and the resistor adjusted), the r.m.s. value of the a.c. is 0.3 A.

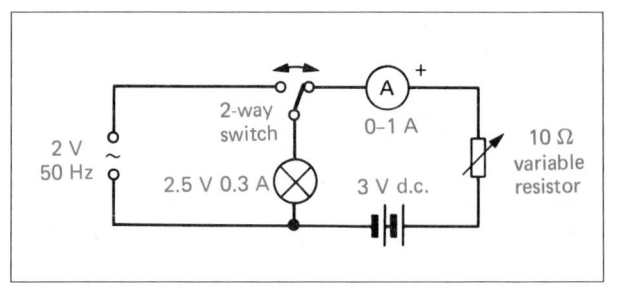

Fig. 7.4

A lamp designed to be fully lit by a current of 0.3 A d.c. will also be fully lit by a.c. of r.m.s. value 0.3 A.

It can be shown that for a sine wave a.c.

$$\text{r.m.s. value} = \frac{\text{peak value}}{\sqrt{2}} \approx 0.7 \times \text{peak value}$$

The r.m.s. voltage of the UK mains supply is 240 V: the peak value is much higher and is given by

$$\text{peak value} = \frac{\text{r.m.s. value}}{0.7} = 1.4 \text{ r.m.s. value}$$
$$= 1.4 \times 240 \approx 340 \text{ V}$$

The value given for an alternating current or voltage is always assumed to be the r.m.s. one, unless stated otherwise. The power P of a device on an a.c. supply is given by the same expression as for d.c., i.e. $P = V \times I$ where V and I are r.m.s. values.

◆ Waveforms

Some of the many types of repetitive waveforms occurring in electronics (apart from the sine wave) are shown in Fig. 7.5.

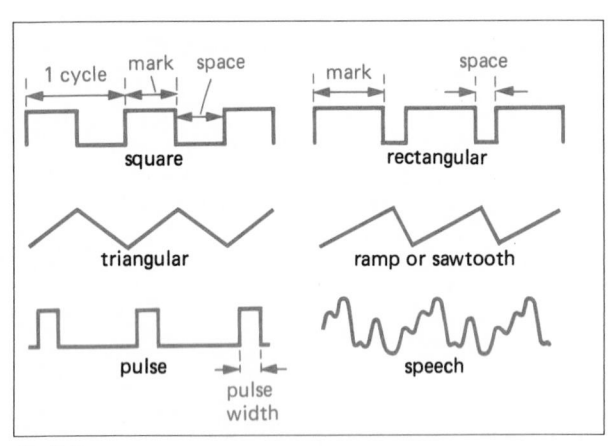

Fig. 7.5

The term *mark-to-space ratio* or *duty cycle* is used in connection with rectangular and square waves. It is given by

$$\text{duty cycle} = \frac{\text{mark time}}{\text{space time}}$$

For a square wave the duty cycle is 1/1 since the mark and space times are equal.

For a pulse waveform, the term *repetition rate* is used and is the number of pulses per second.

◇ Questions

Q1
Does the waveform in Fig. 7.6 represent d.c. or a.c.? Explain your answer.

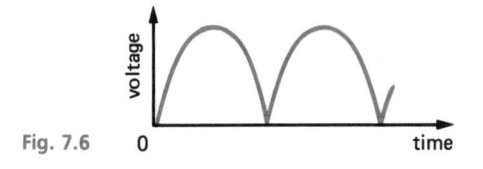

Fig. 7.6

Q2
What is **(a)** the period, **(b)** the frequency, of the a.c. in Fig. 7.7?

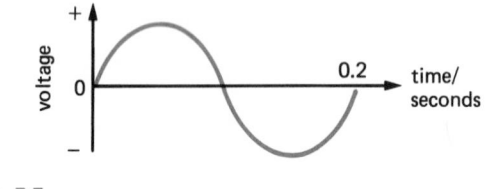

Fig. 7.7

Q3
The waveform of an alternating voltage is shown in Fig. 7.8. What is **(a)** the period, **(b)** the frequency, **(c)** the peak voltage, **(d)** the r.m.s. voltage?

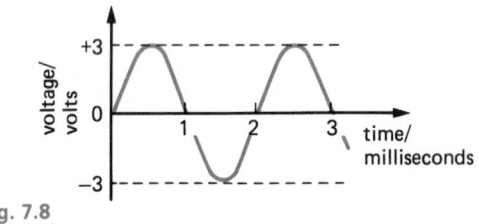

Fig. 7.8

Q4
An a.c. supply lights a lamp with the same brightness as does a 12 V battery. What is **(a)** the r.m.s. voltage, **(b)** the peak voltage, **(c)** the power of the lamp if it takes a current of 2 A on the a.c. supply?

8 Additional questions

◇ **Core level**

Q1

What would you expect the readings to be on the ammeter
Ⓐ and voltmeter Ⓥ in the circuit of Fig. 8.1?

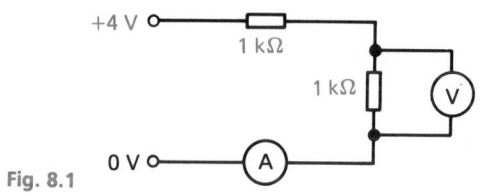

Fig. 8.1

Q2

(a) Calculate the total resistance of the two resistors connected in parallel in Fig. 8.2.

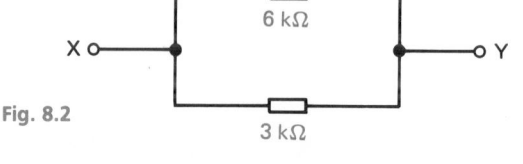

Fig. 8.2

(b) The parallel network in Fig. 8.2 is to be replaced by two
resistors in series, one of which has a value of 1.5 kΩ, Fig. 8.3.
What will be the value of the other resistor R if the total
resistance is to be the same as that of the parallel network?

Fig. 8.3   X o——▢——▢——o Y
            1.5 kΩ R

Q3

In the circuit of Fig. 8.4 what is the reading on Ⓥ when
(a) S_1 and S_2 are both open,
(b) S_1 and S_2 are both closed, and
(c) S_1 is open and S_2 is closed?

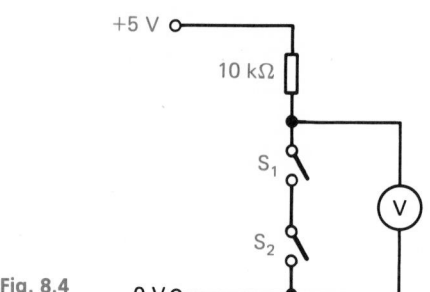

Fig. 8.4

Q4

In the circuit of Fig. 8.5 what is
(a) the total resistance,
(b) the current through R_1,

(c) the p.d. across R_1,
(d) the power dissipated in R_1,
(e) the chance of R_1 overheating if it is rated at 0.25 W?

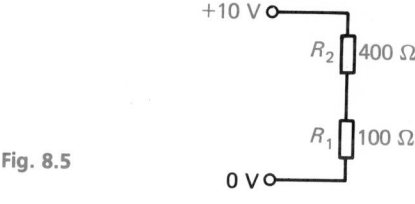

Fig. 8.5

Q5

State the units in which the following quantities are
measured, choosing from:
watt, ohm, ampere, hertz, volt
(a) current, **(b)** p.d., **(c)** resistance, **(d)** power,
(e) frequency.

◇ **Further level**

Q6

Will a 1 kΩ resistor rated at 0.1 W overheat when it is connected across a 20 V supply? Explain your answer.

Q7

For the voltage waveform shown in Fig. 8.6 what is
(a) the peak value,
(b) the r.m.s. value,
(c) the period, and
(d) the frequency?

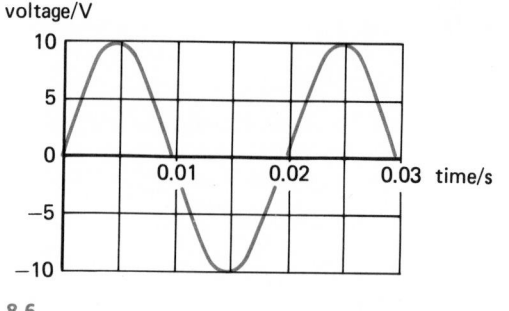

Fig. 8.6

Q8

What are the duty cycles of the waves in Fig. 8.7a,b?

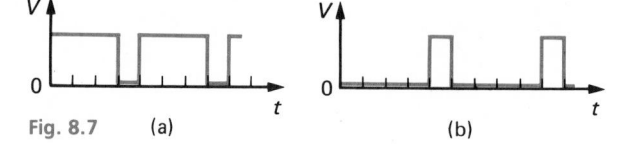

Fig. 8.7   (a)   (b)

Check list **Basic principles**

After studying *Chapter 1: Electric current*, you should be able to

◊ recognize circuit symbols for wires, cells, batteries, switches, lamps and ammeters,

◊ state that electric current is a flow of electrons, measured in amperes by an ammeter,

◊ state and use the fact that the current in a series circuit is the same everywhere in the circuit, and

◊ state and use the fact that the sum of the currents entering a junction in a circuit equals the sum of the currents leaving it.

After studying *Chapter 2: Potential difference*, you should be able to

◊ state that potential difference (p.d.) or voltage causes current and is measured in volts by a voltmeter,

◊ state and use the fact that the sum of the voltages in a series circuit equals the voltage across the whole circuit, and

◊ state and use the fact that there is the same voltage across each component in a parallel circuit.

After studying *Chapter 3: Resistance and Ohm's law*, you should be able to

◊ state that resistance is measured in ohms,

◊ state and use the equation $R = V/I$ in its three forms using different units, and

◊ recognize $I–V$ graphs for ohmic and non-ohmic conductors.

After studying *Chapter 4: Resistor networks*, you should be able to

◊ calculate the effective resistance of a number of resistors in series, and

◊ calculate the effective resistance of two resistors in parallel.

After studying *Chapter 5: Potential divider*, you should be able to

◊ calculate the output voltage from a potential divider, and

◊ state the effect of the load on the output voltage.

After studying *Chapter 6: Electric power*, you should be able to

◊ state that electric power is measured in watts,

◊ use the equations $P = IV$, $P = I^2R$ and $P = V^2/R$ for calculating power, and

◊ calculate the maximum safe current which can be passed through a resistor of a certain power rating.

After studying *Chapter 7: Alternating current*, **you should be able to**

◇ state that in an alternating current the direction of electron flow reverses regularly,

◇ state the meaning of the terms frequency, period, peak value (amplitude), peak-to-peak value, and indicate them on a voltage–time graph of a sine wave,

◇ state that frequency is measured in hertz,

◇ use the equation $T = 1/f$, and

◇ state and use the equation

   r.m.s. value $\approx 0.7 \times$ peak value

Components

9 Resistors and potentiometers

◆ Preferred values and tolerances

Exact values of resistors are not necessary in most electronic circuits and so only a certain number of *preferred values* are made having a particular *tolerance*, i.e. accuracy. This ensures that maximum coverage is obtained with minimum overlapping, using a limited number of resistors.

Resistors with a ±10% tolerance belong to the E12 series which has the twelve basic values given in the table below.

1.0	1.2	1.5	1.8	2.2	2.7
3.3	3.9	4.7	5.6	6.8	8.2

These are available in Ω, kΩ, and MΩ and also with values 10 and 100 times greater. For example,

1.0 Ω, 10 Ω, 100 Ω
1.0 kΩ, 10 kΩ, 100 kΩ
1.0 MΩ, 10 MΩ, 100 MΩ

and similarly for the other eleven values.

A 1.0 kΩ resistor in the E12 series can have any value from (1.0 kΩ + 10% of 1.0 kΩ) to (1.0 kΩ − 10% of 1.0 kΩ). That is, in the range (1.0 + 0.1) = 1.1 kΩ to (1.0 − 0.1) = 0.9 kΩ. For a 10 kΩ resistor, the range is 9.0 kΩ to 11 kΩ. The next higher value is 12 kΩ and this covers the range 12 kΩ ± 10% of 12 kΩ, i.e. 11 kΩ to 13 kΩ approximately, and so on. If a 5.0 kΩ resistor was required, a 4.7 kΩ resistor of the E12 series would be chosen since its value lies in the range (4.7 ± 0.47) kΩ, which near enough is 4.2 kΩ to 5.2 kΩ.

◆ Resistance codes

(a) Colour code. In this method the resistance value and tolerance are shown by four coloured bands round the resistor, each colour standing for a number. The first three bands give the *value in ohms* and the fourth gives the *tolerance* as a percentage.

The table below gives the colour code numbers.

Number	Colour
0	black
1	brown
2	red
3	orange
4	yellow
5	green
6	blue
7	violet
8	grey
9	white

rainbow colours (2–7)

To find the value of a resistor, start at the 1st band nearest one end. (The 4th band, if it is present, is at the other end and will be either gold or silver, these colours not being used for the 1st band.)

The *1st band* gives the first number, the *2nd band* gives the second number and the *3rd band* tells how many 0s come after the first two numbers. Study the examples in Fig. 9.1. If the *4th band* is silver, the tolerance is ±10% (as in the E12 series); if it is gold, the tolerance is ±5%. Resistors with a ±20% tolerance do not have a 4th band.

(b) Printed code. The code is printed on the resistor and consists of letters and numbers. The examples in the table below show how it works.

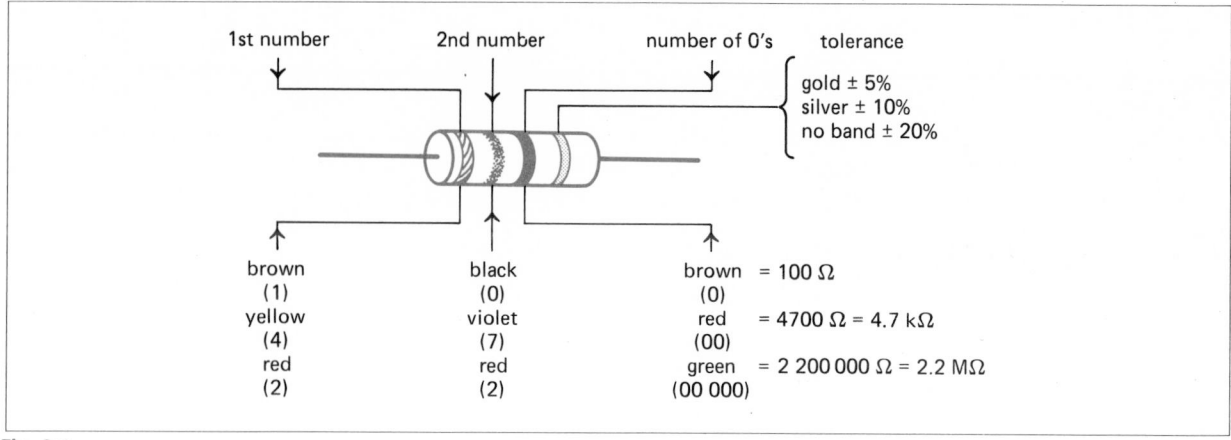

Fig. 9.1

R means ×1, K means ×1000 (10³) and M means ×1 000 000 (10⁶). The position of the letter gives the decimal point.

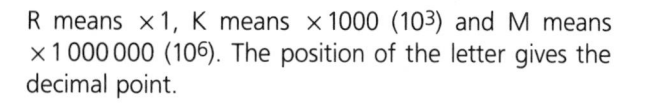

Value	0.27 Ω	3.3 Ω	10 Ω	220 Ω
Mark	R27	3R3	10R	220R
Value	1 kΩ	68 kΩ	100 kΩ	4.7 MΩ
Mark	1K0	68K	100K	4M7

Tolerances are indicated by adding a letter at the end.

J = ±5%, K = ±10%, M = ±20%

For example, 5K6K = 5.6 kΩ ± 10%.

◆ Potentiometers

A variable resistor is also called a *potentiometer* (or 'pot') and is used as a volume or other control in electronic equipment. The construction of one is shown in Fig. 9.2a,b with its symbol.

It consists of a circular resistive *track* (e.g. of carbon) with connecting terminal tags A and C at each end. A metal *wiper* can be moved round the track by rotating a spindle attached to it. A connection to the wiper by terminal tag B allows the resistance to be varied between B and either A or C. If the track is *linear* equal changes of resistance occur when the wiper is turned through equal angles. In a 'log' track the resistance change for equal angular rotations is greater at the end of the track than at the start making it more suitable as a volume control. The effect of a linear track volume control would be all at one end.

When a 'pot' is used as a rheostat to give variable control of the current in a circuit, connections are made to the wiper tag B and one end tag (see Chapter 3). As a *potential divider* (see Chapter 5), all three connecting tags are needed.

Preset variable resistors, Fig. 9.3a,b, are used where small, infrequent adjustments have to be made (with a screwdriver) to the resistance of a circuit.

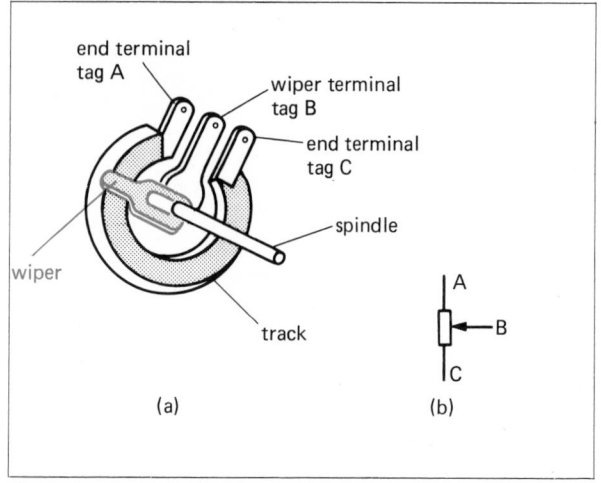

(a)

(b)

Fig. 9.2

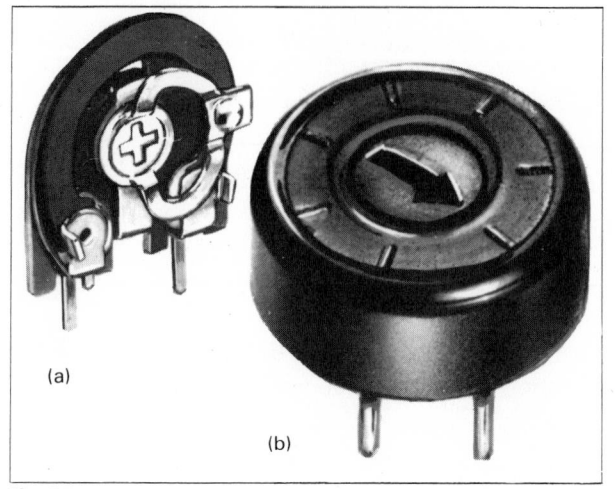

(a)

(b)

Fig. 9.3

◇ **Questions**

Q1
What are the values and tolerances of R_1, R_2 and R_3, colour coded in the table below?

Band	1	2	3	4
R_1	brown	black	red	silver
R_2	yellow	violet	orange	gold
R_3	green	blue	yellow	none

Q2
What are the colour codes for the following:
(a) $150\,\Omega \pm 10\%$, **(b)** $10\,\Omega \pm 5\%$, **(c)** $3.9\,k\Omega \pm 10\%$,
(d) $10\,k\Omega \pm 10\%$, **(e)** $330\,k\Omega \pm 20\%$, **(f)** $1\,M\Omega \pm 10\%$?

Q3
What are the values and tolerances of resistors marked:
(a) 2K2M, **(b)** 270KJ, **(c)** 1M0K, **(d)** 15RK?

Q4
What are the printed codes for:
(a) $100\,\Omega \pm 5\%$, **(b)** $4.7\,k\Omega \pm 20\%$, **(c)** $100\,k\Omega \pm 10\%$,
(d) $56\,k\Omega \pm 20\%$?

Q5
What E12 preferred values would you use if you calculated that a circuit needed resistors having values of:
(a) $1.3\,k\Omega$, **(b)** $5.0\,k\Omega$, **(c)** $72\,k\Omega$, **(d)** $350\,k\Omega$?

10 Capacitors

◆ About capacitors

A capacitor *stores electric charge.* In its simplest form it consists of two flat, parallel metal plates (conductors), close together, but separated by an insulating material (a non-conductor), called the *dielectric*, Fig. 10.1.

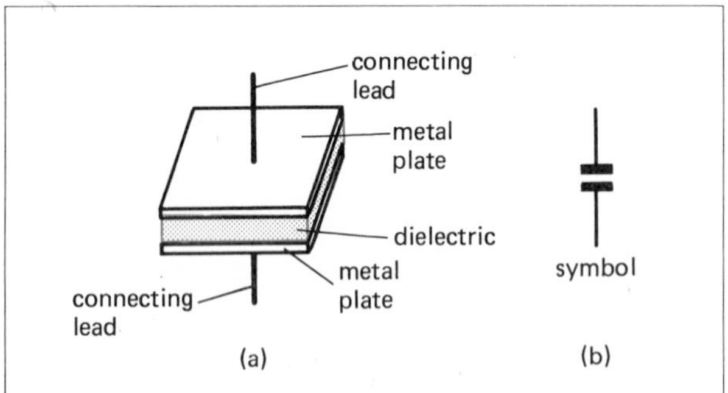

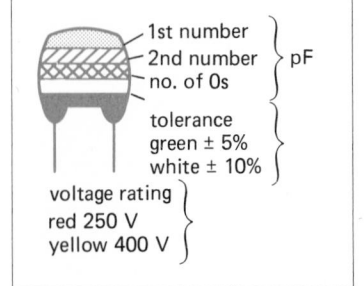

Fig. 10.1

(a) Capacitance. The more charge a capacitor can store the greater is its *capacitance* (symbol C). The capacitance is large if the plates have a large area and are close together, but it also depends on the dielectric.

The unit of capacitance is the *farad* (F) but smaller units such as the *microfarad* (μF), the *nanofarad* (nF) and the *picofarad* (pF) are more convenient in electronics.

$$1\,000\,000\,\mu F = 1\,F$$
$$1000\,nF \quad = 1\,\mu F$$
$$1000\,pF \quad = 1\,nF$$

(b) Voltage rating. This is the maximum voltage (d.c. or peak a.c.) a capacitor can withstand across its plates before the dielectric breaks down (i.e. is damaged). The capacitor is then useless. The voltage rating is often marked on the capacitor, e.g. 30 V, and the higher it is, the thicker the dielectric has to be.

◆ Types of capacitor

Different types are used for different purposes and operating conditions.

(a) Fixed (non-polarized). They have a fixed value and are known by their dielectric. Ceramic and polyester (a plastic) types are shown in Figs. 10.2 and 10.3, respectively. They are made with values ranging from 10 pF to 1 μF with tolerances up to $\pm 20\%$ for polyester and -25 to $+50\%$ for ceramic.

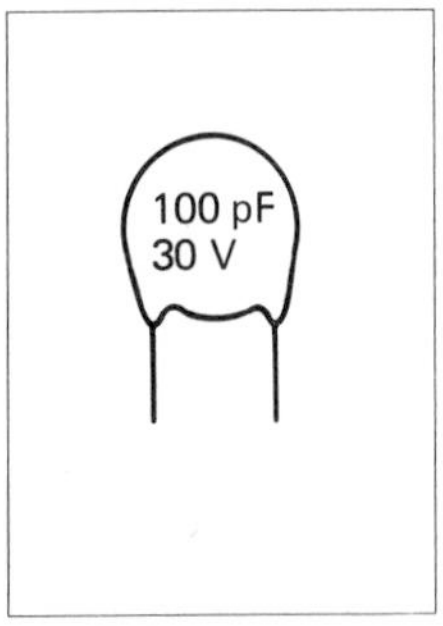

```
100 pF
30 V
```

Fig. 10.2

```
                1st number
                2nd number   } pF
                no. of 0s

                tolerance
                green ± 5%
                white ± 10%

voltage rating
red 250 V
yellow 400 V
```

Fig. 10.3

There is no agreed colour code for capacitors, so the value is usually stamped on them in figures, e.g. 100 pF.

Some polyesters use the resistor colour code to give their value in pF, Fig. 10.3.

(b) Electrolytic (polarized). This type is used where very large, fixed values (up to 100 000 μF or so) are required. They are compact but have a wide tolerance (-10 to $+50\%$) and must be connected so that their $+$ terminal, Fig. 10.4*a*,*b*, leads to the $+$ of the supply. Wrong connection destroys the very thin layer of the aluminium oxide dielectric which is formed on the $+$ plate during manufacture.

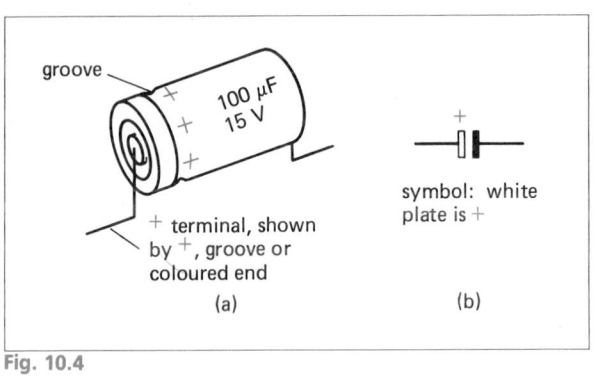

Fig. 10.4

(c) Variable. They are used to tune radio receivers. Their value is varied (e.g. up to 500 pF) by altering the area of overlap between a fixed set of metal plates and a moving set, separated by a dielectric of air. Often two or more are 'ganged', Fig. 10.5*a*,*b*.

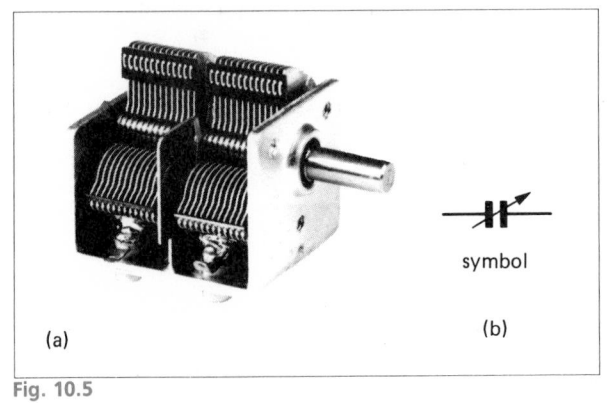

Fig. 10.5

◆ Charging a capacitor

When the capacitor in Fig. 10.6 is connected to the battery, the $+$ of the battery attracts electrons (since they have a $-$charge) from plate X and the $-$ of the battery repels electrons to plate Y. A positive charge

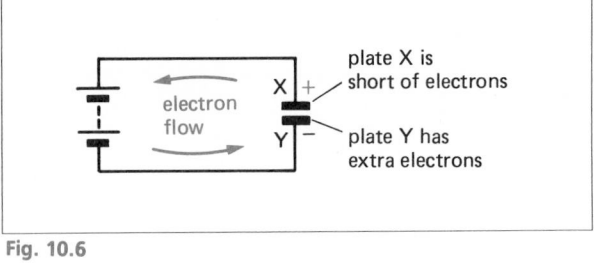

Fig. 10.6

builds up on plate X (since it loses electrons) and an equal negative charge is stored on Y (since it gains electrons). The capacitor is then *charged*.

During the charging, there is a brief flow of electrons, i.e. a current, round the circuit from X to Y. Charging stops when the p.d. built up between X and Y equals (and opposes) the voltage of the battery.

The charge gradually leaks away, i.e. the capacitor *discharges*, when the battery is removed, because the dielectric is not perfect and allows electrons to 'leak' through it. *Leakage currents* are small in most capacitors but not in electrolytics.

◆ Charge and discharge of a capacitor through a resistor

In electronic circuits capacitors are often charged or discharged through a resistor.

(a) Charging. When S is closed in Fig. 10.7*a*, C charges up at a rate which depends on the product $C \times R$, called the *time constant T* of the circuit. If *T* is large, due to C and/or R being large, the charging occurs slowly. In practice C becomes fully charged after a time equal to about 5*T* (where *T* is in seconds if C is in farads and R in ohms).

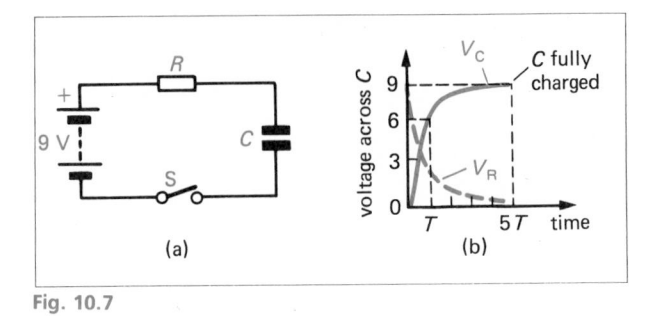

Fig. 10.7

The graph in Fig. 10.7*b* shows how the voltage builds up across C with time on a 9 V supply and also how the voltage V_R across R falls. At the start of charging $V_R = 9$ V and after about 5*T* it is 0 V.

(b) Discharging. The rate at which a capacitor discharges through a resistor also depends on $T(=C \times R)$ and in general it is fully discharged after about $5T$, Fig. 10.8a,b.

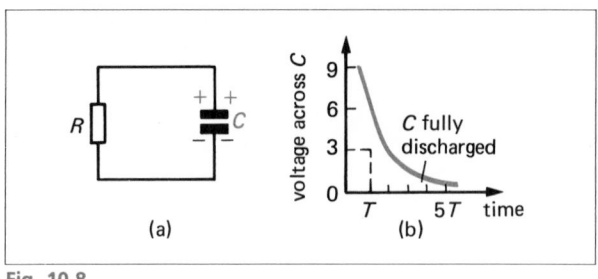

Fig. 10.8

◆ Capacitors block d.c. and pass a.c.

(a) d.c. In Fig. 10.9a the supply is d.c. and the lamp does not light showing that *a capacitor blocks d.c.*

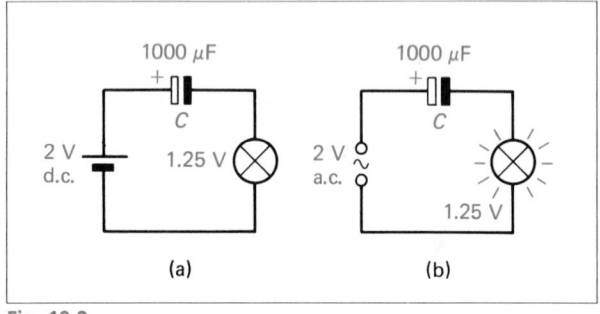

Fig. 10.9

(b) a.c. In Fig. 10.9b the supply is a.c. and the lamp lights showing that *a capacitor passes a.c.* In fact, no current actually goes *through* C since its plates are separated by an insulator. But it *seems* to do so because

electrons flow on and off the plates as the direction of the a.c. reverses (causing C to charge and discharge).

The current is greater, i.e. more electrons flow on and off the plates per second, if

(i) the frequency *f* of the a.c. is high,
(ii) the capacitance *C* is large.

In other words, the opposition of a capacitor to current is *small* when C and *f* are *large*.

The opposition to current in an a.c. circuit is called *impedance* and, like resistance in a d.c. circuit, it is measured in *ohms*.

At high frequencies, the impedance of a circuit containing a capacitor is low. At low frequencies it is large and at zero frequencies (d.c.) it is infinite (the d.c. is blocked).

◇ Questions

Q1
(a) What does it mean if a capacitor is marked '0.1 μF 250 V'?
(b) Why should a capacitor rated at 250 V not be used on a 240 V a.c. supply?

Q2
Arrange the following capacitances in order of increasing value:

100 pF, 4.7 μF, 2.2nF

Q3
If you wanted to stop d.c. passing through a component but allow a.c. to pass, what would you do?

Q4
What precaution must be taken when connecting an electrolytic capacitor into a circuit?

11 Transformers and inductors

◆ About transformers

A transformer changes (transforms) *alternating* voltages and currents to higher or lower values. A *step-up* transformer increases the voltage but the current is decreased. A *step-down* transformer decreases the voltage but the current is increased. In neither case can the power output exceed the power input.

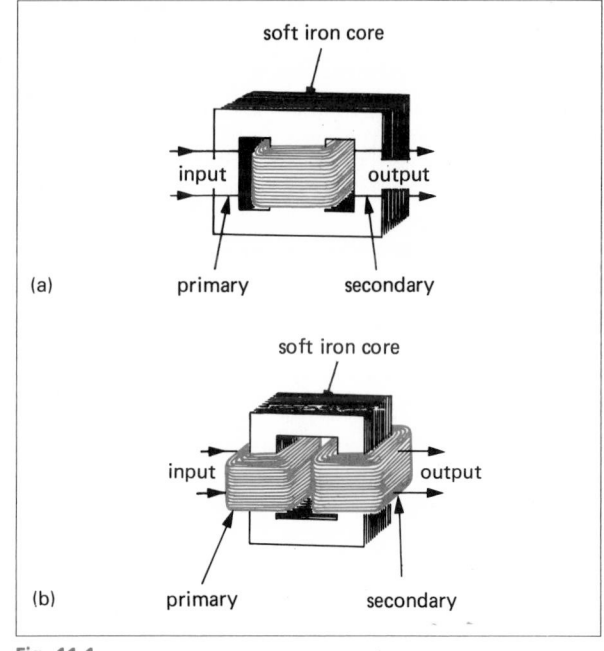

soft iron core

input / output

(a) primary / secondary

soft iron core

input / output

(b) primary / secondary

Fig. 11.1

A transformer consists of two coils of wire called the *primary* and the *secondary* windings which are not connected to each other electrically. The coils are wound on a core of soft iron sheets, either one on top of the other as in Fig. 11.1*a*, or side by side as in Fig. 11.1*b*. An alternating voltage applied to the primary (the *input*) produces a larger or smaller alternating voltage in the secondary (the *output*).

The symbols for step-up and step-down transformers are shown in Fig. 11.2*a,b*.

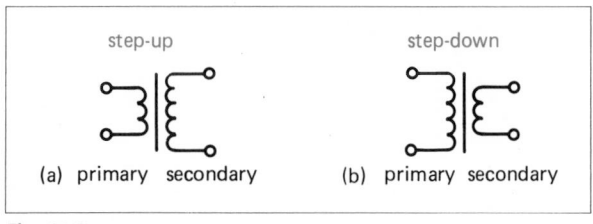

step-up   step-down

(a) primary secondary   (b) primary secondary

Fig. 11.2

◆ Turns ratio

The ratio of the output voltage from the secondary to the input voltage to the primary is approximately equal to the *turns ratio* of the windings. That is

$$\frac{\text{secondary voltage}}{\text{primary voltage}} = \frac{\text{secondary turns}}{\text{primary turns}}$$

In symbols

$$\frac{V_s}{V_p} = \frac{N_s}{N_p}$$

For example, in a step-up transformer, if $N_p = 1000$ turns and $N_s = 2000$ turns, the turns ratio is given by

$$\frac{N_s}{N_p} = \frac{2000}{1000} = \frac{2}{1}$$

Therefore, V_s will be *twice* V_p. If $V_p = 12$ V, $V_s = 24$ V but the secondary (output) current will be about *half* the primary (input) current.

In a step-down transformer, if $N_p = 1000$ turns and $N_s = 500$ turns, $N_p/N_s = 1000/500 = 2/1$ and V_s will be half V_p. Hence if $V_p = 12$ V, $V_s = 6$ V, but the secondary current will be about *twice* the primary current.

◇ Worked example

A transformer steps down the mains supply from 240 V to 12 V to light a lamp, Fig. 11.3.

(a) What is the turns ratio of the windings?
(b) How many turns are on the primary if the secondary has 100 turns?
(c) Estimate the current in the primary if the current in the lamp is 2 A.

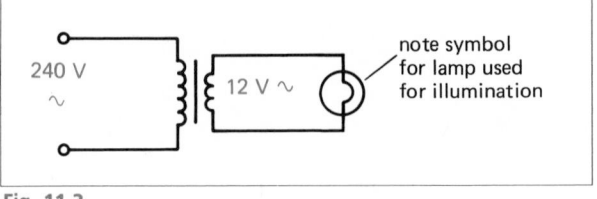

240 V ∼   12 V ∼   note symbol for lamp used for illumination

Fig. 11.3

(a) Primary voltage $V_p = 240$ V.
Secondary voltage $V_s = 12$ V.
Turns ratio $= \dfrac{N_s}{N_p} = \dfrac{V_s}{V_p} = \dfrac{12}{240} = \dfrac{1}{20}$
N_p is 20 times greater than N_s.

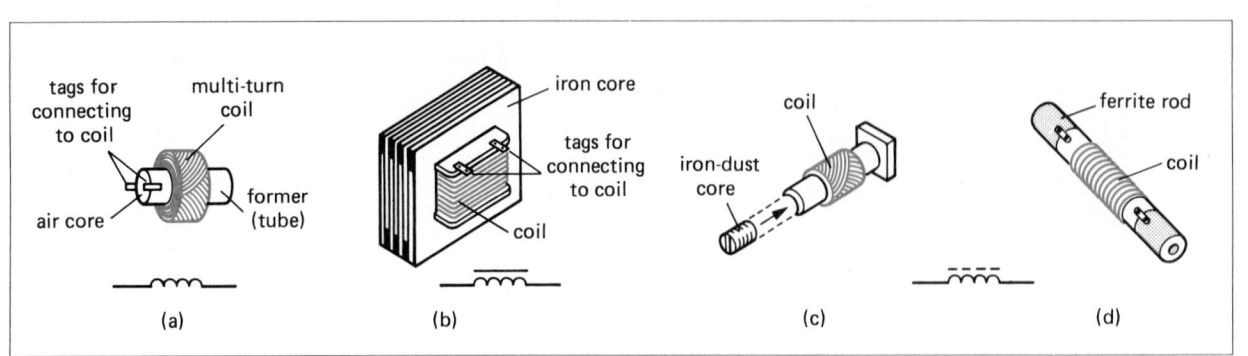

Fig. 11.4

(b) Secondary turns $N_s = 100$.
Therefore primary turns $N_p = 20 \times N_s = 20 \times 100$
$= 2000$ turns.
(c) The voltage is stepped down 20 times, therefore the current is stepped up about 20 times. Hence if

secondary current $= 2\,\text{A}$

primary current $\approx \dfrac{1}{20} \times 2 \approx \dfrac{1}{10} \approx 0.1\,\text{A}$

◆ Inductors

An inductor is a coil of wire with a core of air or a magnetic material. Four types with their symbols are shown in Fig. 11.4.

Inductors oppose current *changes* and are said to have *inductance* (symbol L).

In Fig. 11.5 if the variable resistor R is first adjusted so that the lamps are equally bright when S is closed, the resistance of R then equals the resistance (due to its coil) of the iron-cored inductor L. When S is opened and closed again, the lamp in series with L lights up a second or two *after* that in series with R. L opposes the *rise* of the d.c. from zero to its steady value.

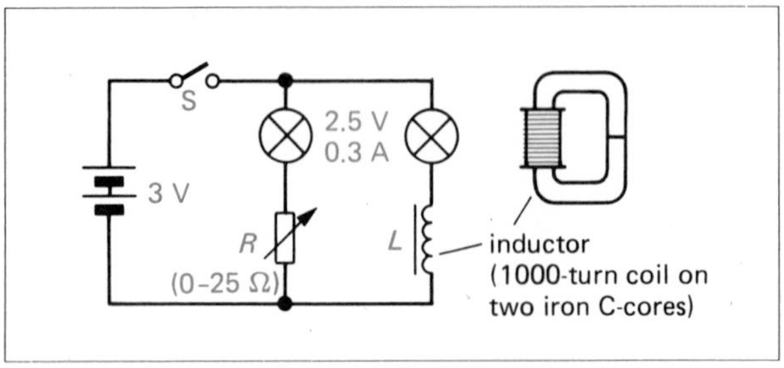

Fig. 11.5

If the 3 V battery is replaced by a 3 V a.c. supply, the lamp in series with L never lights. The alternating current is changing in value all the time and the opposition of L makes it too small to light the lamp.

The current in an inductor is greater if

(i) the frequency f of the a.c. is low, i.e. the current changes in value more slowly (at zero frequency, i.e. d.c., the current is a maximum), and
(ii) the inductance L is small, i.e. the core has fewer turns or no magnetic core.

To sum up, the opposition or *impedance* (see Chapter 10) to the current in an a.c. circuit containing an inductor is *small* if f and L are small.

◇ Questions

Q1
What is the turns ratio of a transformer in which
(a) $N_p = 200$ and $N_s = 400$, **(b)** $N_p = 600$ and $N_s = 300$,
(c) $V_p = 1\,\text{V}$ and $V_s = 4\,\text{V}$, **(d)** $V_p = 10\,\text{V}$ and $V_s = 2\,\text{V}$?

Q2
What is the value of
(a) V_s in Fig. 11.6a, **(b)** V_p in Fig. 11.6b, **(c)** N_s in Fig. 11.6c,
(d) N_p in Fig. 11.6d?

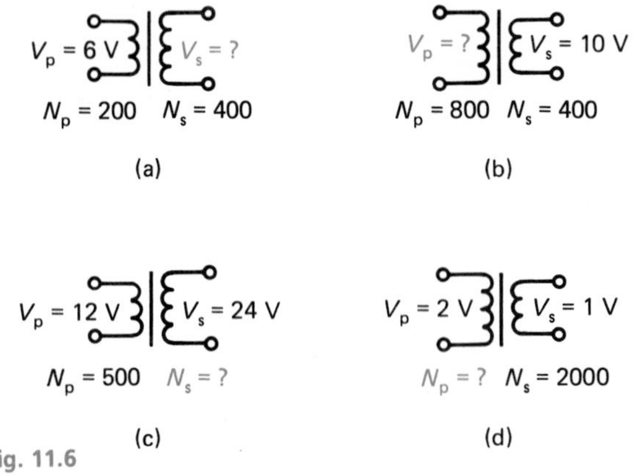

$V_p = 6\,\text{V}$ $V_s = ?$

$N_p = 200$ $N_s = 400$

(a)

$V_p = ?$ $V_s = 10\,\text{V}$

$N_p = 800$ $N_s = 400$

(b)

$V_p = 12\,\text{V}$ $V_s = 24\,\text{V}$

$N_p = 500$ $N_s = ?$

(c)

$V_p = 2\,\text{V}$ $V_s = 1\,\text{V}$

$N_p = ?$ $N_s = 2000$

(d)

Fig. 11.6

Q3
On a 240 V a.c. supply a transformer takes a primary current of 200 mA. What is the *maximum* current that should be delivered in the secondary if the output voltage is 480 V?

12 Transducers

A *transducer* changes energy from one form to another, one of these forms being electrical. An *input* transducer has a non-electrical input and an electrical output. An *output* transducer has an electrical input and a non-electrical output. Both types enable an electronic system (Chapter 23) to communicate with the outside world.

◆ Input transducers

(a) Microphone. A microphone changes sound into electrical energy. The popular, good quality *moving-coil* type is shown in Fig. 12.1 *a,b* with the circuit symbol for a microphone. The *crystal* type does not give as good reproduction but it is inexpensive and much used in cassette recorders.

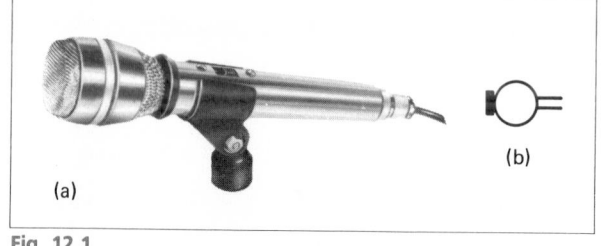

(a)

(b)

Fig. 12.1

(b) Pick-up. A record player pick-up changes the sound stored on a disc (record) into electrical energy.

(c) Thermistor. One is shown in Fig. 12.2*a,b* with its symbol. It is a resistor whose resistance *decreases*

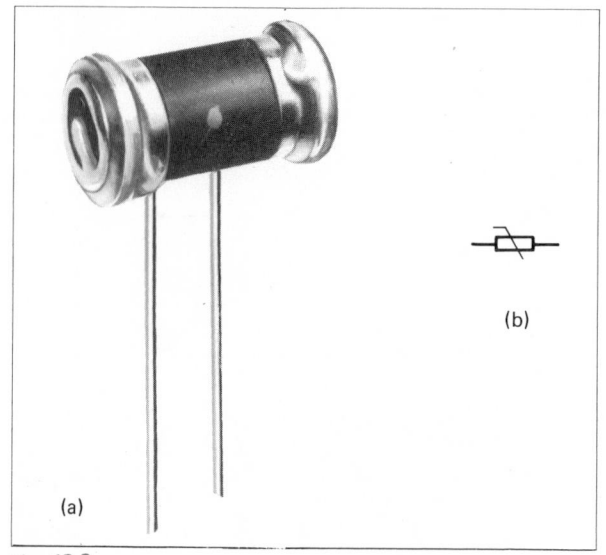

(a)

(b)

Fig. 12.2

considerably when its temperature *rises*. This enables it to change heat into electrical energy.

(d) Light dependent resistor (LDR). Its resistance *decreases* when it is illuminated enabling it to change light into electrical energy. One is shown in Fig. 12.3*a,b* with its symbol. It is also called a photocell.

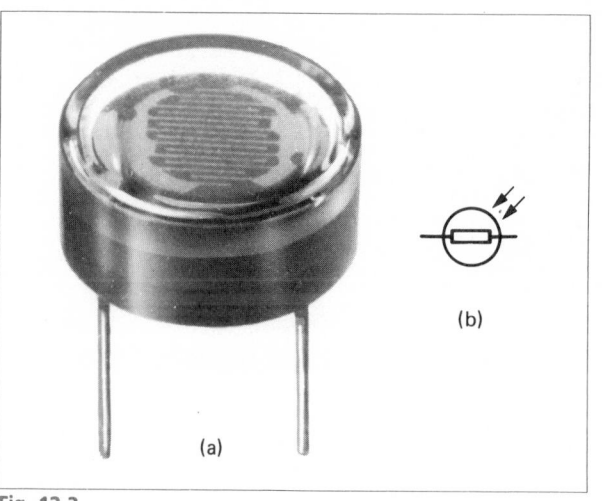

(a)

(b)

Fig. 12.3

(e) Switches. When a switch is operated and completes one or more circuits, we can look upon the mechanical energy supplied by the person operating it as causing the production of electrical energy in the circuit.

Switches have different numbers of *poles* and *throws* (or *ways*). The poles (P) are the number of separate circuits the switch makes or breaks at the same time. The throws (T) are the number of positions to which each pole can be switched. The symbols for various types are given in Fig. 12.4. In a SPDT (single pole double throw) switch there are two positions for the switch (B or C) and only one circuit (that joined to A) is switched.

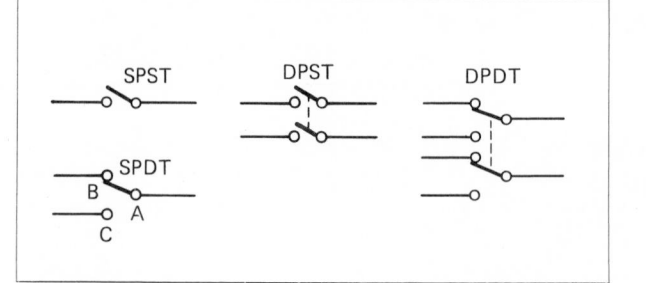

Fig. 12.4

(i) *Push-button.* The one in Fig. 12.5a is a 'push-on, release-off' type; its symbol is given in Fig. 12.5b and that for the 'push-off, release-on' variety in Fig. 12.5c. 'Push-to-change-over' switches are also made; their symbol is shown in Fig. 12.5d.

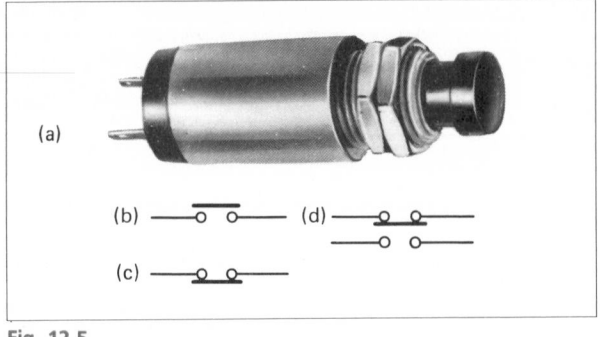

Fig. 12.5

(ii) *Slide.* The slide switch in Fig. 12.6a is a 'change-over' SPDT type.

(iii) *Toggle.* This type is often used on equipment as a power supply 'on-off' switch, either in the SPST form shown in Fig. 12.6b or as a SPDT, DPST or DPDT type.

(iv) *Keyboard.* The one shown in Fig. 12.6c is a SPST push-to-make momentary type which can be mounted on a printed circuit board (p.c.b.).

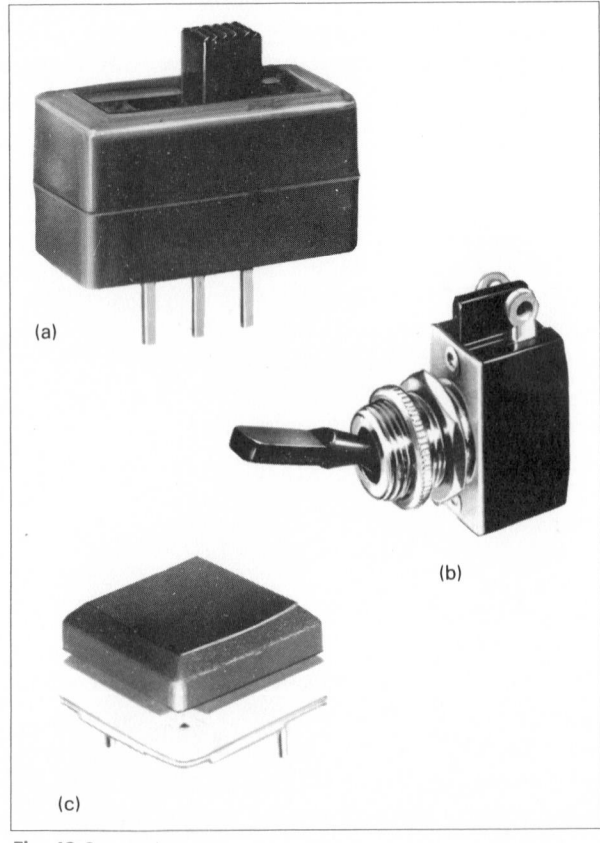

Fig. 12.6

(v) *Rotary wafer.* One or more insulating plastic discs or wafers are mounted on a twelve-position spindle as shown in Fig. 12.7a. The wafers have metal contact strips on one or both sides and rotate between a similar number of fixed wafers with springy contact strips. The contacts on the wafers can be arranged to give switching that is 1 pole 12 throw, 2 pole 6 throw, 3 pole 4 throw, 4 pole 3 throw (as in Fig. 12.7b) or 6 pole 2 throw.

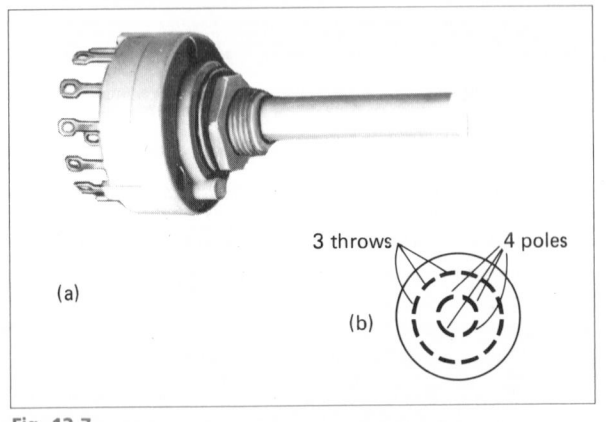

Fig. 12.7

(vi) *Switch ratings.* A switch is rated according to (a) the *maximum current* it can carry and (b) its *working voltage*. These both depend on whether it is to be used in a.c. or d.c. circuits. For example, one with an a.c. rating of 250 V 1.5 A, has a d.c. rating of 20 V 3 A. If these values are exceeded the life of the switch is shortened. This is due to overheating while it carries current or to vaporization of the contacts due to sparking. This happens when the current tries to keep flowing in the air gap when the switch is switched off. In general, sparking lasts longer with d.c. than with a.c. because a.c. falls to zero twice per cycle.

◆ Output transducers

(a) Loudspeaker. A loudspeaker changes electrical energy into sound. One is shown in Fig. 12.8a,b with its symbol.

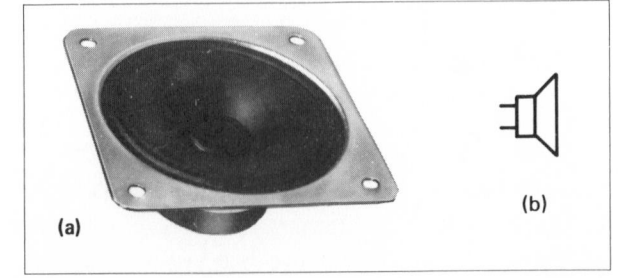

Fig. 12.8

(b) Solenoid. A solenoid is a long coil of wire which becomes a temporary magnet while current passes through it, Fig. 12.9a. Its magnetism is much greater if it is wound on an iron core, Fig. 12.9b. Anything near it which is made of magnetic material moves towards it, i.e. electrical energy is changed to mechanical energy.

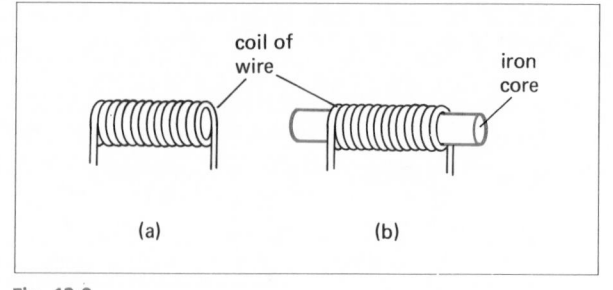

Fig. 12.9

(c) Buzzer and bell. These produce sound from electrical energy and contain an iron-cored solenoid.

(d) Relay. This is an electrically operated switch in which a small current passes through a coil and magnetizes it. Electrical energy is thus changed into mechanical energy (movement).

A relay is used when we want a small current in one circuit to control another circuit containing a device such as a lamp, an electric motor, a bell or a buzzer, which needs a large current.

A relay and its symbol are shown in Fig. 12.10a,b.

A relay with a nominal coil voltage of 12 V may, for example, work off any voltage between 9 V and 15 V.

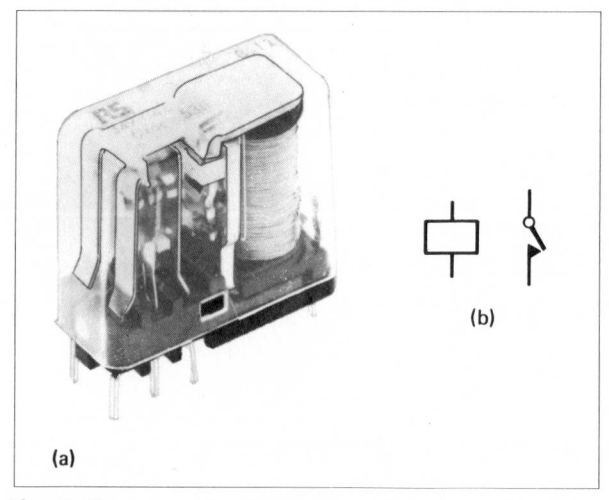

(a)

Fig. 12.10

The coil resistance (e.g. 185 Ω) is also quoted as well as the current and voltage ratings of the contacts. The current needed to operate a relay is called the *pull-in* current, and the *drop-out* current is the smaller current

in the coil when the relay just stops working. For the above relay, the pull-in current I is given by $I = V/R = 12\ \text{V}/185\ \Omega = 0.065\ \text{A} = 65\ \text{mA}$.

(e) Reed switch. A reed switch operates much faster than a relay. The one in Fig. 12.11 consists of two reeds (thin strips) of easily magnetized and demagnetized material sealed in a small glass tube. When current passes through a coil surrounding the switch (or a magnet is brought near) the reeds become oppositely magnetized. Attraction occurs and when they touch, the circuit connected to the terminals is completed. The reeds separate when the current in the coil stops or the magnet is removed.

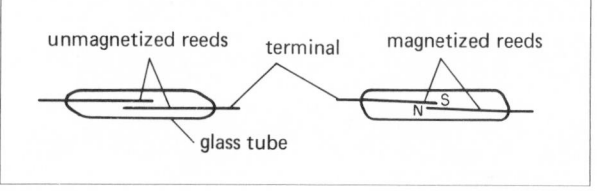

Fig. 12.11

(f) Electric motor. This causes rotation and changes electrical energy into mechanical energy. Many domestic appliances such as vacuum cleaners and washing machines contain one. 'Stepper' motors, driven by current pulses, turn the arm of a robot a fixed amount per pulse. A small motor is shown in Fig. 12.12a, b with its symbol.

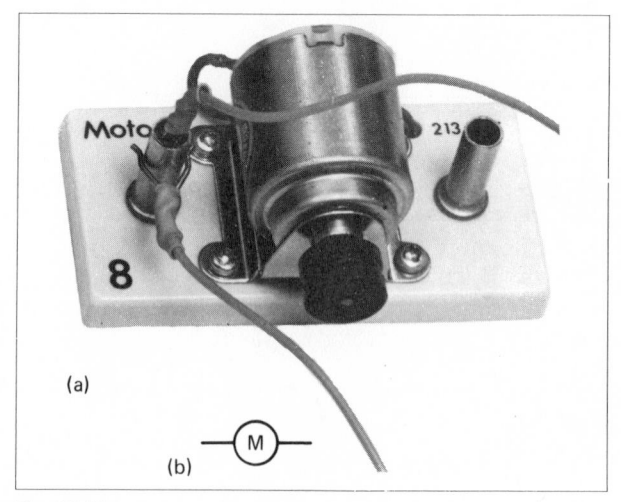

Fig. 12.12

(g) Lamps. They convert electrical energy into light. In an ordinary filament lamp used for illumination, only about 2% of the electrical energy becomes light, the rest is changed to unwanted heat. A LED (Chapter 14) changes electrical energy directly to light and is much more efficient.

◆ Input transducers and potential dividers

Certain input transducers often form a potential divider with a resistor, to supply the input to an electronic system.

(a) Thermistor and resistor. The circuit in Fig. 12.13a is a *temperature sensing unit* in which the output voltage V_{out} falls if the temperature of the thermistor rises due to R_2 decreasing. For example, if $V_{in} = 9$ V, $R_1 = 10\ \Omega$ and $R_2 = 80\ \Omega$ when the thermistor is at room temperature, then using the potential divider equation given in Chapter 5 we get

$$V_{out} = \left(\frac{R_2}{R_1 + R_2}\right) V_{in} = \left(\frac{80}{10 + 80}\right) 9 = \frac{80}{90} \times 9 = 8\,\text{V}$$

If $R_2 = 10\ \Omega$ when the thermistor is heated, then

$$V_{out} = \left(\frac{10}{10 + 10}\right) 9 = \frac{10}{20} \times 9 = 4.5\,\text{V}$$

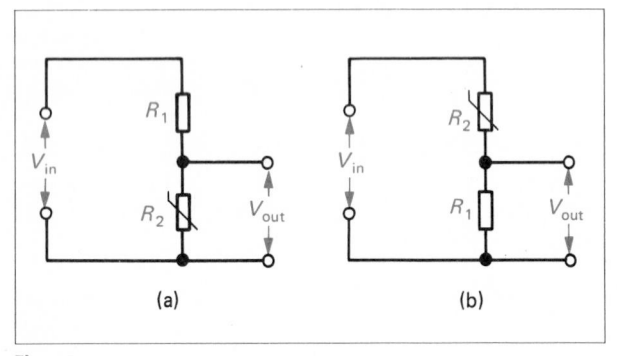

(a) **(b)**

Fig. 12.13

In the circuit of Fig. 12.13b the thermistor and resistor are interchanged, and in this case V_{out} *rises* if the thermistor is heated.

(b) LDR and resistor. *Light sensing units* are shown in Fig. 12.14a,b. In (a) when the LDR is illuminated its resistance R_2 *falls*, as does the voltage across it, i.e. V_{out}. In (b) V_{out} *increases* when the LDR is illuminated.

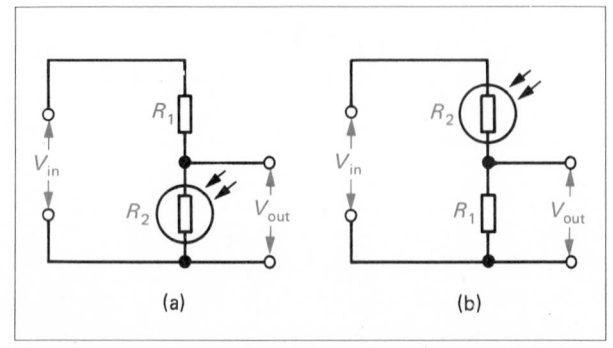

(a) **(b)**

Fig. 12.14

(c) Switch and resistor. In Fig. 12.15a when the switch is open (OFF), R_2 is infinitely large. Compared with R_2, R_1 is negligible and the potential divider equation becomes

$$V_{out} = \left(\frac{R_2}{R_2}\right) V_{in} = V_{in} \qquad \text{(see also Chapter 2)}$$

When the switch is closed (ON), $R_2 = 0$ and

$$V_{out} = \left(\frac{0}{R_1 + 0}\right) V_{in} = 0 \qquad \text{(see also Chapter 2)}$$

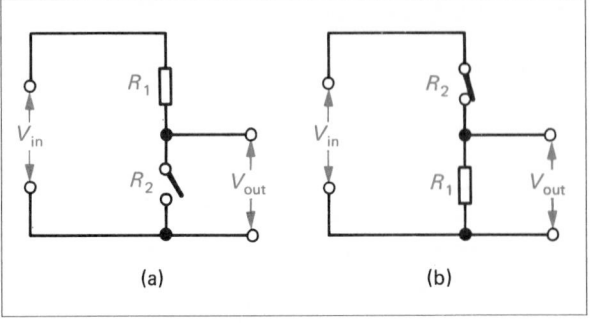

(a) **(b)**

Fig. 12.15

These results are summarized in the table below.

Switch	V_{out}
OFF	V_{in}
ON	0

In Fig. 12.15b the reverse occurs. That is, when the switch is closed, $V_{out} = V_{in}$ and when it is open, $V_{out} = 0$.

In (a) R_1 is a 'pull-up' resistor, i.e. $V_{out} = V_{in}$ unless the switch is closed. In (b) R_2 is a 'pull-down' resistor, i.e. $V_{out} = 0$ unless the switch is closed.

◇ Questions

Q1

Identify the transducers represented by the symbols in Fig. 12.16a to *i* and say what each one does.

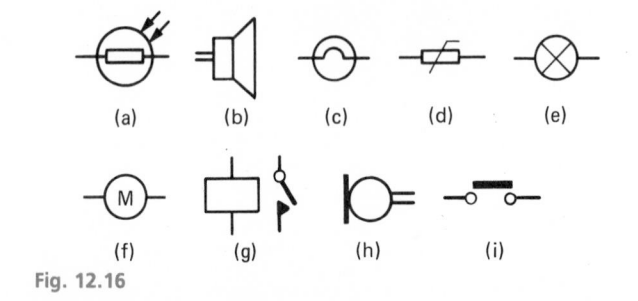

(a) **(b)** **(c)** **(d)** **(e)**

(f) **(g)** **(h)** **(i)**

Fig. 12.16

Q2

In terms of forms of energy, what is the difference between an input and an output transducer?

Q3

If L is just alight in the circuits of Fig. 12.17*a*, *b*, does it get brighter or dimmer in (*a*) if the thermistor is heated and in (*b*) if the LDR is screened from daylight?

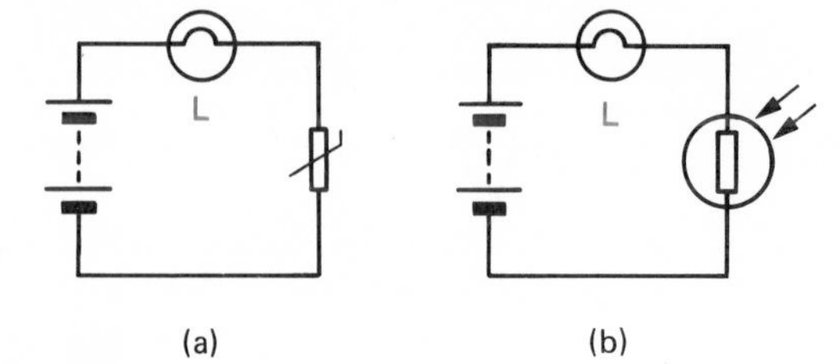

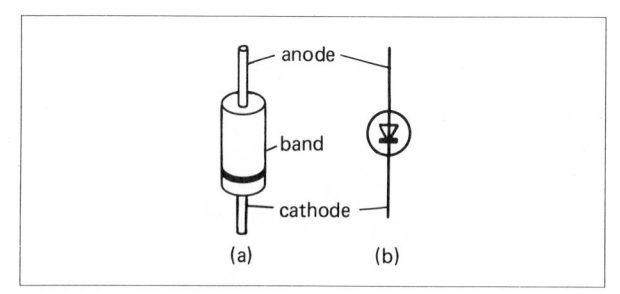

(a) (b)

Fig. 12.17

Q4

What happens to V_{out} in the circuit of
(a) Fig. 12.13*a* when the temperature of the thermistor falls,
(b) Fig. 12.14*b* when the LDR is in the dark?

Q5

What kind of switch is used in Fig. 12.18 to reverse the direction of rotation of the motor?

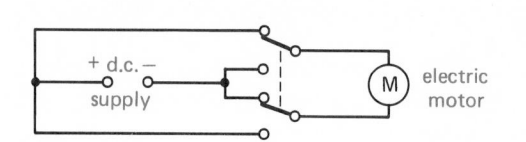

Fig. 12.18

13 Diode and power supplies

◆ The diode

(a) Action. A diode allows current to pass through it in one direction only. One is shown in Fig. 13.1*a*, *b* with its symbol. The end nearest the band round it is called the *cathode* and the other end is the *anode*.

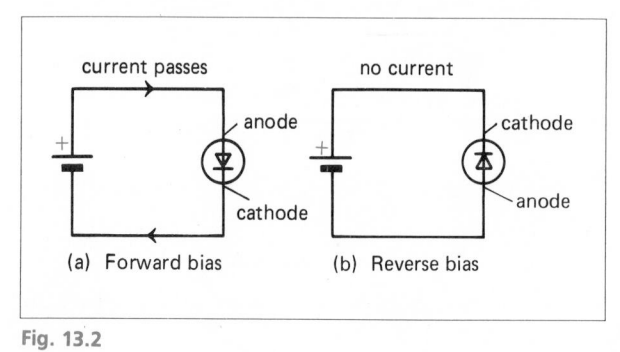

Fig. 13.1

The diode conducts when the anode goes to the + terminal of the voltage supply and the cathode to the − terminal, Fig. 13.2*a*. It is then *forward biased* and has a

very low resistance. Conventional current passes in the direction of the arrow on its symbol, i.e. from anode to cathode. If the connections are the other way round, it has a very high resistance and does not conduct. It is then *reverse biased*, Fig. 13.2*b*.

The semiconductors silicon and germanium are used to make diodes.

(b) Characteristic curve. When a diode is forward biased conduction does not start until the voltage, called the *turn-on voltage*, is about 0.6 V for silicon and 0.1 V for germanium. Thereafter a very small increase in voltage causes a sudden, large increase in current, as the *I–V* graph in Fig. 13.3 for a silicon diode shows.

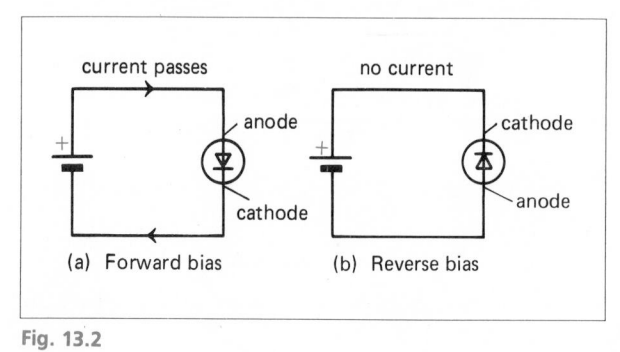

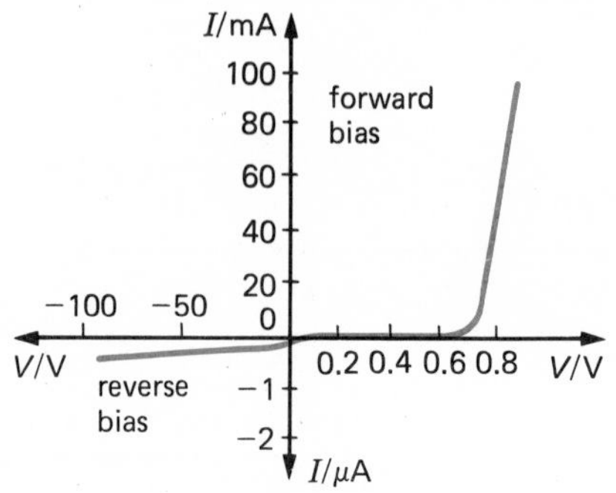

Fig. 13.3

For every diode there is a maximum forward current, called the *forward current rating* I_F, which should not be exceeded. Otherwise overheating occurs and the diode may be destroyed. For the 1N4001 diode $I_F = 1$ A.

(a) Forward bias (b) Reverse bias

Fig. 13.2

If the reverse bias exceeds a certain value, called the *maximum reverse voltage V_{RRM}* (or *peak inverse voltage rating*) of the diode, it conducts suddenly in the wrong direction and may be permanently damaged. For the 1N4001, $V_{RRM} = 50\,V$.

(c) Uses. Diodes are used
(i) as *rectifiers* to change a.c. to d.c. in power supplies (see below), and
(ii) to *prevent damage to a circuit by a reversed voltage supply.* In Fig. 13.4*a* the battery is correctly connected and forward biases the diode. In Fig. 13.4*b* it is incorrectly connected but since it reverse biases the diode, no current passes and no damage occurs to the circuit.

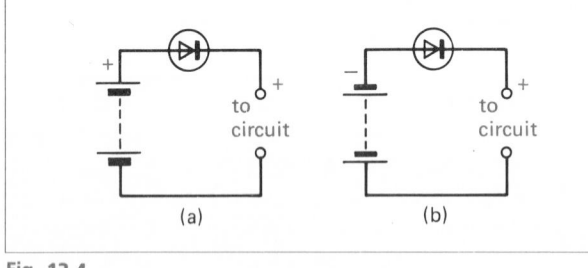

Fig. 13.4

◆ Power supplies

Many electronic systems require a d.c. supply. Batteries are suitable for portable equipment but in general, power supply units operated from the a.c. mains are used. They are more economical and reliable and can provide more power than batteries.

In most power supply units a transformer steps down the mains from 240 V to a much lower voltage, e.g. 12 V. This is then changed to d.c., i.e. *rectified*, by one or more diodes.

◆ Half-wave rectifier

In the circuit of Fig. 13.5, the *load* (i.e. an electronic system such as a radio, a TV set or a computer) is represented by a resistor.

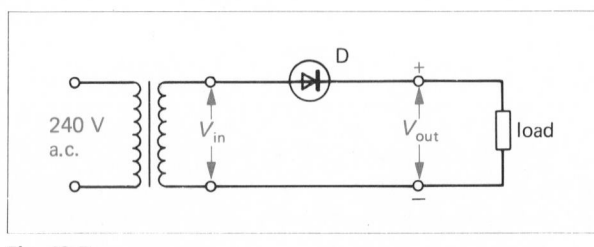

Fig. 13.5

Positive half-cycles of the alternating input p.d. V_{in} from the transformer secondary, forward bias diode D which conducts, producing positive pulses of current. These create a voltage V_{out} across the load having almost the same peak value as V_{in}.

Negative half-cycles of V_{in} reverse bias D, no current passes and V_{out} is zero. Fig. 13.6 shows that V_{out} is a varying but direct (one-way) voltage, i.e. d.c., consisting of only positive half-cycles.

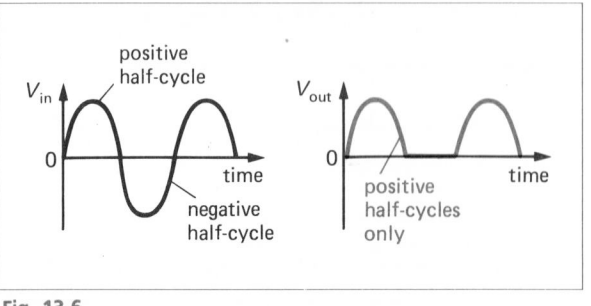

Fig. 13.6

◆ Bridge full-wave rectifier

In this circuit both half-cycles of the a.c. input to be rectified cause current to pass through the load, hence the term 'full-wave'. Four diodes are used in a 'bridge' network and a larger average current is supplied, Fig. 13.7.

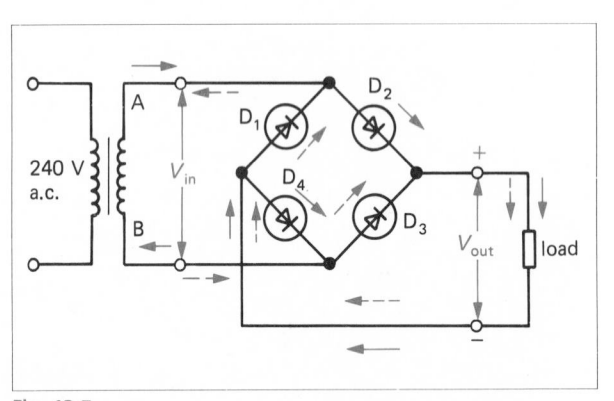

Fig. 13.7

If A is positive and B negative during the first half-cycle of the input V_{in}, D_2 and D_4 are forward biased and conduct. Current takes the path AD_2 load D_4B as shown by the solid arrows. On the next half-cycle when B is positive and A negative, D_1 and D_3 conduct and current takes the path BD_3 load D_1A.

For both half-cycles of V_{in} current passes through the load in the *same* direction. The output V_{out} across the 'load' is a d.c. voltage, varying as in Fig. 13.8.

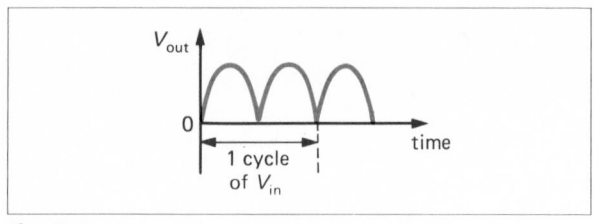

Fig. 13.8

◆ Smoothing

The varying d.c. output voltage from a rectifier circuit must be 'smoothed' to obtain the steady d.c. required by electronic systems. This can be done by connecting a large capacitor C (an electrolytic whose large leakage current does not matter too much in this case), called a *reservoir capacitor*, across the load, as in Fig. 13.9a.

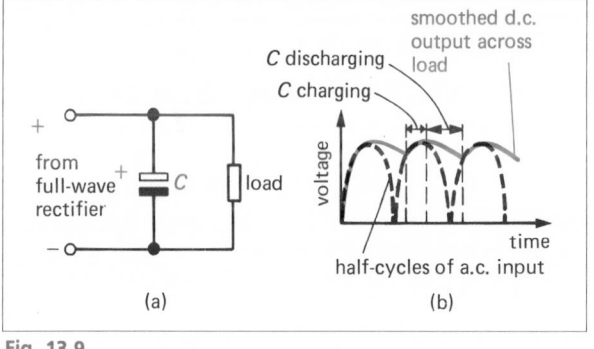

Fig. 13.9

The smoothed d.c. output voltage is shown in Fig. 13.9b. It has a small *ripple voltage* on it which causes 'mains hum'. Smoothing occurs because C is charged up by the half-cycles of a.c. input. When these fall below the p.d. across C, C partly discharges through the load, keeping it supplied with current and acting as a reservoir of charge. C is recharged when the half-cycles of a.c. input rise above the p.d. across C, as Fig. 13.9b shows.

The amplitude of the ripple voltage decreases if
(i) C is increased since a greater charge is held and the p.d. across C falls less when it supplies current, and
(ii) the output current taken by the load decreases because the p.d. across a certain C is less affected if a smaller current is drawn from it.

◆ Heat sinks

High current diode rectifiers are mounted on *heat sinks* with cooling fins (made of aluminium sheet and painted black), as shown in Fig. 13.10a to stop them overheating. Manufacturers state what the *thermal resistance* of the

heat sink should be for a particular rectifier. For example, if it is 2°CW⁻¹, the temperature of the heat sink rises by 2°C above its surroundings for every watt of power it has to get rid of. To dissipate 10 W, the rise will be 20°C. A transistor heat sink is shown in Fig. 13.10b.

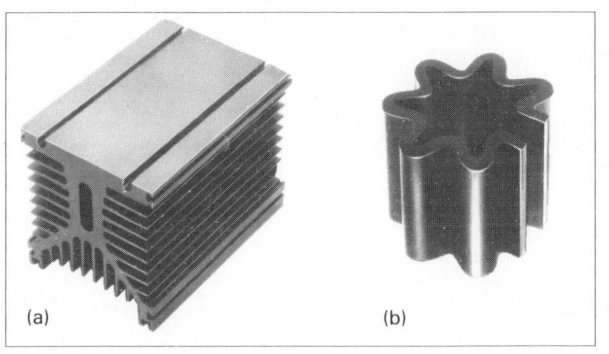

Fig. 13.10

◇ Questions

Q1
In the circuits of Fig. 13.11 say which of the 6 V 60 mA lamps are bright, dim or off.

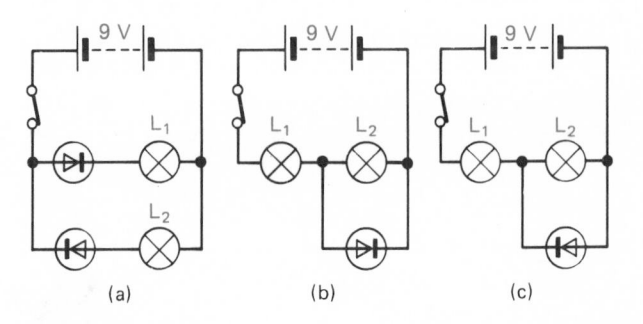

Fig. 13.11

Q2
The voltage drop across a 1N4001 diode is 1 V when the forward current is 1 A. If it is used on a 6 V supply as in Fig. 13.12, calculate
(a) the value of the safety resistor R, and
(b) the power dissipated in the diode.

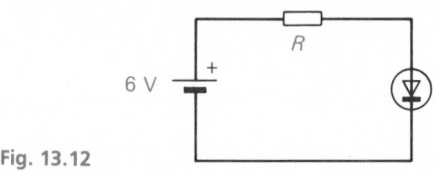

Fig. 13.12

Q3
(a) What is meant by *rectification*? Name a component which is used to achieve it.
(b) What is meant by *smoothing*? Name a component which is used to achieve it.

14 Other semiconductor diodes

◆ Zener diode

A Zener diode, shown in Fig. 14.1a,b with its symbol, is a special kind of silicon diode.

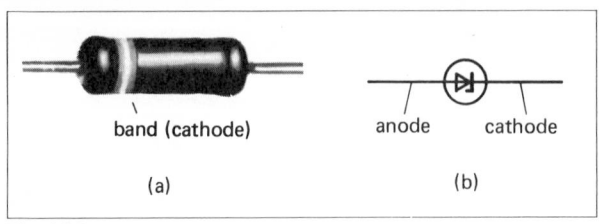

band (cathode)   anode   cathode

(a)   (b)

Fig. 14.1

(a) Characteristic curve. The current–voltage graph in Fig.14.2 shows that when forward biased, a Zener diode turns on at about 0.6 V, like an ordinary silicon diode. However, it is normally used in reverse bias. Then the reverse current is negligible until the reverse p.d. reaches a certain value V_Z, called the *Zener*, *reference* or *breakdown voltage*. At V_Z, the reverse current increases suddenly and rapidly as the graph indicates. At breakdown the diode may be damaged by overheating unless the reverse current is limited by a series resistor. If this is connected, the *p.d. across the diode remains constant at V_Z* over a wide range of reverse current values. It is this property of a Zener diode which makes it useful.

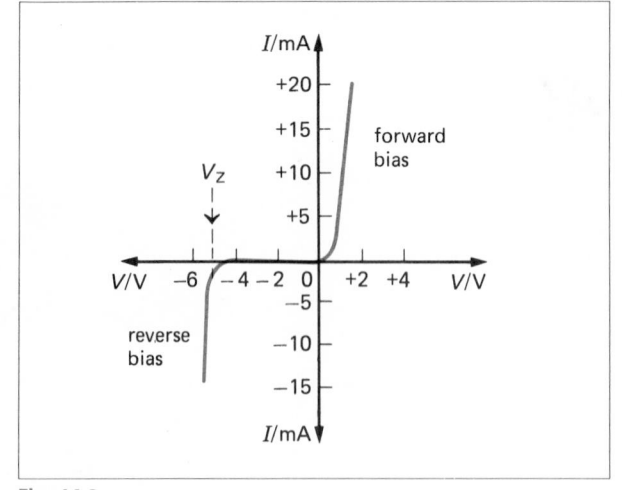

Fig. 14.2

Zener diodes with specified Zener voltages between 2.0 and 200 V are made.

(b) Voltage regulation. Zener diodes are used to regulate or stabilize (i.e. keep steady) the *output voltage*

from a power supply unit or a battery. In an unregulated power supply the output voltage falls if the output current rises and this may upset the working of the electronic system being supplied, i.e. the load. (The output voltage falls because the power supply has *internal* (or source) *resistance* itself through which the output current has also to pass. As a result, some of the voltage the power supply generates is dropped ('lost') across this resistance, thus reducing the output voltage available for the load. When the output current increases, the 'lost' volts also increase and reduce the output voltage further.)

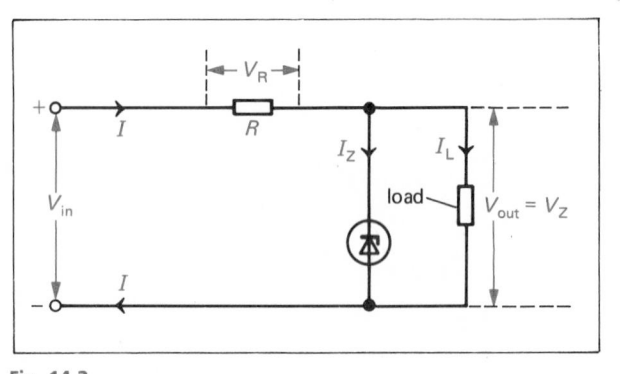

Fig. 14.3

In the regulating circuit of Fig. 14.3, the Zener diode is *reverse biased* and is in parallel with the load. The input voltage V_{in} to the circuit is taken from an unregulated supply, e.g. a battery, and is greater than the output voltage V_{out} that is developed across the load. If I_Z and I_L are the currents in the diode and load respectively, the total current supplied, I, is given by

$$I = I_Z + I_L$$

If I_L rises (or falls), I_Z is found to fall (or rise) by the *same* amount, so keeping I and therefore V_{out} ($= V_Z$) constant. This happens because, even with different reverse currents through it, a Zener diode at breakdown has a constant voltage across it.

(c) Series resistor. The current-limiting resistor in series with the diode should have resistance R which is given by

$$R = \frac{V_R}{I} = \frac{V_{in} - V_Z}{I}$$

since $V_{in} = V_R + V_Z$. For example, in Fig. 14.3, if $V_{in} = 9$ V, $V_{out} = 5$ V, $I_L = 40$ mA and $I_Z = 10$ mA, then

$$I = I_Z + I_L = 10 + 40 = 50 \text{ mA} = 0.05 \text{ A}$$

therefore

$$R = (9\,V - 5\,V)/0.05\,A = 4\,V/0.05\,A = 80\,\Omega$$

The power P_R dissipated in R is given by

$$P_R = V_R \times I = 4\,V \times 50\,mA = 200\,mW = 0.2\,W$$

The power $P_Z = V_Z \times I_Z = 5\,V \times 10\,mA = 50\,mW = 0.05\,W$. *Note*. If the load is disconnected, $I_L = 0$ and $I_Z = 50\,mA$ making $P_Z = 5\,V \times 50\,mA = 250\,mW = 0.25\,W$. The power rating of the diode must therefore be 0.25 W at least, to carry 50 mA safely.

(d) Demonstration. When the input p.d. V_{in} in Fig. 14.4 is gradually increased we see that:
(i) if $V_{in} < 6.2\,V$ (the Zener voltage), $I = 0$ and the output p.d. $V_{out} = V_{in}$ since there is no current through R and so no p.d. across it, and
(ii) if $V_{in} > 6.2\,V$, the diode conducts, even though it is reverse biased, and $V_{out} = 6.2\,V$, any excess p.d. appearing across R.

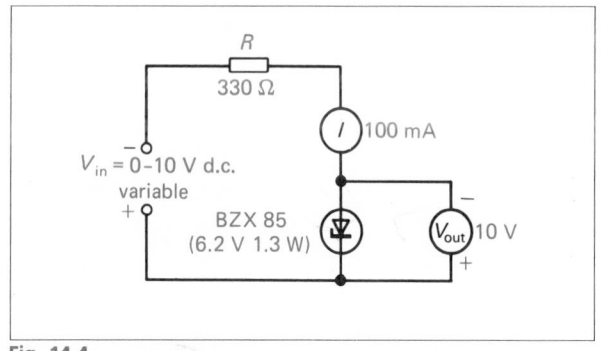

Fig. 14.4

The Zener diode thus regulates V_{out} so long as V_{in} is not less than V_Z (here 6.2 V), i.e. there must be current through it.

◆ Light emitting diode (LED)

(a) What it does. A LED, shown in Fig. 14.5*a,b* with its symbol, is a diode made from the semiconductor

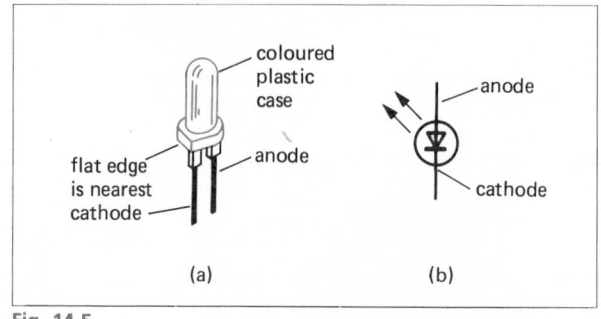

Fig. 14.5

gallium arsenide phosphide. When forward biased it conducts and emits red, green or yellow light. No conduction or emission of light occurs for reverse bias which, if it exceeds 5 V, may damage the LED.

(b) Series resistor. To limit the current through a LED, a resistor R must be connected in series with it, otherwise it could be destroyed, Fig. 14.6.

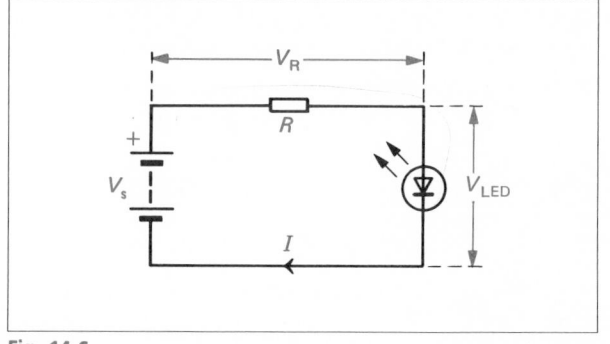

Fig. 14.6

The forward voltage drop V_{LED} across a LED is about 2 V (compared with 1 V for a silicon diode) and a typical current $I = 10\,mA = 0.01\,A$. The value of R depends on the supply voltage V_s and is given by

$$R = \frac{V_R}{I} = \frac{V_s - V_{LED}}{I}$$

since $V_s = V_R + V_{LED}$. For example, if $V_s = 5\,V$ then

$$R = (5\,V - 2\,V)/0.01\,A = 3\,V/0.01\,A = 300\,\Omega$$

(c) Uses. LEDs are used as indicator (or signal) lamps in radios and other electronic systems. Their advantages over filament lamps are small size, reliability, long life, fast response and small current needs.

Many calculators, clocks, cash registers and measuring instruments show their 'output' on several seven-segment, red or green numerical displays, like the one in Fig. 14.7*a*. Each segment is a LED and, depending on which have a p.d. across them, the display lights up the numbers 0 to 9, as in Fig. 14.7*b* (see also Chapter 31).

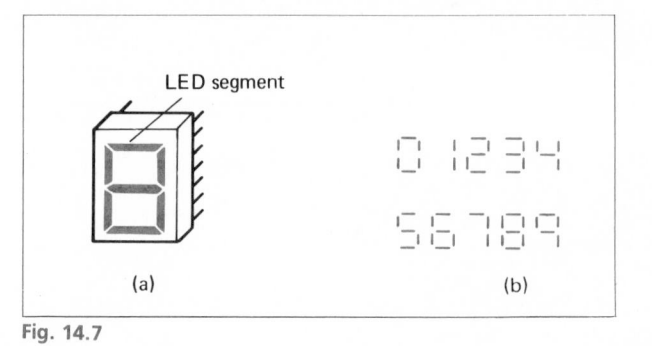

Fig. 14.7

◆ Photodiode

A photodiode is a silicon diode in a case with a transparent 'window' through which light can enter. One is shown in Fig. 14.8*a,b* with its symbol. It is operated in reverse bias and only conducts when light falls on it. It is used as a fast counter which produces a pulse of current every time a beam of light is interrupted, e.g. when counting objects on a moving conveyor belt.

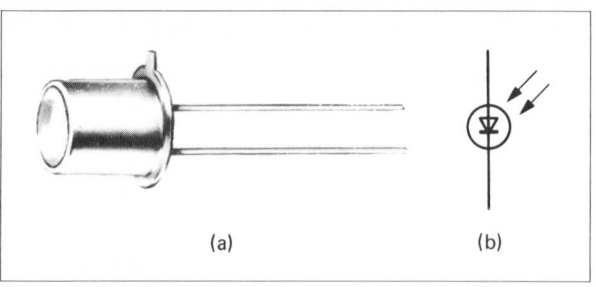

(a)   (b)

Fig. 14.8

◆ Thyristor

This is a silicon diode with a third connection called the *gate*. When forward biased it does not conduct until a positive voltage is applied to the gate. Conduction

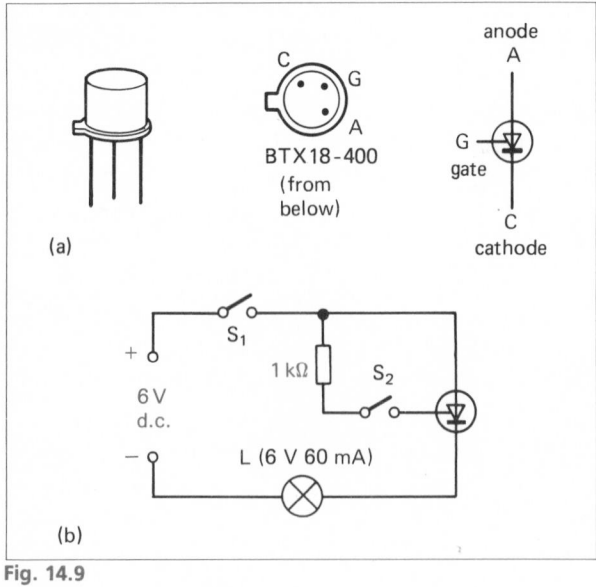

(a)

(b)

Fig. 14.9

continues when the gate voltage is removed and stops only if the supply voltage is switched off or is reversed.

A thyristor, its symbol and a circuit for showing its action are given in Fig. 14.9 *a,b*. When S_1 is closed, the lamp L stays off. When S_2 is closed as well, gate current flows and the thyristor switches on, i.e. it 'fires'. The anode current is large enough to light L, which stays alight even if S_2 is opened.

Thyristors are used as 'latching' switches in alarm circuits (see Chapter 27).

◇ Questions

Q1
In Fig. 14.3 the Zener diode has a breakdown voltage of 3 V. If the input voltage from an unregulated power supply is $V_{in} = 7$ V, what is
(a) the output voltage V_{out},
(b) the voltage V_R across R,
(c) the current I if $I_Z = 5$ mA and $I_L = 35$ mA,
(d) the value of R, and
(e) the power dissipated in the diode?

Q2
In Fig. 14.3, if $V_{in} = 8$ V, $V_{out} = 3$ V and $R = 50$ Ω, what is the value of **(a)** I, **(b)** I_L if $I_Z = 20$ mA?

Q3
Calculate the maximum current a Zener diode can carry without damage, if its breakdown voltage is 10 V and its power rating is 5 W.

Q4
In Fig. 14.10 the LED is bright when the current through it is 10 mA and the voltage across it is 2 V. Calculate the value of the current-limiting series resistor R if the supply is 9 V.

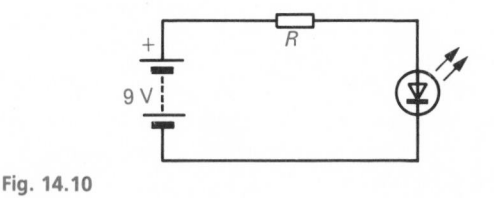

Fig. 14.10

Q5
State one use for **(a)** a Zener diode, **(b)** a LED, **(c)** a photodiode and **(d)** a thyristor.

15 Transistors and ICs

◆ Bipolar transistor

A bipolar transistor has three leads called the *collector* (C), the *base* (B) and the *emitter* (E). The one in Fig. 15.1*a,b* with its symbol is an *n-p-n* type in which C and B must have *positive* voltages with respect to E. In a *p-n-p* type the arrow on the symbol is reversed, Fig. 15.1*c*, and C and B must have *negative* voltages with respect to E.

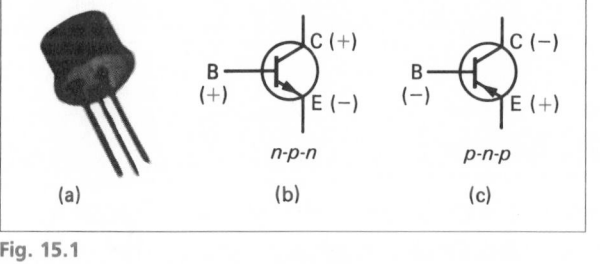

Fig. 15.1

There are two current paths through a transistor. In the *n-p-n* type the *base current* I_B enters by B and the *collector current* I_C by C. Both leave by the emitter, where they combine to form the *emitter current* I_E.

The *action of a transistor* can be shown using the circuit of Fig. 15.2, in which positive voltages are supplied to both C and B by the same battery.

When S is *open*, I_B *is zero* and neither L_1 or L_2 light up, showing that I_C is *also zero* even though the battery is correctly connected across C and E.

When S is *closed*, B is connected through R to the battery+ and L_2 lights up, but not L_1. This shows that I_C

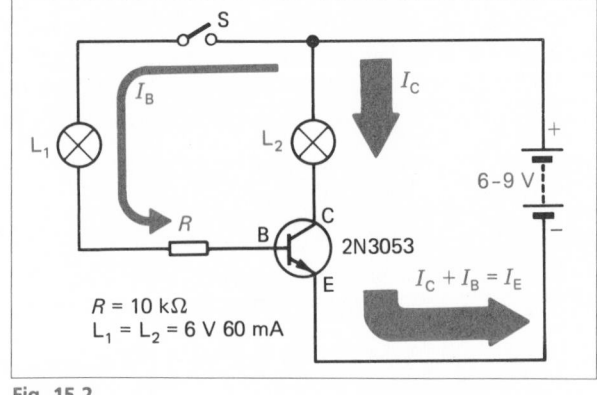

$R = 10\,\text{k}\Omega$
$L_1 = L_2 = 6\,\text{V } 60\,\text{mA}$

Fig. 15.2

is now passing through L_2 and that *it is much greater than* I_B, which passes through L_1, but is too small to light it.

To sum up: I_B *switches on and controls the much greater* I_C, and measurements show that the switch-on does not occur until B is at least 0.6 V positive with respect to E. That is, the *turn-on voltage for a transistor is about 0.6 V or so*. The base–emitter behaves like a diode and must have a forward bias of at least 0.6 V before I_B flows and turns on I_C.

Two further points to note are
(i) R must be in the base circuit *to limit* I_B, otherwise it causes an excessive I_C which destroys the transistor by overheating, and
(ii) the current paths for I_C and I_B have a common connection at E and the transistor is said to be in *common–emitter connection*.

◆ Transistor as a current amplifier

If we think of I_B as the *input* to a transistor and I_C as the *output* from it, then the transistor acts as a *current amplifier* since I_C is greater than I_B.

Typically, I_C is 10 to 1000 times greater than I_B depending on the type of transistor. The *current gain* h_{FE} is an important property of a transistor and is given by

$$h_{FE} = \frac{I_C}{I_B}$$

For example, if $I_C = 5\,\text{mA}$ and $I_B = 0.05\,\text{mA}$ $(50\,\mu\text{A})$

$$h_{FE} = \frac{5\,\text{mA}}{0.05\,\text{mA}} = 100$$

Although h_{FE} is approximately constant for one transistor over a limited range of I_C values, it varies between transistors of the same type due to manufacturing tolerances.

Also note that since the current leaving a transistor equals that entering,

$$I_E = I_B + I_C$$

In the above example $I_E = 5.05\,\text{mA}$.

◇ **Worked example**

In the circuit of Fig. 15.3, if $I_C = 40$ mA and $h_{FE} = 200$, calculate **(a)** I_B, **(b)** R_B *if* $V_{BE} = 0.6$ V *and* $V_s = 6$ V *and* **(c)** I_E.

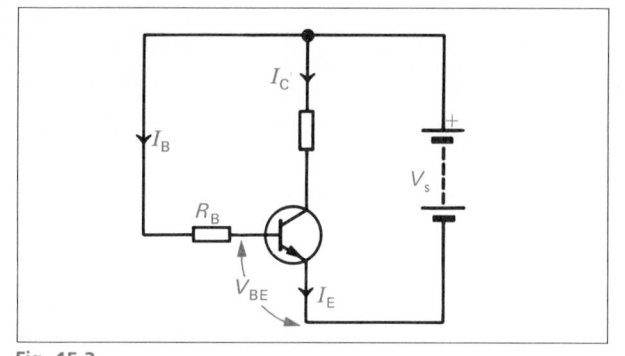

Fig. 15.3

(a) Rearranging $h_{FE} = I_C/I_B$ we get

$$I_B = \frac{I_C}{h_{FE}} = \frac{40}{200} = 0.2 \text{ mA}$$

(b) R_B and the base–emitter form a potential divider across V_s.

Therefore

voltage across $R_B + V_{BE} = V_s$

that is

voltage across $R_B = V_s - V_{BE} = 6 - 0.6 = 5.4$ V

but

voltage across $R_B = I_B \times R_B$
therefore $I_B \times R_B = 5.4$ V

$$R_B = \frac{5.4 \text{ V}}{I_B} = \frac{5.4 \text{ V}}{0.2 \text{ mA}} = \frac{54}{2} = 27 \text{ k}\Omega$$

(c) $I_E = I_B + I_C = 0.2 + 40 = 40.2$ mA

◆ **Field effect transistor (FET)**

A field effect (unipolar) transistor also has three leads but they are called the *drain* (D), the *gate* (G) and the *source* (S), Fig. 15.4a. One type, the *n-channel MOSFET*, Fig. 15.4b, is very compact and lends itself to integrated circuit construction but is easily damaged by electrostatic voltages.

In a bipolar transistor, the small input (base) current controls the larger output (collector) current; it is a *current-* controlled device. In a FET, the input (gate) *voltage* controls the output (drain) current; the input current is usually negligible due to the *high input resistance* of a FET compared with a bipolar transistor.

This feature of a FET is very useful when the input is from a device such as a crystal microphone or pick-up, which cannot supply much current. It also enables it to be used as a *touch switch* since it responds to capacitance changes between a touch plate connected to its gate and the hand of someone touching the plate. When the finger is removed an output pulse is produced which can drive a CMOS IC (see below). The MOSFET type can be used as a *power transistor* to switch very large currents when the input is supplied by a CMOS chip.

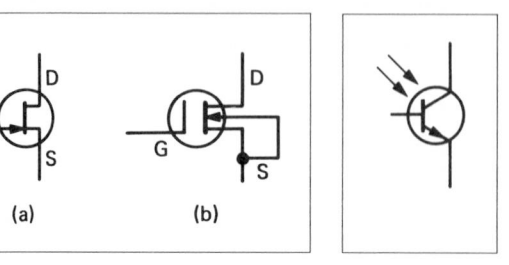

Fig. 15.4

Fig. 15.5

◆ **Phototransistor**

A phototransistor behaves like a photodiode (Chapter 14) which gives current amplification. It has a 'window' to allow light to enter and is about one hundred times more sensitive than a photodiode. Its symbol is given in Fig. 15.5.

◆ **Integrated circuits (ICs)**

Integrated circuits are densely populated electronic circuits which are much smaller, much cheaper to make and much less likely to fail than circuits built from separate components. They may contain thousands of transistors and often diodes, resistors and small capacitors. All are made on a tiny 'chip' of silicon, no

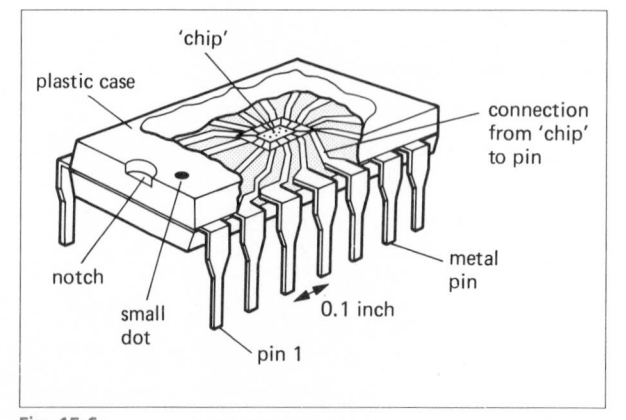

Fig. 15.6

more than 5 mm square and 0.5 mm thick and connected together by thin aluminium strips.

One is shown in Fig. 15.6 with its protective plastic case partly removed to show the leads radiating from the 'chip' to the pins that enable it to make external connections. This type of package is the dual-in-line (d.i.l.) arrangement with the pins (from 6 to 64 in number but often 14 or 16) 0.1 inch apart, in two lines on either side of the case.

◆ Types of IC

There are two broad groups

(a) Linear or analogue ICs. These include *amplifier-type* circuits of many kinds. They handle signals that are often electrical representations, i.e. analogues, of physical quantities such as sound, which change smoothly and continuously over a range of values between a maximum and a minimum, Fig. 15.7a.

One of the most versatile linear ICs is the operational amplifier or op amp (Chapters 36 and 37).

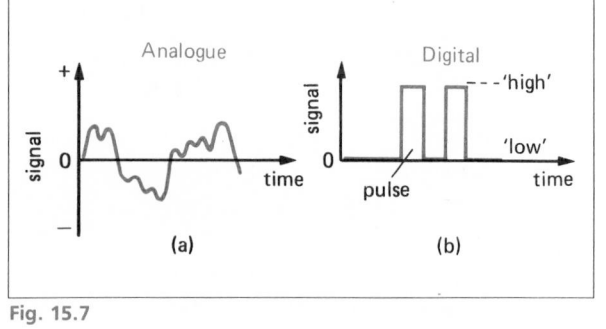

Fig. 15.7

(b) Digital ICs. These contain *switching-type* circuits that process electrical signals which have only one of two values, Fig. 15.7b. Their inputs and outputs are either 'high' (e.g. near the supply voltage, often 5 V) or 'low' (e.g. near 0 V). They include logic gates (Chapters 25 and 28), memories (Chapter 32), microprocessors (Chapter 49) and many other kinds of chip.

There are two main families of digital ICs. One is TTL (standing for Transistor-Transistor-Logic) using bipolar transistors; the other is CMOS (pronounced 'see-moss' and standing for Complementary Metal Oxide Semi-conductor) based on FETs.

Each family has its own advantages and disadvantages which have to be considered when designing a system, e.g. voltage and current required from power supply, output current need to drive indicators and relays etc.,

operating speed, cost. Generally, ICs from both families are not mixed. The table below summarizes their main properties.

Property	TTL	CMOS
Supply voltage	5 V ± 0.25 V d.c.	3 V to 15 V d.c.
Current required	Milliamperes	Microamperes
Switching speed	Fast	'Slow'

While CMOS gains on the first property (since TTL requires a regulated 5 V supply) and the second (because of its very high input resistance due to the use of FETs), it loses out on the third being about one-tenth as fast as TTL. CMOS can also be damaged if static electricity builds up on its pins, but it is preferred for battery-operated equipment. Greater output currents are available from TTL, which is better for industrial environments.

◇ Questions

Q1
In the labelled circuit of Fig. 15.8 which path through the transistor is taken by **(a)** the base current, **(b)** the collector current?

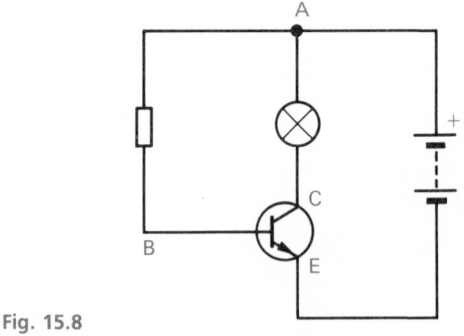

Fig. 15.8

Q2
In which circuit(s) in Fig. 15.9 will L light up (if R is not too large)?

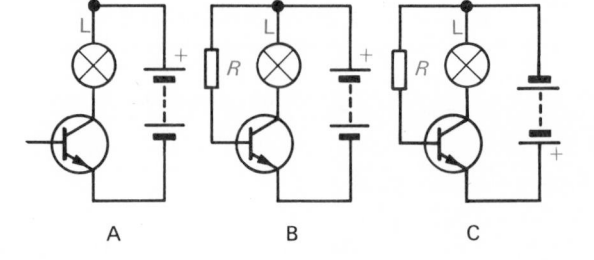

Fig. 15.9

Q3
(a) What is the approximate value in volts of the *turn-on voltage* of a silicon transistor?
(b) What happens at the turn-on voltage?

Q4
What is the *current gain* of a transistor in which a base current of 1 mA causes a collector current of 200 mA?

Q5
In the circuit of Fig. 15.3 if $I_B = 0.3$ mA and h_{FE} for the transistor is 50, calculate **(a)** I_C, **(b)** R_B if $V_{BE} = 0.6$ V and $V_C = 6$ V.

Q6
(a) What are the names of the leads on a FET?
(b) How does the input resistance of a FET compare with that of a bipolar transistor?

Q7
(a) What is an integrated circuit?
(b) Which digital IC family would you use in designing **(i)** a wrist watch, **(ii)** a high-speed computer and **(iii)** an electronic ignition control system for a boiler?

16 Additional questions

◇ **Core level**

Q1
(a) What are the values of the following colour coded resistors R_1, R_2 and R_3?
R_1—brown black orange
R_2—yellow violet yellow
R_3—orange orange black
(b) What are the colour codes for the following resistors?
(i) 22 kΩ **(ii)** 6.8 kΩ **(iii)** 10 MΩ
(c) If a 100 kΩ resistor has a tolerance of 10%, calculate its possible maximum and minimum values.

Q2
(a) Draw the circuit symbols for:
(i) a potentiometer, **(ii)** a capacitor, **(iii)** a transformer, **(iv)** a LDR, **(v)** a loudspeaker, **(vi)** a microphone, **(vii)** a diode, **(viii)** a Zener diode, **(ix)** a LED, **(x)** a bipolar transistor.
(b) From the list of components in **(a)**, select one having the property stated in each of the following sentences.
(i) It rectifies a.c.
(ii) Its resistance decreases as the light intensity increases.
(iii) It passes a.c. but blocks d.c.
(iv) It changes electrical energy to sound.
(v) It has three leads called the collector, the base and the emitter.

Q3
If the thermistor in Fig. 16.1 has a resistance R_1 of 400 Ω at 20°C and 100 Ω at 70°C, calculate V_{out} at **(a)** 20°C, **(b)** 70°C.

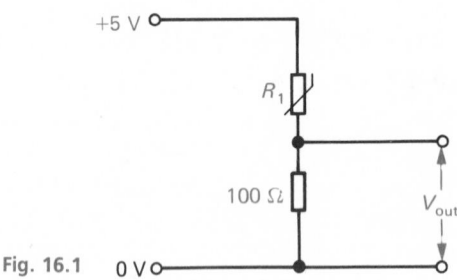

Fig. 16.1

Q4
The current–voltage graph for a Zener diode is shown in Fig. 16.2a.
(a) What is its reverse breakdown voltage?
(b) If it is used in the circuit of Fig. 16.2b, what is V_{out} when the battery is **(i)** new with a voltage of 9 V, **(ii)** old with a voltage of 6 V and **(iii)** very old with a voltage of 3 V?

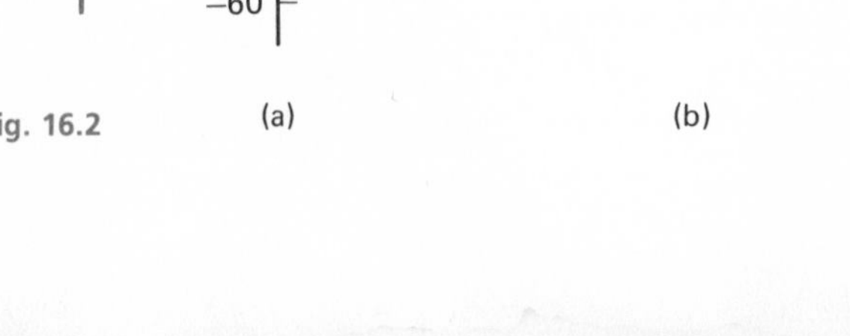

Fig. 16.2   (a)   (b)

Q5

In the circuit of Fig. 16.3

(a) What type of switch is S?

(b) Name component A.

(c) How does L behave when S is **(i)** pushed, **(ii)** released?

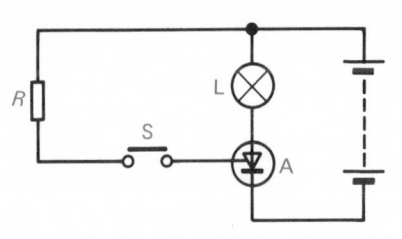

Fig. 16.3

Q6

Under the following conditions would you use TTL or CMOS integrated circuits?

(a) Only a 9 V power supply available.

(b) Large static charges present.

(c) Fast switching essential.

(d) Very low power consumption necessary.

◇ **Further level**

Q7

(a) For the resistor R–capacitor C circuit of Fig. 16.4 draw a graph of *voltage* (*y*-axis) against *time* (*x*-axis) to show what happens to the voltage across C when S is closed.

(b) On the same axes draw another two graphs, one for a *smaller* value of C (label it 'smaller C') and one for a *larger* value of R (label it 'larger R').

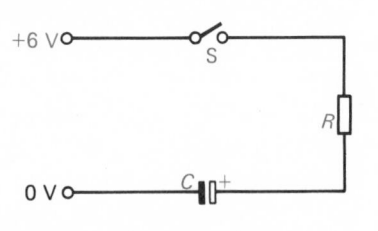

Fig. 16.4

Q8

The Zener diode in the circuit of Fig. 16.5 has a Zener voltage of 5 V.

(a) Sketch a graph of V_{out} against V_{in} for values of V_{in} from 0 to +9 V.

(b) When $V_{in} = 9$ V calculate **(i)** I, **(ii)** I_L and **(iii)** I_Z.

(c) If the power rating of the diode is 0.5 W what is the maximum current it can carry?

(d) State a use for this circuit.

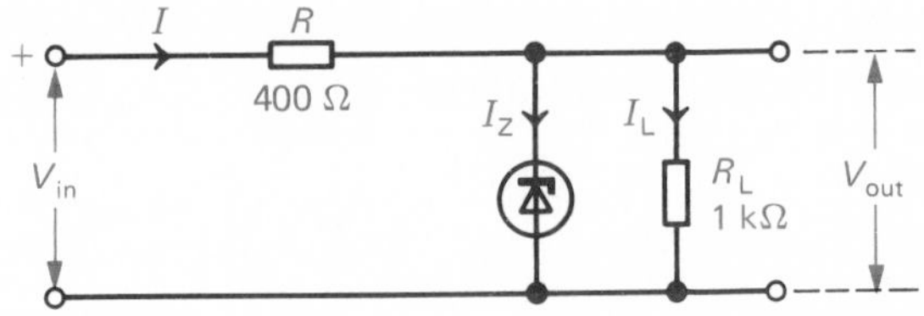

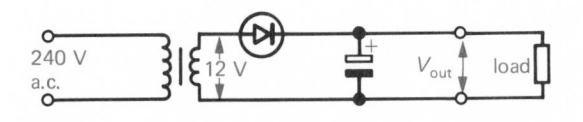

Fig. 16.5

Q9

This question refers to Fig. 16.6.

(a) What is the function of

(i) the transformer,

(ii) the diode and

(iii) the electrolytic capacitor?

(b) What would be the effect of using a capacitor of larger capacitance?

(c) How would V_{out} be affected if the resistance of the load decreased?

Fig. 16.6

Q10

Draw a bridge rectifier circuit and say why it is better than the single diode circuit of Fig. 16.6.

Check list **Components**

After studying *Chapter 9: Resistors and potentiometers,* **you should be able to**

◇ state the resistance of a resistor from the colour code or printed code,

◇ state the tolerance of a resistor from the colour code or printed code, and hence calculate the maximum and minimum resistances possible,

◇ select an appropriate preferred value from the E12 series of resistors, and

◇ state what a potentiometer is and say how it is used as **(a)** a potential divider and **(b)** a rheostat.

After studying *Chapter 10: Capacitors,* **you should be able to**

◇ state that a capacitor stores charge,

◇ state that capacitance is measured in farads (usually microfarads),

◇ interpret the markings on a capacitor to determine its capacitance and voltage rating,

◇ state that some types of capacitor are polarized (electrolytic) and must be connected with the correct polarity,

◇ realize the difference in use of non-polarized and polarized capacitors because of their different capacitance values,

◇ draw and interpret, in terms of time constants, voltage–time graphs for a capacitor charging and discharging through a resistor,

◇ state that a capacitor blocks d.c., and

◇ state that a capacitor passes a.c. and that the higher the frequency and the larger the capacitance,the smaller is the impedance (opposition) to the a.c.

After studying *Chapter 11: Transformers and inductors,* **you should be able to**

◇ state what a transformer does,

◇ recall the transformer turns ratio equation $V_s/V_p = N_s/N_p$ and use it to solve simple problems on step-up and step-down transformers, and

◇ state that an inductor opposes a.c. and that the higher the frequency and the larger the inductance, the greater is the impedance to the a.c.

After studying *Chapter 12: Transducers,* **you should be able to**

◇ state what an input transducer does and give examples, e.g. microphone, pick-up,

◇ state what an output transducer does and give examples, e.g. loudspeaker, bell, buzzer, electric motor, lamp,

◇ recognize symbols for various transducers,

◇ state that the resistance of a thermistor decreases as the temperature increases,

◇ state that the resistance of a light dependent resistor (LDR) is very high in the dark and decreases as the illumination increases,

◇ recognize various types of switch and be familiar with their use in circuits, e.g. SPST, DPST, DPDT, SPDT, push button,

◇ state that a relay is a switch which is operated by a small direct current and can be used to control larger currents,

◇ recognize the circuit symbols for different transducers, and

◇ recognize potential divider input circuits for electronic systems which contain an input transducer, e.g. thermistor, LDR, switch.

After studying *Chapter 13: Diode and power supplies,* you should be able to

◇ state that a diode conducts in one direction only,

◇ explain the meaning of the terms 'forward bias' and 'reverse bias',

◇ sketch a current–voltage graph for a silicon diode,

◇ draw, describe and explain the action of **(a)** a half-wave rectifier, and **(b)** a bridge full-wave rectifier,

◇ sketch graphs to show the variations of output voltages with time for half- and full-wave rectifiers,

◇ explain the use of a capacitor in parallel with the load to produce smoothing,

◇ describe with the aid of a graph what is meant by ripple, and

◇ explain the effect on the amplitude of the ripple voltage caused by changing **(a)** the value of the smoothing capacitor and **(b)** the output current.

After studying *Chapter 14: Other semiconductor diodes,* you should be able to

◇ state that a Zener diode has a specified reverse breakdown voltage,

◇ sketch and interpret a current–voltage graph for a Zener diode,

◇ explain why the output voltage falls as the output current from an unstabilized power supply increases,

◇ draw and perform simple calculations on a Zener diode voltage regulation (stabilization) circuit containing a current-limiting series resistor,

◇ state that a light emitting diode (LED) emits light when forward biased and calculate the value of an appropriate current-limiting series resistor,

◇ describe the action of a photodiode, and

◇ describe a thyristor and explain how the gate controls the anode current.

After studying *Chapter 15: Transistors and ICs,* you should be able to

◇ name the three leads of a bipolar transistor,

◇ state that a transistor is a current amplifier in which a small base current switches on a much larger collector current when the base-emitter voltage exceeds $+0.6$ V (the turn-on voltage),

◇ state and use the equations $h_{FE} = I_C/I_B$ and $I_E = I_C + I_B$,

◇ calculate the value of the current-limiting series base resistor,

◇ name the three leads of a FET and recall that a FET has a very high input resistance compared with a bipolar transistor,

◇ recall that the two main groups of integrated circuits (ICs) are linear (or analogue) and digital, and

◇ recall that the two chief families of digital ICs are TTL and CMOS and compare the advantages and disadvantages of each.

Meters, measurements and safety

17 Test meters

◆ Ammeters and voltmeters

When a meter is connected to a circuit to make a measurement it should cause the minimum disturbance to the conditions which existed before.

An *ammeter* is inserted in *series* in a circuit. It must have a *low* resistance compared with the rest of the circuit, otherwise it changes the current to be measured.

A *voltmeter* is connected in *parallel* with the component, e.g. a resistor, across which the voltage is to be measured. It should have a *high* resistance compared with the resistor. Otherwise the total resistance of the whole circuit is reduced by the 'loading' effect of the voltmeter and the voltage to be measured changes.

◆ Multimeters

A multimeter measures alternating and direct currents and voltages, and resistance, all on several ranges.

(a) Analogue multimeter. In this type, Fig. 17.1, the deflection of a pointer over a scale represents the value of the quantity being measured.

Currents and voltages are measured by turning the selector switch so that the arrow on it points to the appropriate setting on the scale round it. The multimeter is then connected into the circuit (*observing the correct polarity for d.c.*) as an ordinary ammeter or voltmeter would be. For a.c. measurements, a diode rectifier produces pulses of varying d.c. to which the meter responds. Its a.c. scales are calibrated to read r.m.s. values of currents and voltages that have sine waveforms.

Fig. 17.1

Resistance is measured by selecting a resistance range. This brings an internal variable resistor R (often marked 'ohms adjust' or 'zero Ω') and internal battery E (1.5 or 15 V) into the *ohmmeter* circuit.

To make a measurement, the meter leads are first held together, Fig. 17.2a, making the external resistance between its terminals X and Y zero (and the current through the meter a maximum). If necessary, R is adjusted (to allow for battery voltage changes) until the pointer gives a full-scale deflection to the right, i.e. is on the zero of the ohms scale.

The leads are then connected across the unknown resistance R_X.

The current is now less and the pointer indicates R_X in ohms, Fig. 17.2b.

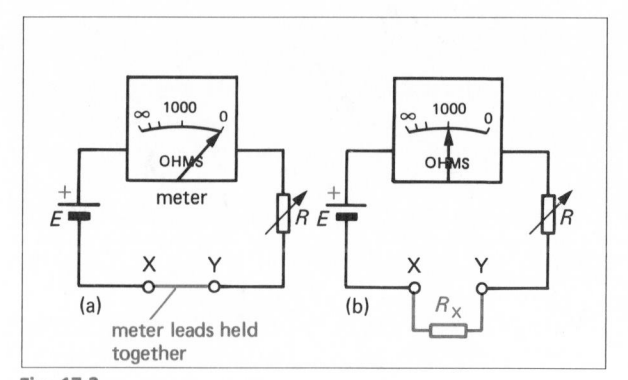

Fig. 17.2

If X and Y are not connected, the resistance between them is infinite and the pointer sets on the ∞ (infinity) mark at the left end of the ohms scale.

(b) Digital multimeter. The measurement is shown on a LED or LCD (liquid crystal) digital decimal display (Chapter 31), often with four figures, Fig. 17.3.

Fig. 17.3

◆ Practical points

1 Before use, check that the reading is zero; if it isn't, correct it by the 'zero adjustment' screw.
2 For d.c. currents and p.ds., the positive terminal must be connected to the circuit so that it is nearer the supply's positive terminal than is the negative terminal of the meter.
3 Switch to the highest range first.
4 Check you are reading the correct scale.
5 When finished leave the multimeter on the highest d.c. voltage range.

◆ Fault-finding

Multimeters are useful for locating faults in electronic circuits and components. Sometimes, when measuring resistance, use is made of the fact that in analogue meters, the negative (black) terminal has positive (+) polarity (due to the internal battery) and the positive (red) terminal has negative (−) polarity. With digital meters the polarity is given in the instruction booklet (but often the terminal marked 'mA' is positive).

(a) Diodes. A diode should have a low resistance when the cathode (the end with the band round it) is connected to the terminal with negative polarity and the anode to the terminal of positive polarity. The connections using an analogue multimeter are shown in Fig. 17.4. Reversing the connections gives a high resistance reading in a 'healthy' diode.

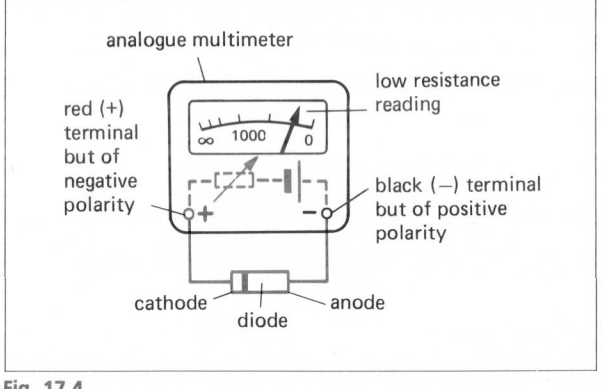

Fig. 17.4

(b) Transistors. In a bipolar transistor the resistance should be *high* between the collector and emitter for *both* methods of connection to the multimeter. This enables the base to be identified since for an *n-p-n* transistor, the resistance is lower when the multimeter terminal of positive polarity (i.e. the black one marked −) is connected to the base and the other terminal to the emitter or collector than it is with the leads reversed, Fig. 17.5.

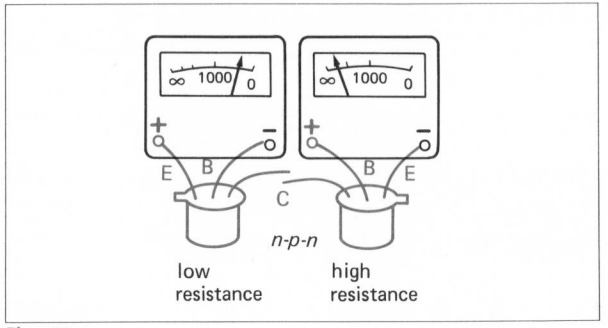

Fig. 17.5

(c) Non-polarized capacitors (Chapter 10). If the resistance of the capacitor is less than about 1 MΩ, it is allowing d.c. to pass (from the battery in the multimeter), i.e. it is 'leaking' and is faulty. With large value capacitors there may be a short initial burst of current as the capacitor charges up.

(d) Polarized capacitors (Chapter 10). For the dielectric to form in these, a positive voltage must be applied to the positive lead of the capacitor (marked by a +) from the multimeter terminal of positive polarity. When first connected, the resistance is low but rises as the dielectric forms.

(e) 'Dry' joints. These are badly soldered joints which have a high resistance. In the circuit of Fig. 17.6, if there is a 'dry' joint at X, the voltmeter reading to the right of X will be +6V and to the left 0V because there is infinite resistance at X.

Any other type of poor connection which breaks the continuity of a circuit shows up in the same way.

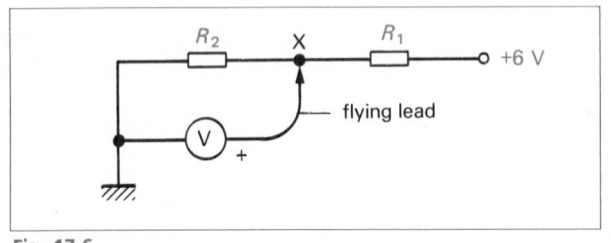

Fig. 17.6

(f) Bulbs, fuses, connecting wire. Their resistance should be low, if not they are faulty.

◆ Comparison of multimeters

Property	Analogue	Digital
Reading errors	Can occur especially when pointer between marks	Less likely
Input resistance as a voltmeter	Moderate, e.g. 20 kΩ Varies with range	High, e.g. 10 MΩ on d.c.
Scale/display	Scale continuous	Display changes by 1 digit
Response to input	Continuous	Samples taken regularly
Power used	None except as an ohmmeter	Small if LCD

◆ Logic probe

In circuits carrying digital signals (Chapter 15) we sometimes need to know for testing (and other) purposes whether the output from the circuit is 'high' (e.g. near the supply voltage, often +5 V) or 'low' (e.g. near 0 V). A simple logic probe is useful for this, consisting of a suitable current-limiting resistor (330 Ω for 5 V circuits) in series with a LED (Chapter 14).

When the probe is connected to the output P of the circuit on test, as in Fig. 17.7a, the LED lights only if P is 'high'.

When is is connected to P as in Fig. 17.7b, the LED only lights if P is 'low'. If P is 'high' the voltage across the probe is (5 − 5) = 0 V.

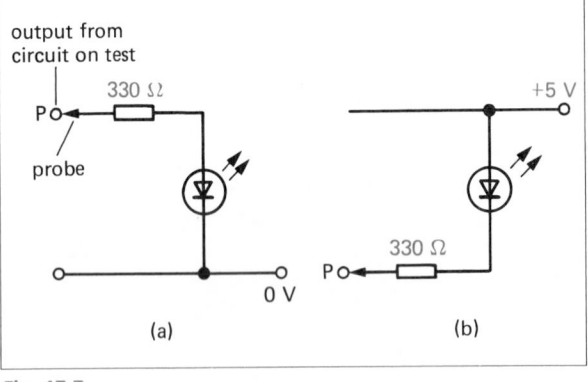

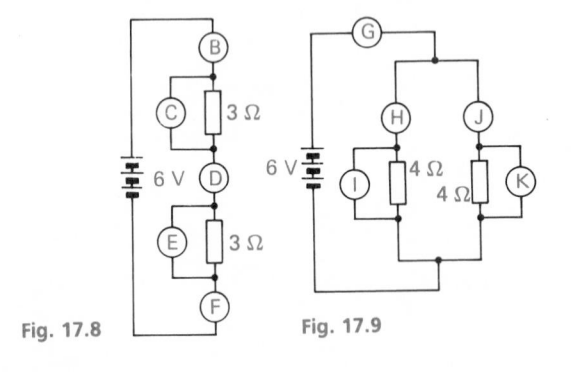

Fig. 17.7

◇ Questions

Q1

In Fig. 17.8 the circles are either ammeters or voltmeters. State which each is and the reading it would show.

Fig. 17.8　　　　**Fig. 17.9**

Q2

Repeat question 1 for Fig. 17.9.

Q3

Do you think a measurement is more likely to be *read* wrongly on an analogue multimeter than on a digital one?

Q4

How would you check that a diode is not faulty?

Q5

Two of the connections, X, Y, Z on a transistor, Fig. 17.10, were connected in turn to a multimeter on the resistance range. The resistances obtained ('high' or 'low') with the polarities shown are given in the table below.

X	Y	Z	Resistance
+	−		high
−		+	high
	+	−	low
	−	+	high
−	+		low
+		−	high

(a) Which connection is the base?
(b) Is the transistor 'healthy'?

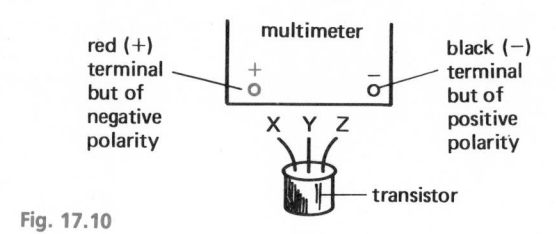

Fig. 17.10

Q6

Why would the LED in Fig. 17.11 not light up?

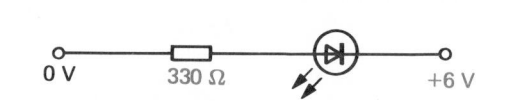

0 V   330 Ω   +6 V

Fig. 17.11

18 Oscilloscope

◆ Description

The cathode ray oscilloscope (CRO), Fig. 18.1, is one of the most important scientific instruments ever to be invented. It contains, like a television set, a cathode ray tube which has four main parts, Fig. 18.2.

(a) Electron gun. This shoots out a beam of electrons which travels at high speed along the middle of an evacuated glass tube. The number of electrons coming

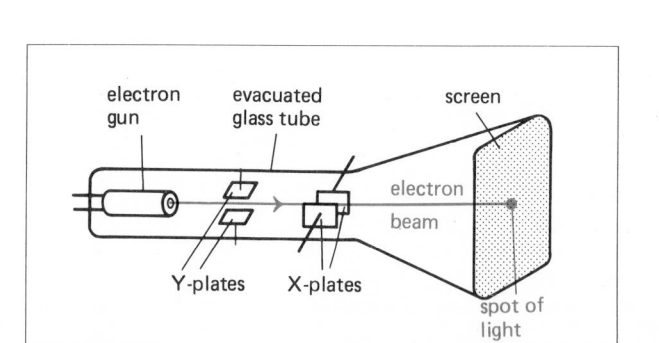

Fig. 18.2

from the gun is controlled by the BRILLIANCE or BRIGHTNESS control on the front of the CRO. The FOCUS control alters the width of the beam.

(b) Screen. A bright spot of light is produced on the screen where the electron beam hits it. A narrow beam causes a small spot.

(c) Y-plates. These are two horizontal metal plates which deflect the beam vertically up or down when a voltage is applied across them via the Y-INPUT terminals (often marked 'high' and 'low') on the front of the CRO. The Y-input voltage is usually amplified by an amount which depends on the setting on the Y-AMP GAIN control before it gets to the Y-plates.

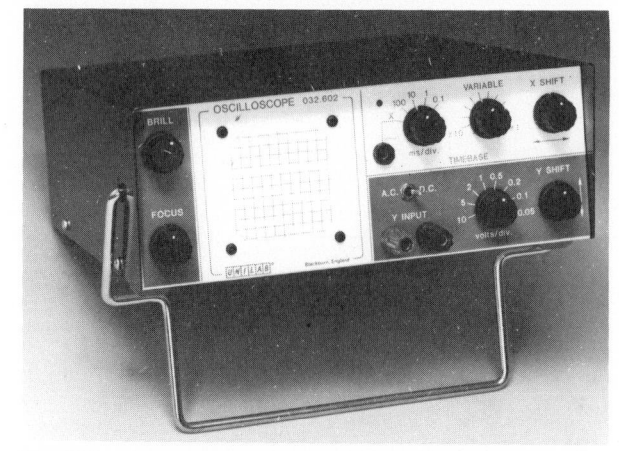

Fig. 18.1

In Fig. 18.3a the voltage between the Y-plates is zero and the beam is not deflected.

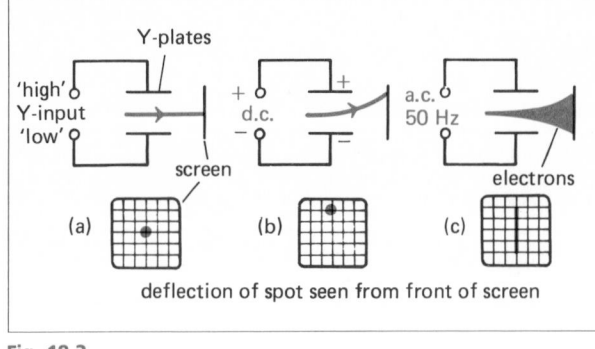

Fig. 18.3

In Fig. 18.3b the d.c. voltage makes the upper plate positive and the beam of negatively charged electrons is attracted upwards towards it. In Fig. 18.3c the 50 Hz a.c. input makes the beam move up and down so rapidly that it produces a continuous vertical line on the screen (which increases in length if the Y-AMP GAIN is turned up).

(d) X-plates and time base. The X-plates are vertical. The voltage applied to them has a *ramp* or sawtooth waveform (see Fig. 7.4) and comes from a circuit inside the CRO called the *time base*. It makes the spot sweep across the screen horizontally from left to right at a steady speed determined by the setting of the TIME BASE controls (the coarse one is often marked 'ms/div' and the fine one 'variable'). At the end of the sweep the spot flies back very quickly to its starting point on the left of the screen.

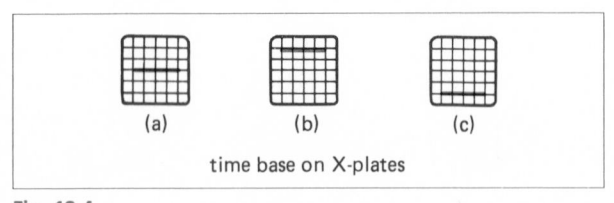

time base on X-plates

Fig. 18.4

In Fig. 18.4a,b,c the time base is on. In (a) the Y-input voltage is zero, in (b) it is d.c. which makes the upper Y-plate positive, in (c) it is d.c. which makes the lower Y-plate positive. In all cases the spot traces out a horizontal line which appears to be continuous if the time base speed is high enough.

◆ Practical points

1 The BRILLIANCE or BRIGHTNESS control, which is usually the ON/OFF switch as well, should be as low as possible when there is just a spot on the screen, otherwise screen 'burn' occurs which damages the fluorescent material on the screen. If possible, it is best to defocus the spot or to draw it into a line by having the TIME BASE on.

2 When preparing the CRO for use, set the BRILLIANCE (or BRIGHTNESS), FOCUS, X- and Y-SHIFT controls (the last two allow the spot to be moved 'manually' over the screen in the X and Y directions respectively) to their mid-positions. The TIME BASE and Y-AMP GAIN controls can then be adjusted to suit the Y-input.

3 When the a.c./d.c. SELECTOR switch is on the 'd.c.' (or 'direct') position, both d.c. and a.c. can pass to the Y-input. In the 'a.c.' (or 'via C') position, a capacitor blocks d.c. in the input but allows a.c. to pass.

◆ Measuring voltages

A d.c. or a.c. voltage applied to the Y-input terminals (time base off) can be measured from the deflection of the spot if the Y-AMP GAIN control is calibrated (i.e. has a scale marked round it).

For example, if it is on 1 V/div (1 volt per division), Fig. 18.5a, a deflection of 1 vertical division on the screen graticule (like graph paper) would be given by a 1 V d.c. input to the Y terminals, Fig. 18.5b.

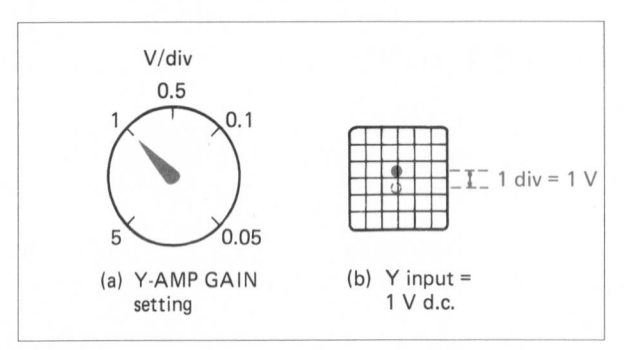

(a) Y-AMP GAIN setting

(b) Y input = 1 V d.c.

Fig. 18.5

A vertical line 4 divisions long would be produced by an a.c. input of 4 V *peak-to-peak*, that is, of *peak* value 2 V, Fig. 18.6.

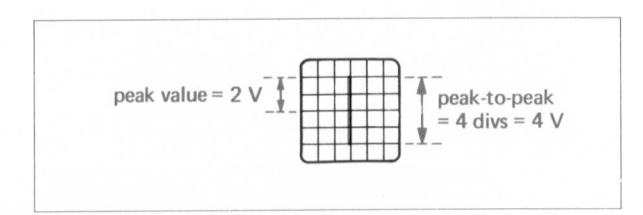

Fig. 18.6

A CRO can be used as a voltmeter with a very high resistance.

◆ Displaying and measuring waveforms

In this widely used role the *time base is on* and the CRO acts as a 'graph plotter' to show the waveform of the voltage applied to the Y-input, i.e. how it varies with time.

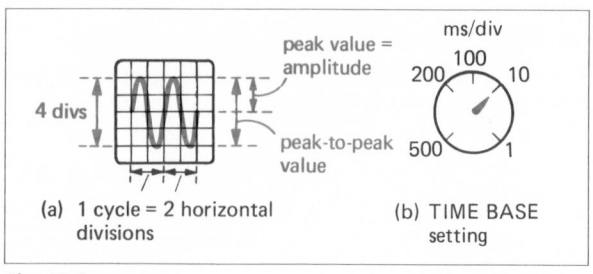

Fig. 18.7

The display in Fig. 18.7*a* is for an a.c supply voltage. If the Y-AMP GAIN control is on 5 V/div, the peak-to-peak value of the voltage is 4 divs = 4 × 5 V = 20 V and its peak value or amplitude is 10 V.

The *period T* and *frequency f* of the a.c. can be found if the TIME BASE is calibrated. For example, if it is set on 10 ms/div, Fig. 18.7*b*, the spot takes 10 milliseconds to move 1 horizontal division across the screen graticule. Then since 1 complete cycle occupies 2 horizontal divisions, we can say

$$T = \text{time for 1 cycle} = 2 \text{ div} \times 10 \text{ ms/div}$$
$$= 20 \text{ ms} \qquad \text{(NB 1000 ms = 1 s)}$$
$$= \frac{20}{1000} \text{ s} = \frac{1}{50} \text{ s}$$

Therefore, 50 cycles will occur in 1 s and so

$$f = 50 \text{ cycles per second} = 50 \text{ Hz}$$

Two other common waveform displays are shown in Fig. 18.8*a,b*.

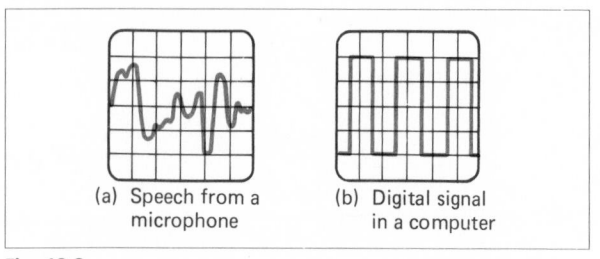

Fig. 18.8

◆ Dual beam and dual trace CROs

These are useful for comparing two traces simultaneously. In the dual beam type the CRT has two electron guns, each with its own Y-plates but having the same time base. In the commoner dual trace type, electronic switching produces two traces from a single beam. The switching is done by a square wave having a frequency much higher than that of either input. The top of the wave connects one input (Y_1) to the Y-plates and the bottom connects the other (Y_2). This occurs so rapidly that there appear to be two separate traces, one above the other, on the screen.

◇ Questions

Q1
When a d.c. voltage is applied across the Y-plates of a CRO via the Y-input terminals, the spot on the screen moves downwards, Fig. 18.9. Which plate, the upper or the lower, is connected to the positive of the d.c. voltage?

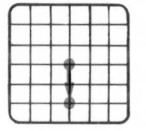

Fig. 18.9

Q2
Which of the displays in Fig. 18.10 could appear on the screen of a CRO if an alternating voltage is applied to the Y-plates with the time base **(a)** off **(b)** on?

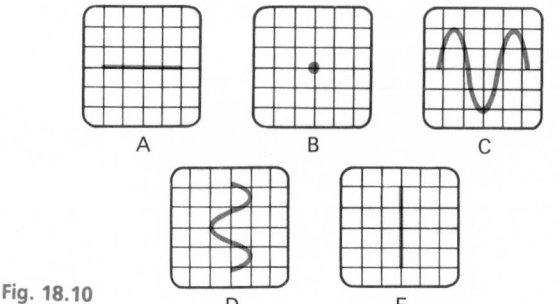

Fig. 18.10

Q3
The waveform in Fig. 18.11*a* is displayed on a CRO. A student then alters *two* controls and obtains the waveform in Fig. 18.11*b*.

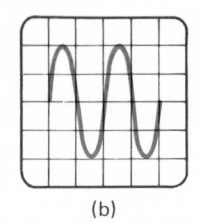

Fig. 18.11   (a)   (b)

The two controls adjusted were:

    A time base and Y-shift,
    B Y-amp gain and X-shift,
    C Y-amp gain and time base,
    D focus and Y-amp gain,
    E time base and focus.

Q4

(a) What is **(i)** the peak-to-peak voltage and **(ii)** the amplitude of the waveform display in Fig. 18.12 if the Y-AMP GAIN control setting on the CRO is as shown?

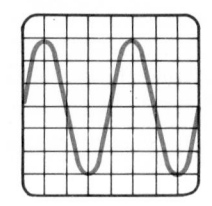 

V/div
0.5

Y-AMP GAIN setting

Fig. 18.12

(b) Repeat **(a)** for the waveform in Fig. 18.13 which was obtained on another CRO with different Y-AMP GAIN control settings *(Note.* 1000 millivolts (mV) = 1 volt (V).)

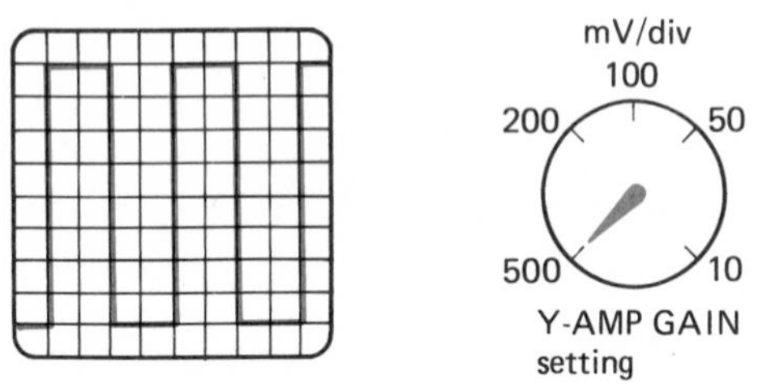

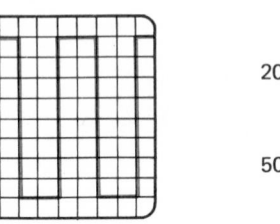

mV/div
100

Y-AMP GAIN setting

Fig. 18.13

Q5

(a) What is **(i)** the period and **(ii)** the frequency of the waveform display in Fig. 18.14 if the TIME BASE control setting on the CRO is as shown?

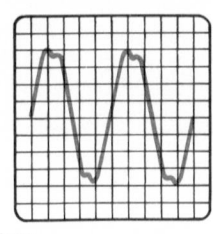 

ms/div
100

TIME BASE setting

Fig. 18.14

(b) Repeat **(a)** for the waveform in Fig. 18.15 which was obtained with a different TIME BASE control setting. *(Note.* 1000 milliseconds (ms) = 1 second (s).)

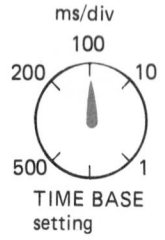

ms/div
100

TIME BASE setting

Fig. 18.15

19 Signal generators

A signal generator is an instrument for producing a signal in the form of a.c. of known but variable frequency, and having a waveform of known shape. It is used for testing, fault-finding and experimental work. There are several types depending on the frequency range covered and facilities provided.

If the maximum output voltage (e.g. 6 V r.m.s.) is not required it can be fed into an attenuator which controls the output by **(i)** reducing it in steps by a factor of 10 or 100, and **(ii)** allowing it to be varied continuously from 0 V up to the maximum.

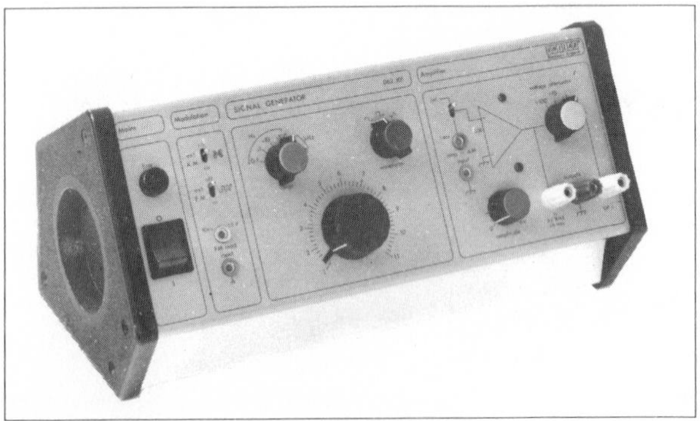

◆ Audio frequency generator

A typical instrument, Fig. 19.1, covers frequencies from 0.1 Hz to 100 kHz in several ranges. The output may have a sine, square or triangular waveform.

To allow matching to different loads (Chapter 24), there are usually 'low' and 'high' impedance outputs, e.g. 1 Ω and 100 Ω respectively. The former would be used for direct connection to a 4 Ω loudspeaker and the latter when providing a signal to an oscilloscope.

Fig. 19.1

One use for an AF signal generator is to test the response of an audio amplifier (Chapter 41) to different frequencies by supplying it with a square wave, Fig. 19.2a. If all the many (sine-wave) frequencies which make up a square wave are amplified equally, the output from the amplifier is seen on the oscilloscope to be a square wave. The waveforms obtained for other responses are given in Fig. 19.2b.

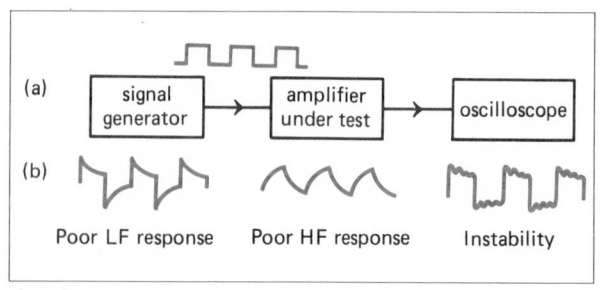

Fig. 19.2

◆ Function generator

The instrument in Fig. 19.3. is marketed as a function generator and covers frequencies from 0.2 Hz to 2 MHz in six ranges with sine, square or triangular waveforms. The output can be varied up to a maximum of about 7 V r.m.s.

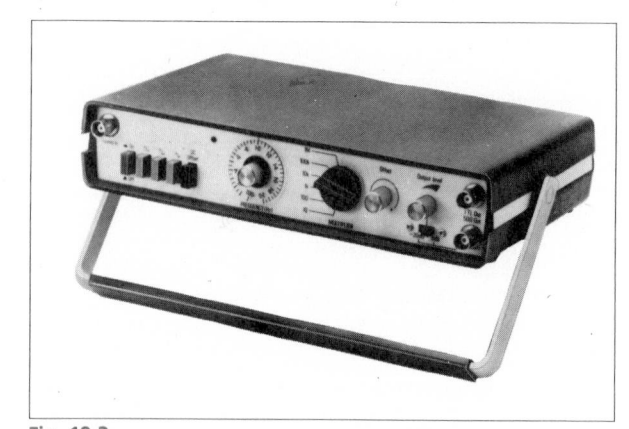

Fig. 19.3

◆ Radio frequency generator

The frequency coverage of this type is from 100 kHz to 450 MHz or so. The output is a pure sine wave which can usually be amplitude or frequency modulated (Chapter 42) for fault-finding in radio receivers.

An attenuator allows the output, normally about 100 mV, to be reduced when smaller signals are required.

The oscillator producing the RF usually contains some type of *LC* circuit (Chapter 42), coarse adjustment of the frequency being obtained by switching in different coils and fine adjustment by altering a variable capacitor.

A typical instrument is shown in Fig. 19.4.

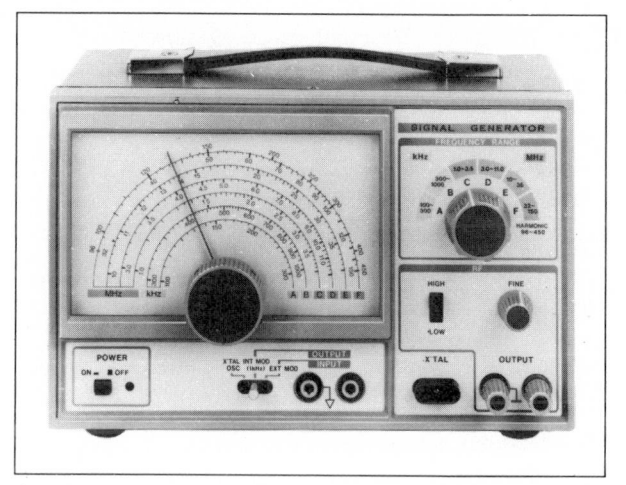

Fig. 19.4

◆ Frequency meter

The frequency of a signal can be measured directly using a frequency meter like the one in Fig. 19.5 which has a range from 5 Hz to 600 MHz. The frequency is shown on an eight-digit LED seven-segment display.

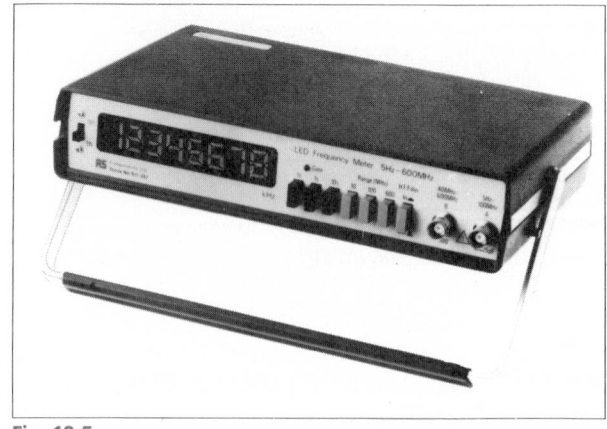

Fig. 19.5

◇ Question

Q1
If you wanted to know the approximate frequency of a signal and did not have a frequency meter, what other piece of equipment would you use?

20 Dangers of electricity

Electricity cannot be seen, smelt or heard, but it can be felt and under certain conditions it can have fatal results.

Electric shock is the main cause of serious electrical injuries and deaths, especially from the mains supply. The danger is increased in a damp atmosphere or wet conditions, since water conducts. Working in poor lighting or cramped conditions are other adverse environmental factors.

Fortunately, many modern circuits use low voltages and with a few exceptions (e.g. portable television sets), battery-operated equipment is unlikely to give shocks *but it is wise to be careful.*

◆ Mains supply

The electricity mains supply from a power station is a.c. and is delivered to consumers by two wires, called the *live* (L) and the *neutral* (N).

The *neutral* is earthed, often by connection to a metal plate buried in the ground at the electricity sub-station, and so there is no risk of a shock for anyone in contact with the ground who touches it.

The *live* is alternately, on successive half-cycles, 240 V r.m.s. (340 V peak) positive and negative above earth. It is the one that can give an electric shock if touched, especially by anyone making a good earth connection, e.g. by standing on a damp concrete floor

◆ Electric shock

(a) Effects. An electric current passing through the body causes electric shock. Effects are produced especially on the heart (upsetting its rhythm and the flow of blood), the muscles and the nervous system. Their severity depends on the value of the current, see table below, and the time for which it passes, although age, general health and moistness of the skin are also factors.

Current in mA	Effect
1	Maximum safe current
2–5	Begins to be felt by most people
10	Muscular spasm, i.e. unable to let go and could become fatal
100	Probably fatal if through heart

The value of the current depends on the voltage applied to the body and its resistance. The latter may exceed 10 kΩ or it might be less than 1.5 kΩ if the skin is moist *so never operate or handle electrical equipment with wet hands.* If the voltage is 240 V and the body resistance is 1.5. kΩ, the current through someone directly in contact with the earth is 240 V/1.5 kΩ = 160 mA (which would be fatal), Fig. 20.1*a*. In Fig. 20.1*b* the current is less (e.g. 50 mA) because the resistance of the tiles and the wood floor has to be added to that of the body, but a severe shock would still be experienced.

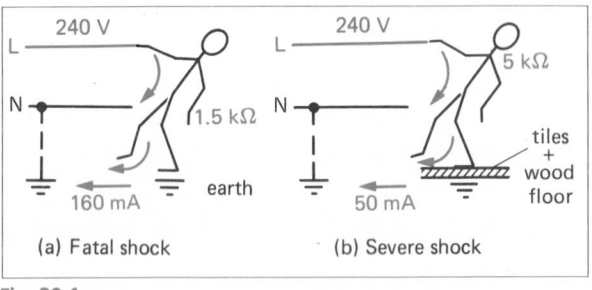

Fig. 20.1

(b) Treatment. If the shocked person is still touching live equipment, *switch off the supply at once.* If this is impossible, pull the victim away using a dry non-conducting article such as a stick, loop or rope or coat and preferably stand on a good insulator (e.g. a rubber mat). *Do not use your bare hands.* Send for qualified medical assistance immediately.

If the heart has stopped, try to restart it by striking the chest smartly three times over the heart.

If breathing has stopped, apply the 'kiss of life' by
(i) laying the patient on his or her back and clearing any obstruction from the mouth,
(ii) tilting the head well back, lifting the chin up to open the air passage and pinching the nostrils closed, Fig. 20.2*a*,

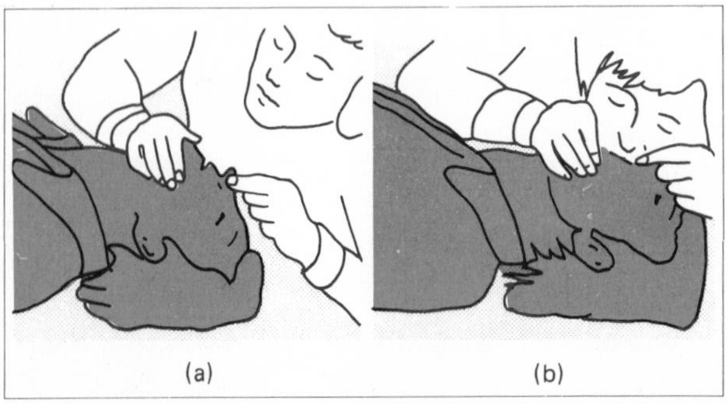

(a)   (b)

Fig. 20.2

(iii) taking a deep breath, opening your mouth wide, sealing your lips round the patient's mouth, blowing into his or her lungs, Fig. 20.2b, watching for the chest to rise, then removing your mouth, and

(iv) taking a deep breath while the chest falls and repeating the process rapidly six times, then ten times a minute until the patient starts breathing or medical help arrives.

If the patient is shocked but still breathing, keep him or her warm and lying still. Should the patient be unconscious, position on his or her side and do not give drinks since there is a risk of choking.

If a victim can be kept alive for a few minutes, the chances of complete recovery are good.

◆ Other dangers

(a) Burns. These may be external, for example on the hands, due to an electric shock or to touching a hot soldering iron. The treatment is to cool the affected part with cold water till the pain goes. Extensive burns require medical care.

Internal burns can result, with little feeling of electric shock, if high frequency currents pass through the body.

(b) Large capacitors. These may hold a lethal charge for a long time even though the equipment is disconnected from the supply. They can be discharged by holding a metal bar with a good insulating handle across the terminals.

(c) Fires. Each year in the UK about 30 000 house fires and 8000 industrial/commercial fires have an electrical origin. The main causes include defective insulation on wiring, producing excessive currents when conductors touch (i.e. short circuit), over-loaded conductors, poor connections, sparking at switch contacts and over-heating of electric motors, cooking, lighting and heating appliances.

Electrical fires are best fought with carbon dioxide or powder extinguishers. Water or foam types may cause short circuits.

(d) Explosions. Care is needed when electrical equipment is used in hazardous atmospheres. These are created not only by flammable gases and vapours but by carbon-based dusts (produced, for example, when grain, sugar or coal are ground) since they form explosive concentrations if mixed with air in certain proportions. An explosion can be started by an electric spark or by an electrical appliance with a surface temperature high enough to ignite any vapour or dust present.

◇ Questions

Q1
(a) Name the electrical quantity which causes electric shock.
(b) Why is the risk of a fatal shock greater for someone using electrical equipment outdoors (e.g. an electric lawn-mower)?

Q2
How can large capacitors in electronic equipment be dangerous?

Q3
Describe the steps you would take to help someone who has received an electric shock.

Q4
A piece of mains-operated equipment suddenly bursts into flames. Outline the steps you would take to tackle this emergency.

21 Safety precautions

◆ Protective measures

(a) Proper earthing. In most serious accidents some-one receives a 'shock to earth'. To prevent this, there is a legal requirement that one point of every supply system shall be earthed. This is usually done at the electricity sub-station by connecting the neutral wire to a metal plate buried deep in the ground.

Each consumer also has an earth connection, e.g. to the outer metal sheath on the incoming supply cable, or to a copper stake driven into the ground, or to a cold water *metal* pipe at a point where it leaves the ground.

If a fault occurs, for instance if the live wire (because it is loose or the insulation on it is worn) touches the exposed metal case of an appliance, then a large 'fault current' passes to earth, Fig. 21.1. This has two results:
(i) it blows the fuse, thereby breaking the circuit and cutting off the supply, and
(ii) it stops the case becoming 'live' and giving anyone touching it a shock.

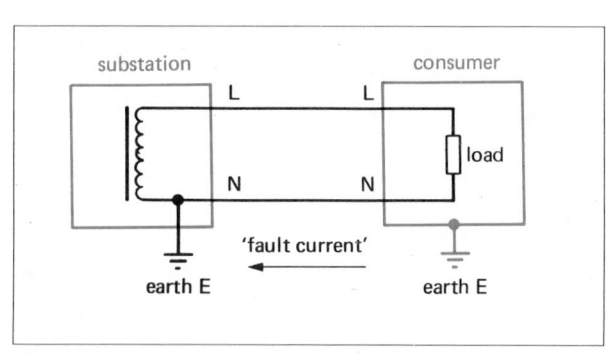

Fig. 21.1

For the fault current to be large enough to do this, good earth connections are essential so that the path to earth has a low resistance.

(b) Fuses. A fuse is a short length of wire of material with a low melting point (often tinned copper) which melts and breaks the circuit when the current through it exceeds a certain value.

A 3 A fuse may need 5 A to blow it at once; it will carry up to 3 A indefinitely. Two types of fuse are shown in Fig. 21.2.

Excessive currents, due for example to 'short circuits' or overloaded circuits, will, without a fuse, *make the wiring hot* (since for every cable there is a maximum safe current) and could cause a fire.

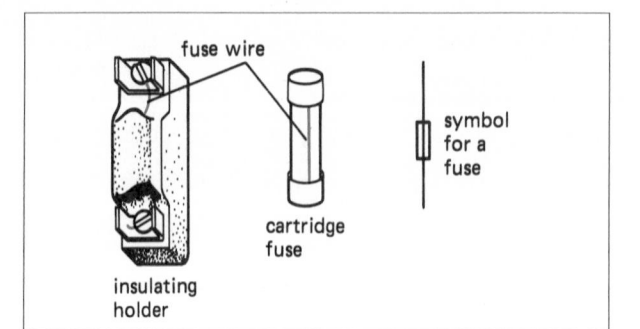

Fig. 21.2

To calculate the current rating of the fuse that is needed to protect a given appliance, we use the expression given in Chapter 6 for power,

$$P = V \times I$$

where P is the power in watts (W), V is the voltage across the appliance in volts (V) and I is the current through it in amperes (A). This can be rearranged as

$$I = \frac{P}{V}$$

and remembered using Fig. 21.3.

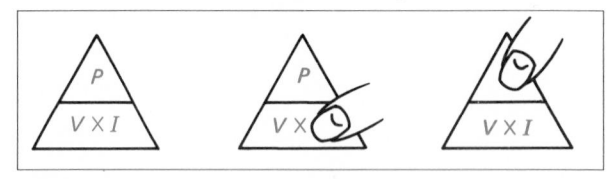

Fig. 21.3

For example, if $P = 1\,\text{kW} = 1000\,\text{W}$ and $V = 240\,\text{V}$ then

$$I = \frac{P}{V} = \frac{1000}{240} \approx 4\,\text{A}$$

A 5 A fuse would give adequate protection.

A fuse should always be in the live wire. If it was in the neutral wire, lamp and power sockets would be 'live' even when the fuse had 'blown', as Fig. 21.4 shows.

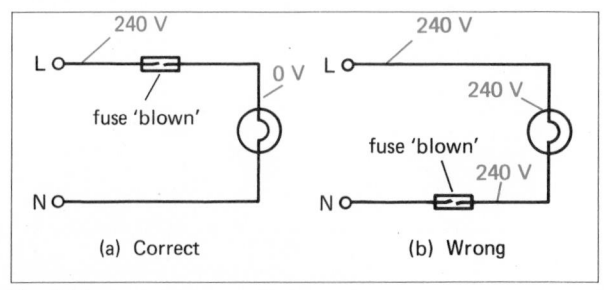

Fig. 21.4

(c) Switches. Single pole switches should always be in the *live* wire, for the same reason as a fuse must be.

(d) Mains power plug. The correct way to wire a three pin plug is shown in Fig. 21.5*a,b*. It has its own fuse in the live lead, 3 A (blue) for appliances with powers up to 720 W, and 13 A (brown) for those between 720 W and 3 kW. The wires in the cable from an appliance have colour-coded insulation and must be connected in the plug so that

BROWN goes to the LIVE terminal,
BLUE goes to the NEUTRAL terminal,
YELLOW–GREEN goes to the EARTH terminal.

The third pin, the earth (E) pin, connects the metal case of an appliance to a wire behind the socket, into which the plug fits, that goes to the consumer's earth connection. This is a safety precaution to prevent electric shock should the appliance develop a fault, as was explained earlier.

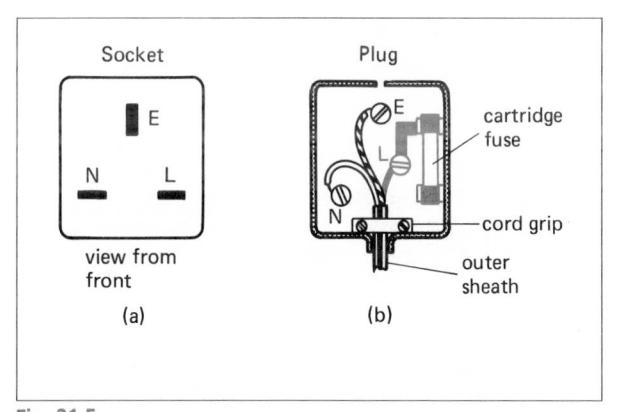

Socket   Plug

E

N   L

view from front

(a)   (b)

cartridge fuse

cord grip

outer sheath

Fig. 21.5

(e) Cables. The outer sheath of the cable in a plug should be firmly secured by the *cord grip*, Fig. 21.5*b*. It should also be firmly clamped inside the cabinet to which it is attached to prevent any strain on the connections.

If a cable continually rubs where it enters the metal case of a cabinet, the insulation wears. A rubber or plastic grommet offers protection, Fig. 21.6*a,b*.

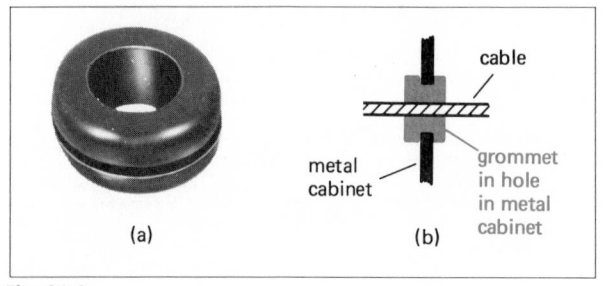

cable

metal cabinet

grommet in hole in metal cabinet

(a)   (b)

Fig. 21.6

◆ Other protective devices

(a) Residual current device (RCD) or earth leakage circuit-breaker (ELCB), Fig. 21.7. This is used as an extra safety device, and is especially suitable for plugging into sockets supplying power to outside portable appliances such as electric lawnmowers and hedge trimmers where the risk of electric shock is greater.

It operates on the principle that normally the current in the live wire equals that in the neutral wire. However, if a fault develops there is a *difference* between them and when it exceeds a safe level, the RCD breaks the circuit and switches off the supply. It is a fast-acting device which is sensitive to small current differences (e.g. 3 mA) and is reset for re-use simply by pressing a button.

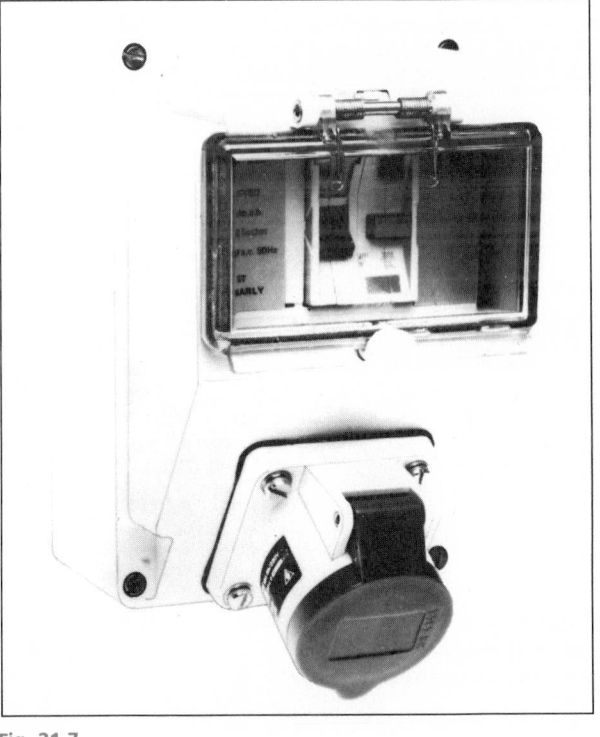

Fig. 21.7

(b) Isolating transformer. This gives greater safety where mains equipment is being worked on. The primary and secondary windings are well insulated from each other and have a turns ratio of 1 to 1. The output voltage equals the input voltage but neither of the secondary leads is live with respect to earth. Touching just one or the other does not give a shock; touching both will, and the voltage is just as high, so care is still needed.

As a general safety precaution mains transformers have an earthed metal screen between the windings, which is shown in circuit diagrams as in Fig. 21.8, overleaf.

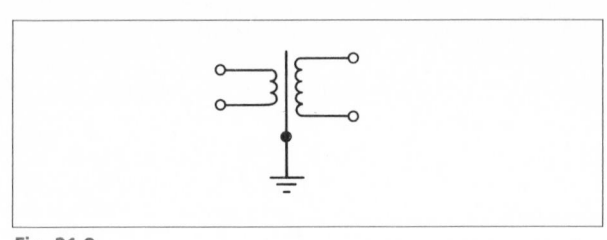

Fig. 21.8

(c) Double insulation. This is the alternative to earthing mains-operated equipment. It is used in domestic appliances such as vacuum cleaners, hair dryers and food mixers and is shown by the sign ▣ on their specification plate.

Connection to the supply is by *two* wires, with no earth wire, and the equipment or appliance, which may be in a metal case, is enclosed in an outer insulating plastic case. If the metal inner case becomes live due to a fault, the outer case is still safe to touch.

(d) Thermal trips. To stop an appliance overheating, a thermal trip can be placed in contact with it so that it opens the circuit at a certain temperature. The principle of such a device is shown in Fig. 21.9, using a bimetal strip in which metal A expands more than metal B when heated. The strip bends upwards and breaks the contact.

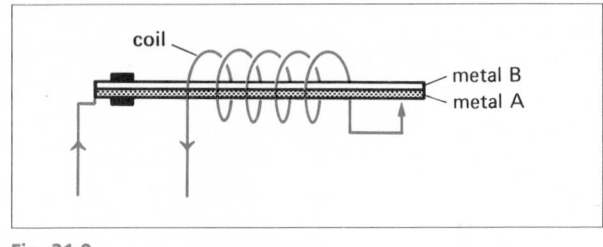

Fig. 21.9

(e) Neon mains indicator. A small neon lamp connected across the mains supply to a piece of equipment lights up when it is 'on'. It is a useful indicator because of its very low power consumption and long life. A current-limiting series resistor is required (270 kΩ for 240 V mains), unless one is incorporated in the lamp itself.

◆ Prevention of accidents

Observing the following rules helps to prevent accidents.

1 Do not work alone unsupervised in a laboratory.
2 Know how to get help in any emergency.
3 Replace damaged plugs and cables.
4 Disconnect equipment from the mains before working on it or removing the cover.

◇ Questions

Q1
(a) Name the three terminals on a three pin plug.
(b) State the colour of the insulation on the wire connected to each terminal.
(c) What is the purpose of the cord grip in a plug?

Q2
(a) Why are fuses used in circuits?
(b) Calculate the current rating of the fuse that is suitable for protecting **(i)** a 480 W appliance, **(ii)** a 3 kW appliance, on a 240 V supply.

Q3
(a) What do the letters RCD stand for?
(b) What is the purpose of an RCD?
(c) When is an RCD especially useful?
(d) What is the principle on which an RCD works?
(e) State *three* advantages of RCDs over fuses.

Q4
Why is double-insulated equipment safe even though it has no earth connection?

22 Additional questions

◇ Core level

Q1

A multimeter has the following d.c. ranges:

Voltage: 3 V, 10 V, 30 V, 100 V
Current: 500 μA, 1 mA, 10 mA, 100 mA, 1 A.

Which range would be best for measuring
(a) the voltage of a 4.5 V battery,
(b) the voltage of about 0.6 V across a semiconductor diode,
(c) the current of 5 mA or so through a LED, and
(d) the base current of about 300 μA in a transistor?

Q2

A 560 Ω resistor with a tolerance of ± 5% is required for a circuit.
(a) What will be the colours of the bands A, B, C and D on the required resistor, Fig. 22.1?

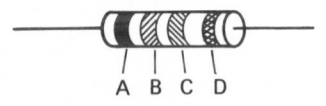

Fig. 22.1   A   B   C   D

(b) To see if the resistor was within the tolerance limit, the voltage across it and the current through it were measured using two multimeters, Fig. 22.2.

Fig. 22.2

(i) What is the reading on multimeter 1 if it is on the 10 V range?
(ii) What is the reading on multimeter 2 if it is on the 10 mA range?
(iii) Calculate the resistance of the resistor.
(iv) Is its value inside the required tolerance?

Q3

(a) What is the colour code on the earth wire of a three pin plug?
(b) What is the purpose of the earth lead in a mains plug?
(c) To ensure that the mains cable to a piece of equipment is safe what would you check **(i)** at the plug, **(ii)** on the cable itself and **(iii)** at the equipment?
(d) State *three* of the four important actions that should be taken if someone receives an electric shock from the mains supply.

Q4

For the waveform displayed on a CRO in Fig. 22.3, the Y–AMP GAIN control is set on 2 V/div and the TIME BASE on 1 ms/div.

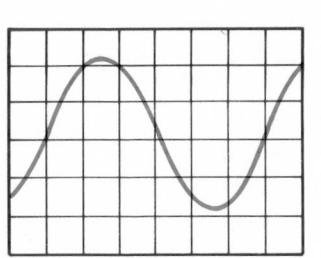

Fig. 22.3

(a) What is the amplitude of the signal in volts?
(b) What is the period in milliseconds?
(c) What is the frequency in hertz of the signal?

◇ Further level

Q5

The waveform seen on the screen of a CRO is shown in Fig. 22.4 along with some of the graticule markings. The Y–AMP GAIN control was set at 0.1 V/div and the TIME BASE at 100 μs/div.

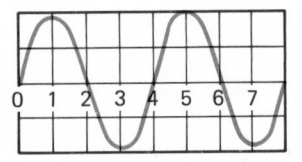

Fig. 22.4

Obtain as much information as you can about the waveform.

Q6

A student who wanted to build a power supply unit as a project proposed the circuit in Fig. 22.5 for the part between the mains input and the transformer.
(a) What is the purpose of each of the parts F, S, T, N and R?
(b) Comment on the positions of F, S and N in the circuit.
(c) Where should an earth connection be made?

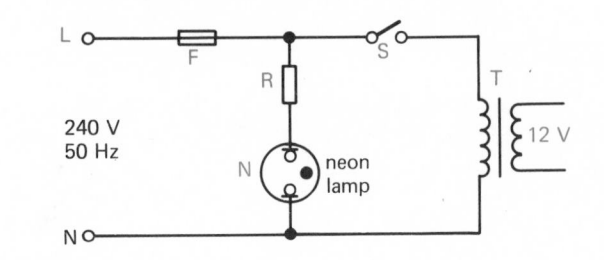

Fig. 22.5

Check list
Meters, measurements and safety

After studying *Chapter 17: Test meters*, **you should be able to**

◇ state how an ammeter is used and explain why it should have a very low resistance,

◇ state how a voltmeter is used and explain why it should have a very high resistance,

◇ state that a multimeter measures resistance, a.c. and d.c. voltages and currents,

◇ describe a simple ohmmeter circuit and its use to measure resistance,

◇ state how to use a multimeter to check for faulty diodes, transistors, capacitors, joints, connecting wire, bulbs and fuses,

◇ compare analogue and digital multimeters, and

◇ explain how a logic probe works.

After studying *Chapter 18: Oscilloscope*, **you should be able to**

◇ describe briefly the four main parts of an oscilloscope and what they do, and

◇ describe and use an oscilloscope to **(a)** measure direct and alternating voltages, **(b)** display waveforms and **(c)** measure the period and frequency of a repeating waveform.

After studying *Chapter 19: Signal generators*, **you should be able to**

◇ state what a signal/function generator does.

After studying *Chapter 20: Dangers of electricity*, **you should be able to**

◇ recall that the mains electricity supply is delivered by the live and neutral wires,

◇ state how environmental factors (e.g. damp atmosphere) affect the dangers of electricity,

◇ describe the effects on the human body of different electric currents,

◇ state the procedures for treating someone who has suffered electric shock,

◇ appreciate how burns can be caused by electricity and how to treat them,

◇ appreciate that large capacitors can store a lethal charge even though they are disconnected from the supply, and

◇ appreciate how fires and explosions can be caused by electricity.

After studying *Chapter 21: Safety precautions*, you should be able to

◇ explain why a proper earth connection is necessary for safety in many mains-operated pieces of equipment and devices,

◇ describe the purpose and action of the fuse in a circuit,

◇ select an appropriate value for a fuse for a device of known power,

◇ state that and know why fuses and single pole switches should be in the live wire of mains-operated equipment,

◇ state the colour coding of the wires on a modern three pin mains plug,

◇ wire a three pin mains plug correctly and ensure that proper strain relief is provided at both ends of the cable,

◇ appreciate how the insulation on cables can wear and what has to be done to stop this,

◇ explain the purpose of **(a)** a residual current device, **(b)** an isolating transformer, **(c)** a thermal trip and **(d)** double insulation,

◇ discuss the advantages of using a neon lamp as a mains-on indicator, and

◇ state 'rules' for the prevention of accidents and explain why they should be obeyed.

Electronic systems and society

23 Electronic systems I

◆ The systems approach

In the systems approach we consider what it is that a system does. We think about it in terms of its overall function, rather than trying to analyse it as a collection of parts. For example, a radio receiver is regarded, not as something consisting of resistors, capacitors, ICs, etc., but as a system which has

(a) an *input transducer* in the form of an *aerial*, which changes the input signal (a radio wave) into an electrical voltage, and passes it on to

(b) several *processing sub-systems* which 'process' the electrical voltage so that it can operate

(c) an *output transducer* in the form of a *loudspeaker*, which produces the output signal, i.e. sound.

All electronic (and other) systems can be described in this way, no matter how complex they are. They can be represented by a *system* or *block diagram* like the one in Fig. 23.1, in which the lines between the blocks indicate the *flow of information*, rather than connecting wires.

Input and output transducers were discussed in Chapter 12.

◆ Processing sub-systems

These are a set of building blocks or basic modules which can be used to build, i.e. *synthesize*, different electronic systems, depending on which are used and how they are connected. Each one performs some basic process, e.g. switching, a logic operation, amplifying, timing, counting or storing the signal represented by the electrical voltage at its input.

On the other hand, if we know from a block diagram what processing sub-systems a system uses, it helps us to work out, i.e. *analyse*, what the system does.

Before either of these tasks can be undertaken we need to know a little about the various sub-systems. The summary of the properties of some common ones given here should enable you to carry out practical work using the systems approach. Each sub-system will be analysed in more detail in later chapters.

◆ Electronic switches

These deal mostly with input and output voltages that are either 'high', e.g. near the supply voltage, often 5 or 6 V, or 'low', e.g. near 0 V. They handle only two voltage levels and are *digital devices* that process digital signals (see Chapter 15). It is usual to represent a 'high' voltage by '1' and a 'low' voltage by '0'.

(a) Transistor switch or signal sensitive switch or inverter. If the input to a transistor switch is 0, the output is 1 and vice versa, Fig. 23.2a. This behaviour is summarized by a *truth table*, Fig. 23.2b. The processes occurring in a transistor switch are *very rapid switching*

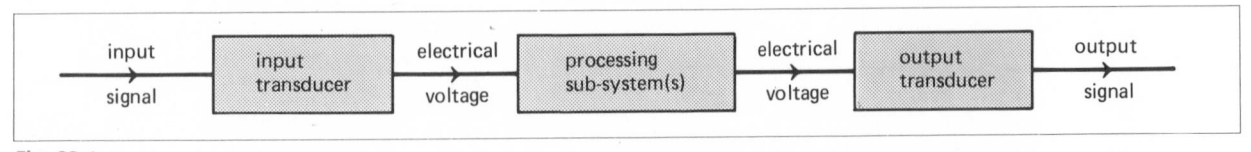

Fig. 23.1

of the output from one state to another, and *inversion* of the input since 'high' (1) and 'low' (0) can be regarded as opposites. They are used to operate low power output transducers, e.g. a buzzer, which does not require much current.

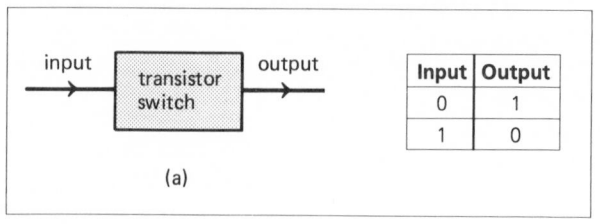

Fig. 23.2

(b) Transducer driver or buffer. This is also a rapidly acting inverting switch, but it can control output transducers of greater power, e.g. motors, lamps and solenoids, which require a large current (e.g. 1 A). It is a *current amplifier* with the same truth table as the transistor switch.

(c) Latch. In many latches, when the input goes 'low' (0), the output goes 'high' (1) and stays 'high', no matter what happens afterwards at the input, i.e. it is *latched* to a 'high' output. The output can only be set 'low' again by pressing the reset button. Like **(a)** and **(b)**, it is an inverting switch.

◆ Burglar alarm

The block diagram in Fig. 23.3*a* is for a burglar alarm system which operates when an intruder passes through a light beam. In Fig. 23.3*b* it is shown built from *Alpha boards*.[1]

When the light beam is broken so that illumination is cut off, the output from the *light sensing unit* (which has a circuit like that in Fig. 12.14*b*) goes from 'high' to 'low', causing the output from the *latch* to go 'high'. This brings on the *transistor switch* which operates the *buzzer*. The latter is kept on by the *latch*, even when the light beam is no longer broken.

Normally, the light beam falling on the *light sensing unit* keeps its output 'high'. The input to the *latch* is then 'high' also and its output is 'low'. The *transistor switch* is therefore off and the *buzzer* silent. If a lamp is used as an alarm instead of a buzzer, the *transistor switch* would be replaced by a *transducer driver*.

◆ Logic gates

These are also digital switches which respond to and produce 'high' and 'low' voltage signals. Each type of gate usually has two inputs and one output. It processes its inputs by performing on them a certain logical operation that is different for each type. As a result the output is switched very rapidly to its 'high' or 'low' state.

The operation depends on, and is always the same for, a particular combination of inputs. The behaviour of gates can be summarized by *truth tables*. 'High' and 'low' are also called *logic levels* 1 and 0 respectively.

(a) AND gate. It gives a 'high' (1) output only when inputs (1) *and* (2) are both 'high', Fig. 23.4 (overleaf).

[1]Unilab Ltd., Blackburn, BB1 3BT

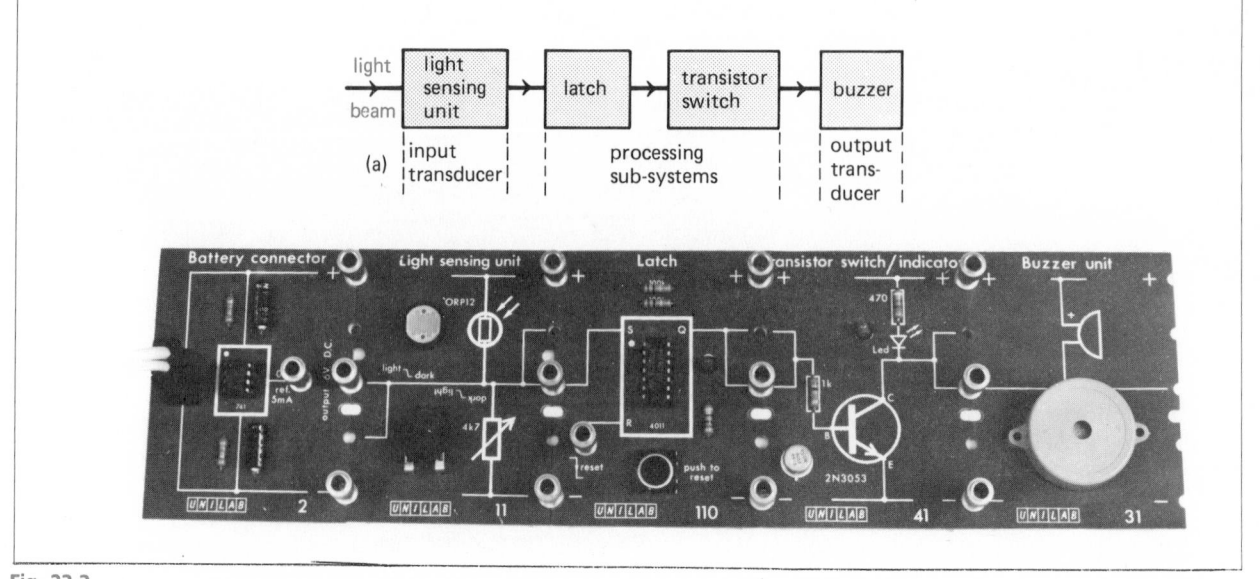

Fig. 23.3

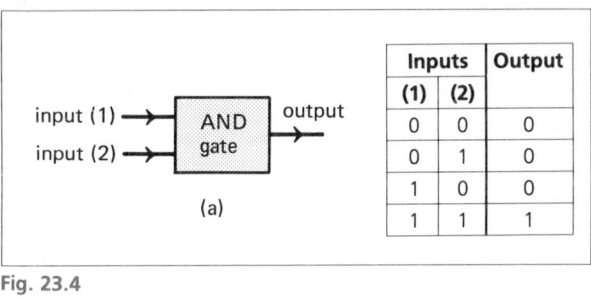

Fig. 23.4

Inputs		Output
(1)	**(2)**	
0	0	0
0	1	0
1	0	0
1	1	1

(a)

Fig. 23.5

Inputs		Output
(1)	**(2)**	
0	0	1
0	1	1
1	0	1
1	1	0

(a)

Fig. 23.6

Inputs		Output
(1)	**(2)**	
0	0	0
0	1	1
1	0	1
1	1	1

(a)

Fig. 23.7

Inputs		Output
(1)	**(2)**	
0	0	1
0	1	0
1	0	0
1	1	0

(a)

(b) NAND gate. In this case the output is 'high' for all input combinations *except* when both are 'high', Fig. 23.5. It is the opposite of the AND gate.

(c) OR gate. The output is 'high' if either input (1) *or* input (2) *or* both are 'high', Fig. 23.6.

(d) NOR gate. The output is 'high' if neither input (1) *nor* input (2) are 'high', Fig. 23.7. It is the reverse of the OR gate.

(e) NOT gate. This is the same as an inverter, such as the transistor switch, Fig. 23.2*a,b*. It has only one input and the output is 'high' if the input is *not* 'high' and vice versa.

NOTE. If you are required to use the special symbols for logic gates you will find them in Chapter 28 where the topic is considered in more detail.

◆ Safety system for machine operators

The system could prevent a machine (e.g. an electric motor) being switched on before a protective safety guard had operated another switch *only* when it was in the correct position.

In Fig. 23.8*a* the *switch units* 1 and 2 (which have a circuit like that in Fig. 12.15*b*) supply the two inputs to the *AND gate*. They produce 'high' outputs when the push buttons are pressed. The *motor* requires a *transducer driver*. Fig. 23.8*b* shows the system built from *Alpha boards*.

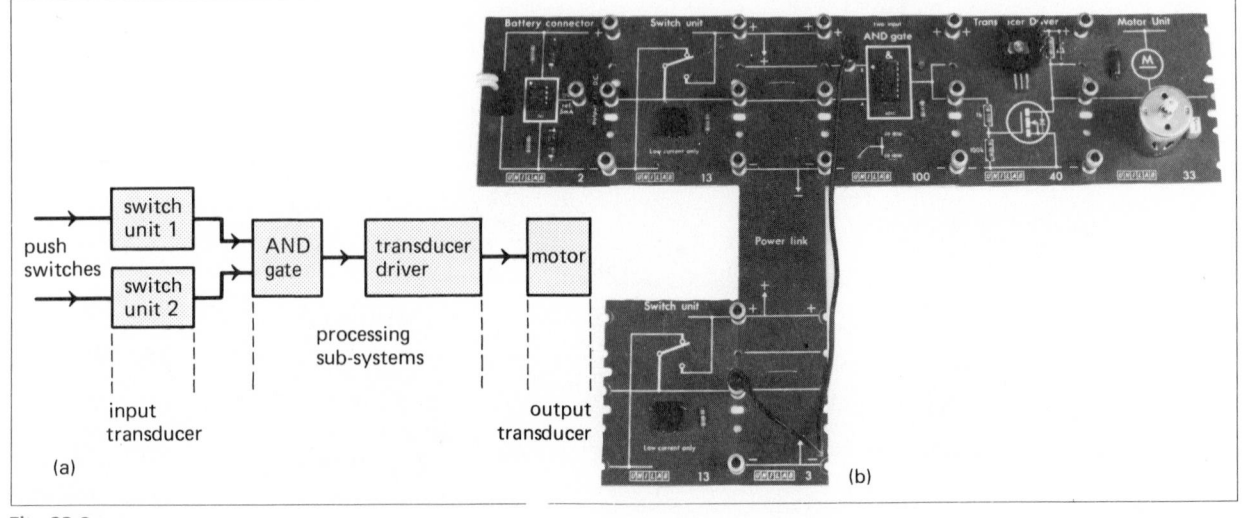

Fig. 23.8

◇ Questions

Q1
Describe the following in systems approach terms, by naming the input transducer, the output transducer and the processing sub-system(s).
(a) a lift,
(b) a shower,
(c) a door bell, and
(d) the steering system of a car.

Q2
Name the input and output transducers in
(a) a cassette tape recorder,
(b) a pocket calculator,
(c) a record player, and
(d) a television receiver.

Q3
Draw the block diagram for a system which would waken you at the crack of dawn.

Q4
A burglar alarm system is required which sounds and keeps on an alarm when light from an intruder's torch falls on a sensing unit in a dark room. Draw the block diagram for such a system.

Q5
Identify each of the gates A,B,C and D whose truth tables are given in the table below.

Inputs		Outputs			
		A	B	C	D
0	0	0	0	1	1
0	1	1	0	0	1
1	0	1	0	0	1
1	1	1	1	0	0

24 Electronic systems II

◆ Amplifiers

Amplifiers are generally used to produce an output voltage that is larger than the input voltage, i.e. they are *voltage amplifiers*. However, they can also be used as

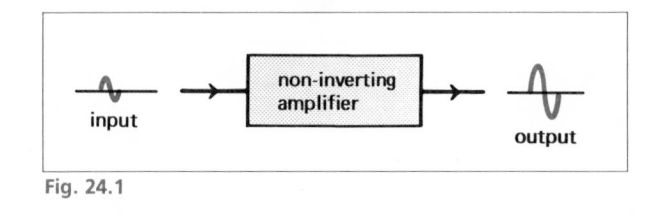

Fig. 24.1

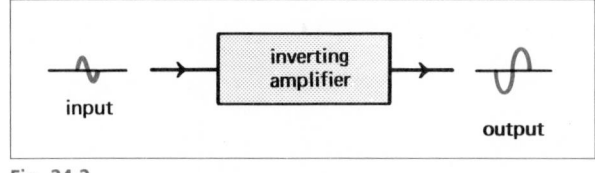

Fig. 24.2

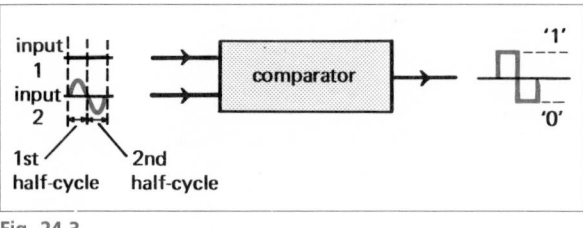

Fig. 24.3

current amplifiers (Chapter 15), as *power amplifiers* (Chapter 41), as *comparators* to compare voltages, as *summing amplifiers* to add voltages and as *difference amplifiers* to subtract them.

(a) Non-inverting amplifier. The output voltage is several times greater than the input voltage and is of the same sign. That is, its waveform is the same as that of the input but magnified, Fig. 24.1.

(b) Inverting amplifier. The output voltage has the same waveform as the input voltage but it is inverted and amplified, Fig. 24.2.

(c) Comparator. It compares two input voltages and gives a *digital* output, i.e. a '1' (e.g. near the positive of the supply voltage, say + 3 V) or a '0' (e.g. near the negative of the supply voltage, say − 3 V).

If input 1 is 0 V and input 2 is a.c., the output is 'high' (a '1') during the first half-cycle of the a.c. when input 2 is *greater* than input 1. During the second half-cycle, when input 2 is *less* than input 1, the output is 'low' (a '0'), Fig. 24.3. In effect it changes an analogue signal (input 2) into a digital one.

(d) Summing amplifier. Like the comparator it has two inputs and the output voltage equals the algebraic sum (i.e. signs are taken into account) of the two input voltages, Fig. 24.4a,b, overleaf.

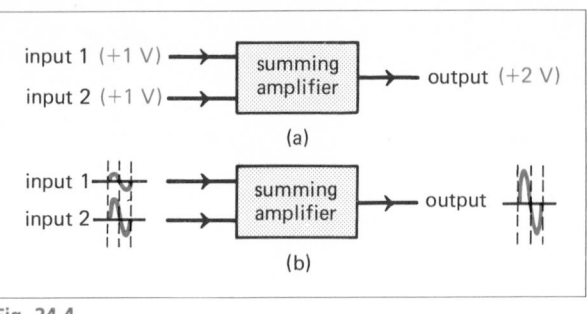

Fig. 24.4

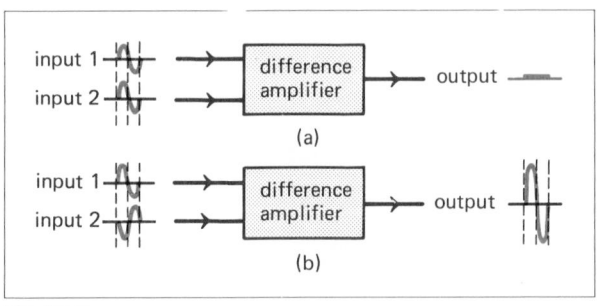

Fig. 24.5

(e) Difference amplifier. The output voltage is an amplification of the difference between the voltages at its two inputs (a.c. or d.c.), Fig. 24.5a,b.

◆ Automatic garage door system

The system has to respond to the horn of a car a few metres away by operating the electric motor which opens the garage door. The block diagram for a system is given in Fig. 24.6a.

When the sound is loud enough, the output from the *sound sensing unit* (containing a microphone) to input 1

of the *comparator*, becomes greater than the voltage to input 2. (This is supplied from within the *comparator* by a potential divider and is not shown in the diagram. Input 2 can be varied by a control knob on the *comparator* and it fixes the level at which sound from the horn operates the *comparator*, i.e. the distance of the car from the garage before the system responds.) Thereafter the *comparator* triggers the *latch* which causes the *transducer driver* to operate the motor. Without the *latch* the horn would have to be sounded continuously.

The system using *Alpha boards* is shown in Fig. 24.6b.

◆ Timers and generators

(a) Pulse generator or astable multivibrator. This produces an output voltage that is a continuous square wave (Chapter 7), the frequency being variable (e.g. between 0.5 Hz and 500 Hz), Fig. 24.7. It is used to produce timing pulses for electronic systems.

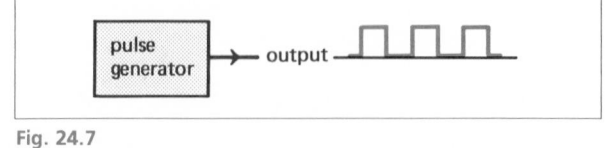

Fig. 24.7

(b) Triggered pulse producer or delay unit or monostable multivibrator. *One* output voltage pulse is produced lasting for a fixed time (e.g. between 3 s and 10 s depending on the potentiometer control setting on the unit) when a trigger signal is received which rises from 'low' to 'high', Fig. 24.8. It is useful as a timer which, for example, can control the number of pulses (from a pulse generator) that pass through a logic gate.

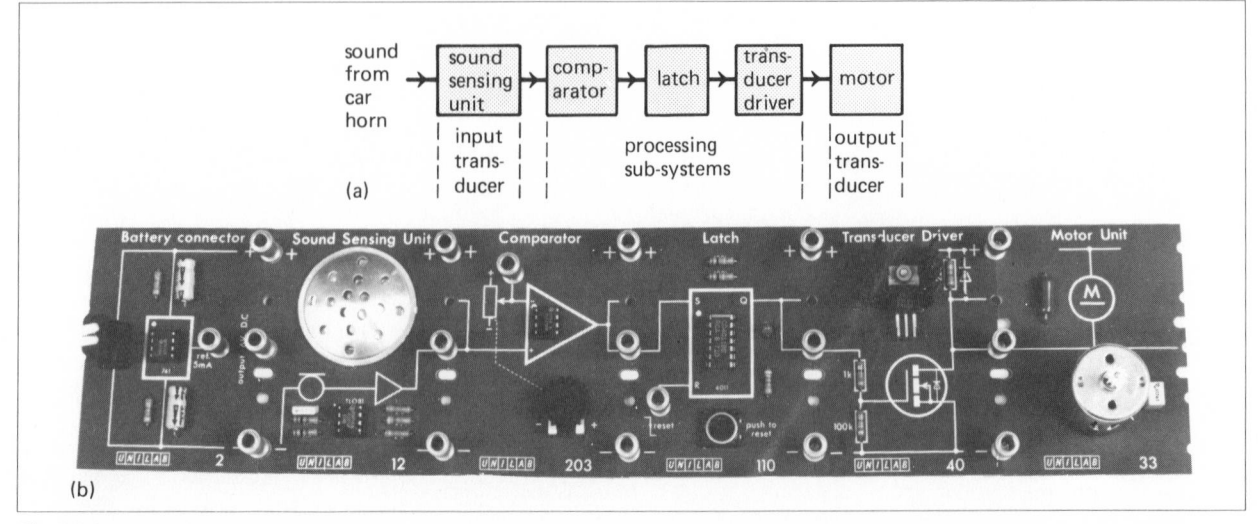

Fig. 24.6

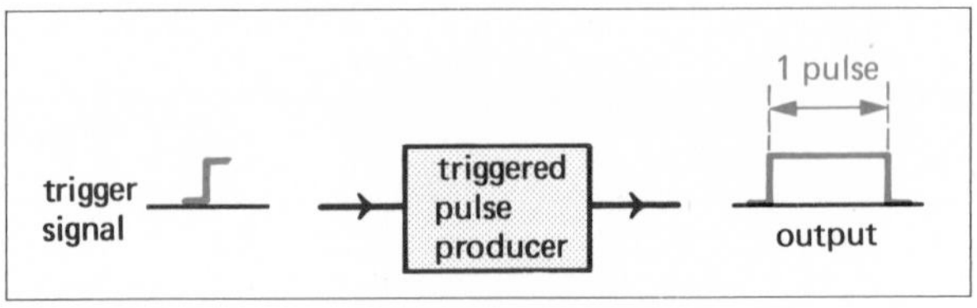

Fig. 24.8

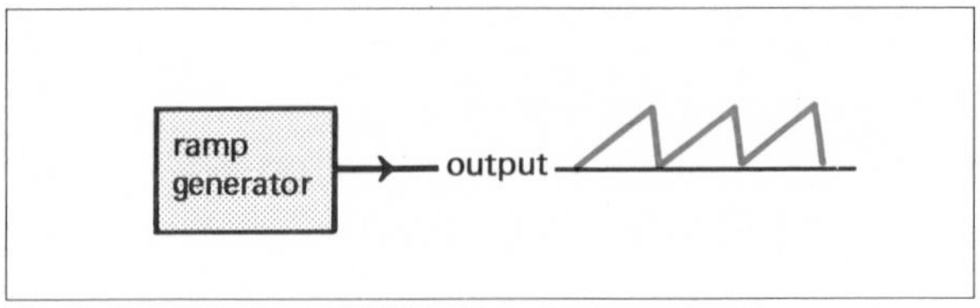

Fig. 24.9

(c) Ramp generator. The output voltage has a linear ramp (sawtooth) waveform like that in Fig. 24.9. It is used as a CRO time base sweep and for changing analogue to digital voltages in a digital multimeter (see later).

◆ Pulsed flashing lamp

The block diagram is shown in Fig. 24.10a. Suppose the *triggered pulse producer* is set on 6 s and the *pulse generator* on 1 Hz. When the *switch unit* is switched from 'off' to 'on', it triggers the *triggered pulse producer* which supplies a 6 s pulse to one input of the AND gate and allows 6 pulses at the other input to pass through the gate from the *pulse generator*. (The AND gate only 'opens' when both its inputs are 'high'.) The six 'high' outputs from the AND gate operate the *transducer driver* causing the *lamp* to flash six times.

Figure 24.10b shows the system using *Alpha boards*.

◆ Counter–decoder–display

A *counter* responds to the pulses at its input and produces an output in binary form (see Chapter 29). This is converted by a *decoder* into a form which causes the appropriate segments of a *seven-segment LED display* (Chapter 14) to light up and show, in decimal form, the total number of pulses received at the counter's input, Fig. 24.11a. Fig. 24.11b shows pulses from a *pulse generator* being counted using *Alpha boards*.

◆ Digital voltmeter

A simplified block diagram is shown in Fig. 24.12 and the waveforms below it help us to follow the action when the input voltage is a steady d.c.

The action is:

(i) a *trigger pulse* sets the *counter* to zero and starts the *ramp generator* which produces a repeating sawtooth waveform,
(ii) the *comparator* output changes from 'high' to 'low' when the ramp voltage equals the input voltage,
(iii) the AND gate inputs are supplied by the *comparator* and a steady train of pulses from the *pulse generator*; the latter pass through the gate until the *comparator* output goes 'low' and the number which does so depends on the time taken by the ramp voltage to equal the input voltage, i.e. it is proportional to the input voltage (if the ramp is linear),
(iv) the *counter* records the number of output pulses from the AND gate,

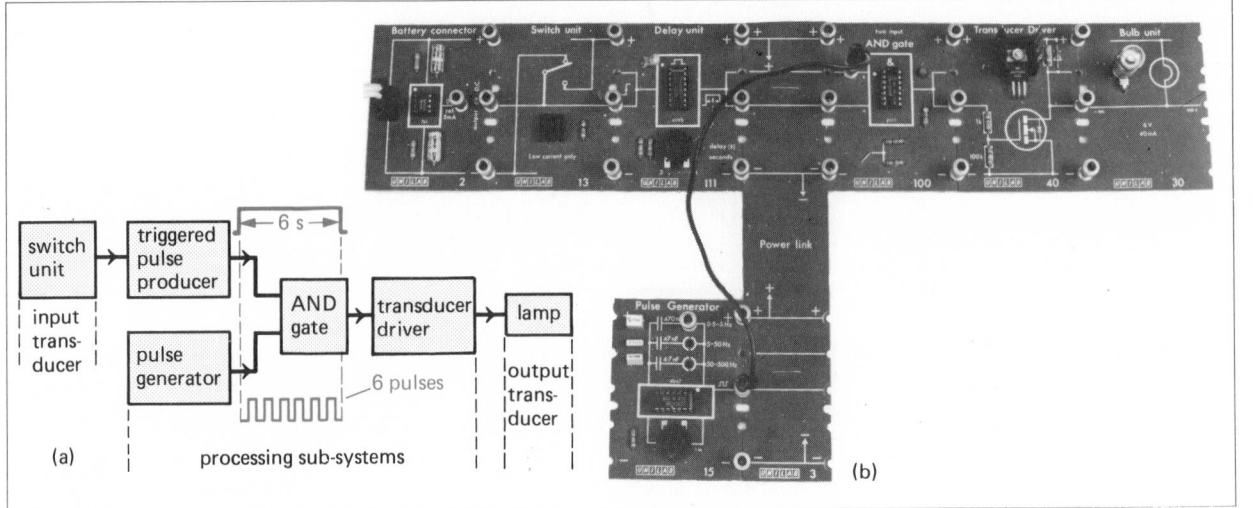

Fig. 24.10

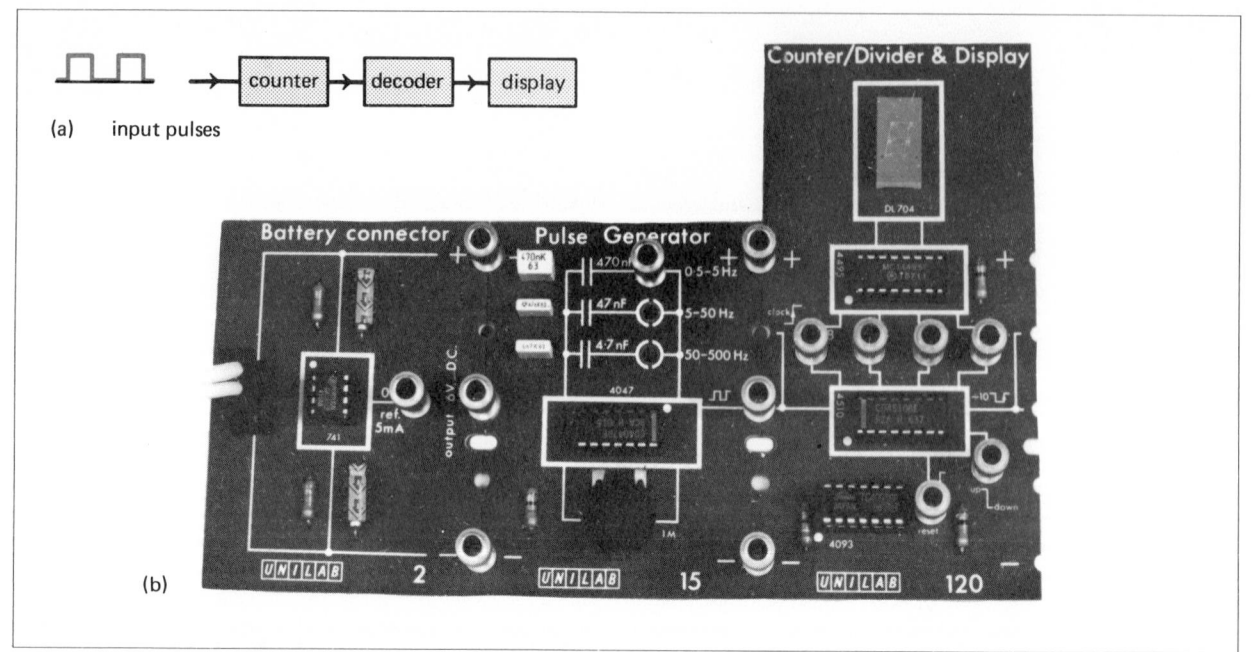

Fig. 24.11

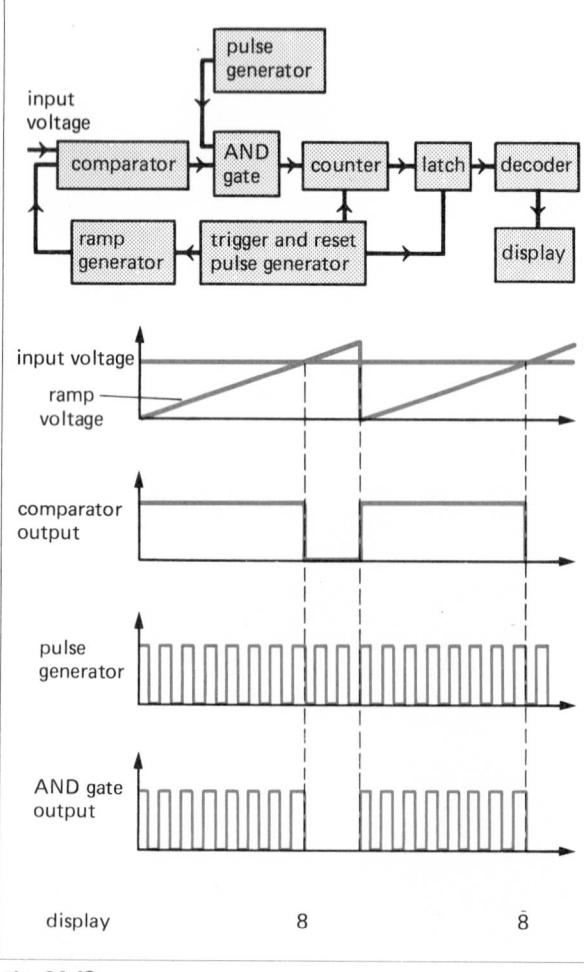

Fig. 24.12

(v) the *latch* passes this number to the *decoder* for conversion to decimal before it reaches the *display*, where it is held until the next count enters the *latch*.

With some additional circuitry the voltmeter can be used as a multimeter to measure a.c. voltages, currents and resistance (Chapter 17).

◆ Interfacing

Two conditions must be satisfied when the stages of a system, e.g. transducers and processing sub-systems, are joined.

Firstly, each stage must be able to supply the *current* required by the following stage. For example, an output transducer such as a lamp requiring a large current, must be supplied by a *transducer driver* (Chapter 23) as an interfacing device. A crystal microphone is an input transducer which can supply only a tiny current and if it is to provide the input to an amplifier using bipolar transistors, a *buffer* or *current amplifier* (Chapter 15) is needed as an interfacing device.

Secondly the *voltage* range and levels of each stage must match the next stage. For example, if the input voltage to an amplifier has too large an amplitude, the output wil be distorted (Chapter 35). Or again, if TTL and CMOS ICs are used in the same system, steps are needed to ensure that there is matching of the voltage levels at which switching occurs.

Other interfacing devices are *decoders* (at the output of a system), *encoders* (at the input to a system, Chapter 46), *analogue-to-digital converters* and *digital-to-analogue converters* (Chapter 47).

◆ Impedance matching

When the parts of a system are joined together it is usually necessary to ensure that there is *maximum voltage transfer* from one part to the next. This occurs only if the *output* and *input impedances* (since we are very often dealing with a.c. and circuits that contain capacitance and sometimes inductance, as well as resistance, Chapter 10) are matched.

For example, suppose a crystal microphone (Chapter 12) produces an output V_{out} of 100 mV and has an *output impedance* Z_{out} (which is the a.c. equivalent of the internal resistance of a battery) of about 1MΩ, Fig. 24.13. If it supplies an amplifier as the next stage of a system with an *input impedance* Z_{in} of 1 kΩ, then since Z_{in} and Z_{out} are in series with V_{out}, only about 1/1000 of the supply voltage V_s is available at the amplifier input, i.e. V_{in} = 1/1000 of 100 mV = 0.1 mV, due to Z_{in} being 1/1000 of Z_{out}. The impedance matching is very poor. What is required for maximum voltage transfer is an amplifier (or a buffer) that has a large Z_{in} compared with

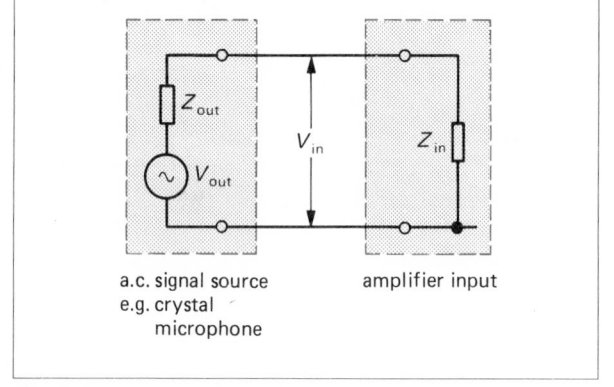

a.c. signal source
e.g. crystal
microphone

amplifier input

Fig. 24.13

Z_{out}. Then, very little of V_{out} will be 'lost' across Z_{out} and $V_{in} \approx V_{out}$.

For *maximum power transfer* it can be shown that this occurs when $Z_{out} = Z_{in}$. For example, a transistor

amplifier (Chapter 35) with its output connected directly to a loudspeaker with a typical input impedance of 8 Ω would not deliver maximum power to it because the output impedance of the amplifier is very much greater. An interfacing device such as a current-amplifying buffer would be needed between them.

◇ Questions

Q1
What is the difference between
(a) a non-inverting amplifier and an inverting amplifier,
(b) a comparator and a difference amplifier?

Q2
The input voltages (d.c.) to a difference amplifier are shown in Fig. 24.14a,b,c. What are the output voltages *x*, *y* and *z*?

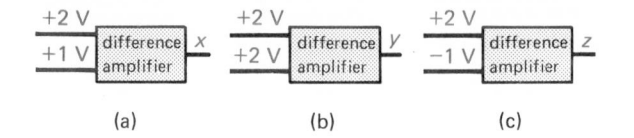

(a) (b) (c)

Fig. 24.14

Q3
Design a system for counting people coming through a doorway.

Q4
Draw the block diagram for a photographic dark room timer in which a light comes on for a certain time when a switch is operated.

Q5
In a digital multimeter name
(a) the input transducer,
(b) the output transducer, and
(c) the processing sub-systems which convert an analogue voltage into a digital one.

Q6
(a) State *two* conditions which must be satisfied when the stages of a system are joined together.
(b) Name *five* interfacing devices and say what each one does.
(c) State the impedance matching requirements for **(i)** maximum voltage transfer and **(ii)** maximum power transfer, between the stages of a system.

25 Electronic systems III

This chapter deals with the use of truth tables to design automatic control systems containing logic gates. Once it is known what a system has to do, a truth table can be constructed.

◆ Street lights

A system is required which allows street lights either to be turned on manually by a *switch* at any time, or automatically by a *light sensing unit* (LSU) when it is dark, Fig. 25.1.

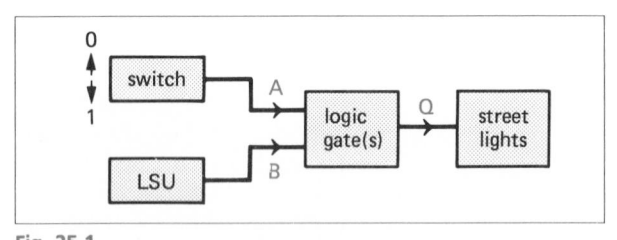

Fig. 25.1

(a) Input transducer output levels. Suppose the outputs from the two transducers (i.e. inputs A and B to the logic gates(s)) are those in Table 25.1.

Output from	Switch	LSU
High (1)	Down (on)	In daylight
Low (0)	Up (off)	In the dark

Table 25.1

It shows that when the *switch* is 'down' (on) it gives a 'high' (1) output and when 'up' (off) it gives a 'low' (0) output. The LSU gives a 'high' (1) output 'in daylight' and a 'low' (0) output 'in the dark'.

(b) Truth table. It can now be completed for each of the four possible input combinations, A and B, to the logic gates(s), as in Table 25.2.

Input A from switch	Input B from LSU	Output Q from logic gate(s)
0	0	1
0	1	0
1	0	1
1	1	1

Table 25.2

If the street lights should be 'on', we enter a '1' for Q. If they should be 'off', we enter a '0' for Q.

For the first combination, 0 and 0, the *switch* is 'off' (0) but the LSU is 'in the dark' (0) so the lights should be 'on' and we put '1' for Q.

For the second combination, 0 and 1, the *switch* is still 'off' (0) and the LSU is 'in daylight'. The lights should be 'off', so we put '0' for Q.

For the third and fourth combinations, the *switch* is 'on', therefore the lights should be 'on', so we put '1' for Q in both cases.

(c) Logic gates required. The truth table is not for one of the basic logic gates. It would be that of an OR gate, see Table 25.3, if output Q on the first two input combinations of Table 25.2 was inverted (i.e. 0 changed to 1 and vice versa). This suggests that an OR gate is required with a NOT gate in the B input to invert it, and so also Q, Fig. 25.2. (Putting the NOT gate in the A input would not make Q = '0' in the second input combination because B = '1' and thus would keep Q = '1'.) In effect, Table 25.3 then becomes Table 25.2.

Inputs		Output
A	**B**	**Q**
0	0	0
0	1	1
1	0	1
1	1	1

Table 25.3

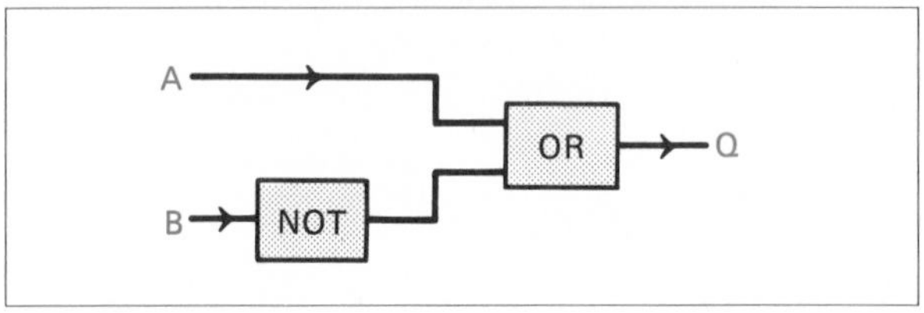

Fig. 25.2

(d) System check. A check can be made to ensure that the correct output is obtained with each input combination, Fig. 25.3a,b,c,d.

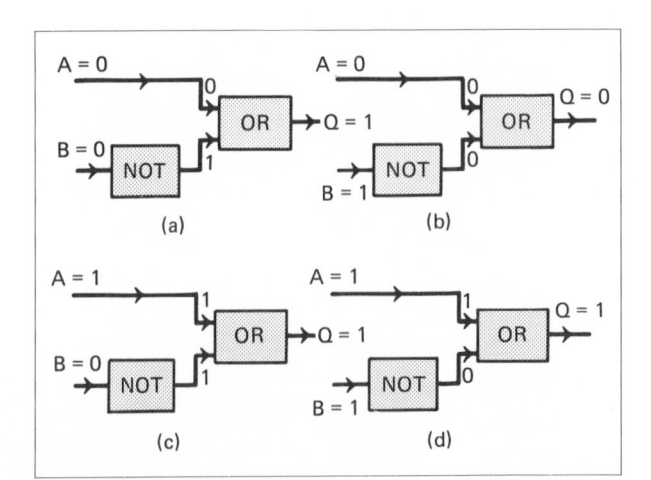

Fig. 25.3

◆ Heater control

The system must switch on a heater control if the room temperature falls below 20°C during the day. The block diagram using a *temperature sensing unit (TSU)* and a *light sensing unit (LSU)* is given in Fig. 25.4.

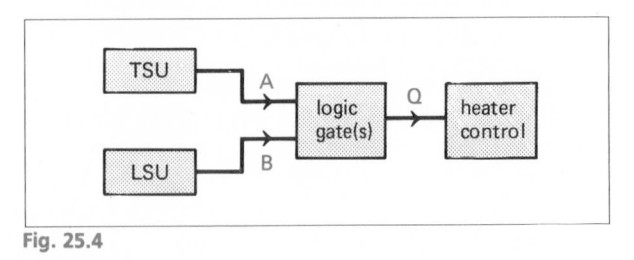

Fig. 25.4

(a) Input transducer output levels. These are given in Table 25.4.

Output from	TSU	LSU
High (1)	Temp. above 20°C	In daylight
Low (0)	Temp. below 20°C	In the dark

Table 25.4

(b) Truth table. If the heater control should be 'on', a '1' is entered for Q; if it should be 'off', we enter '0', as in Table 25.5.

Input A from TSU	Input B from LSU	Output Q from logic gate(s)
0	0	0
0	1	1
1	0	0
1	1	0

Table 25.5

The heater control is only 'on' when the TSU is '0' (i.e. temperature below 20°C) and LSU is '1' (i.e. in daylight).

(c) Logic gates required. The truth table of an AND gate, see Table 25.6, like Table 25.5, has only one '1' output, but it occurs when A = '1' and B = '1', not when A = '0' and B = '1' as in Table 25.5. This indicates that the system can be realized using an AND gate with a NOT gate in the A input, Fig. 25.5. A check can be made as before to confirm that it does so.

Inputs		Output
A	**B**	**Q**
0	0	0
0	1	0
1	0	0
1	1	1

Table 25.6

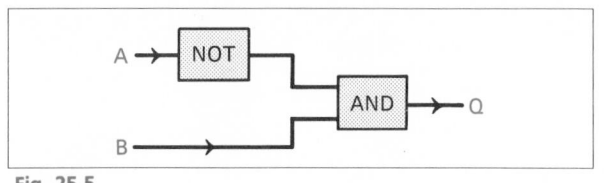

Fig. 25.5

◆ Truth tables from logic diagrams

Sometimes the truth table for a system has to be obtained from a diagram of the system.

Example 1. The diagram is given in Fig. 25.6*a* and the truth table in Fig. 25.6*b*.

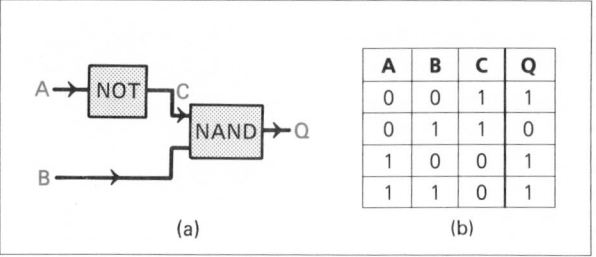

A	B	C	Q
0	0	1	1
0	1	1	0
1	0	0	1
1	1	0	1

(a)   (b)

Fig. 25.6

The NOT gate makes C = '1' if A = '0' and C = '0' if A = '1'. Q is obtained by remembering that the output from a NAND gate is always '1' except when both inputs are '1'.

Note. The above truth table is the same as Table 25.2 for the 'street lights' system. The logic gates circuit of Fig. 25.6*a* could therefore be used instead of that in Fig. 25.2 to produce the same outputs.

Example 2. The diagram is given in Fig. 25.7*a* and the truth table in Fig. 25.7*b*.

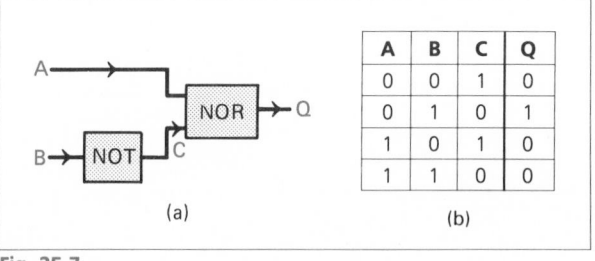

A	B	C	Q
0	0	1	0
0	1	0	1
1	0	1	0
1	1	0	0

(a)   (b)

Fig. 25.7

In this case the B input is inverted by the NOT gate, i.e. if B = '0', C = '1' and if B = '1', C = '0'. For a NOR gate the output is always '0' unless both inputs are '0'.

Note. This truth table is the same as that in Table 25.5 for the 'heater control'. The circuit could be used instead of the one in Fig. 25.5.

◇ **Questions**

Q1
The block diagram of a system which switches on the cooling fan of a car engine when it is too hot, providing the ignition is switched on, is given in Fig. 25.8.

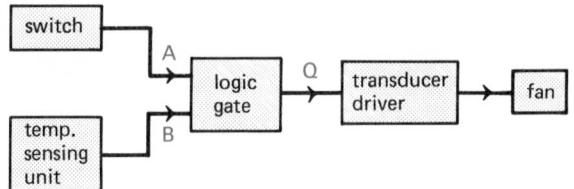

Fig. 25.8

The output levels of the two input transducers are shown for different conditions in Table 25.7.

Output from	Switch	Temp. sensing unit
High (1)	Down (on)	Engine too hot
Low (0)	Up (off)	Engine normal

Table 25.7

(a) Draw up a truth table for the logic gate putting Q = '1' if the fan is to be 'on', and Q = '0' if it is to be 'off'.
(b) What type of logic gate is required?

Q2
The block diagram for a gas-heated hot water system which uses a logic gate to obtain electronic control is shown in Fig. 25.9. When the temperature gets above a certain value or the flame goes out, an alarm is to be sounded.

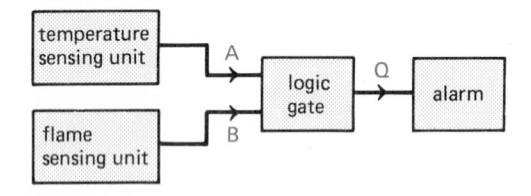

Fig. 25.9

The output levels of the two inputs transducers are given in Table 25.8.

Output from	Temp. unit	Flame unit
High (1)	Temp. not too high	Flame on
Low (0)	Temp. too high	Flame out

Table 25.8

(a) Draw up a truth table for the logic gate putting Q = '1' if the alarm is to sound and Q = '0' if it is not.
(b) What type of logic gate is required?

Q3
What must be the levels of inputs A and B from the moisture sensing unit and switch respectively in Fig. 25.10, for the buzzer to sound, i.e. Q = 1? Give a use for this system.

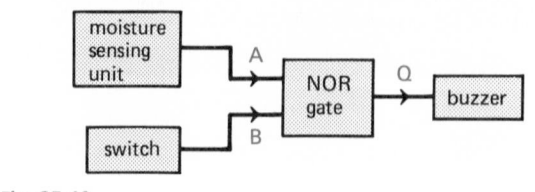

Fig. 25.10

Q4
Using any of the basic logic gates, draw a circuit which has the truth table shown in Table 25.9.

Inputs		Output
A	B	Q
0	0	0
0	1	0
1	0	1
1	1	0

Table 25.9

Q5
Copy and complete the truth table for the circuit in Fig. 25.11.

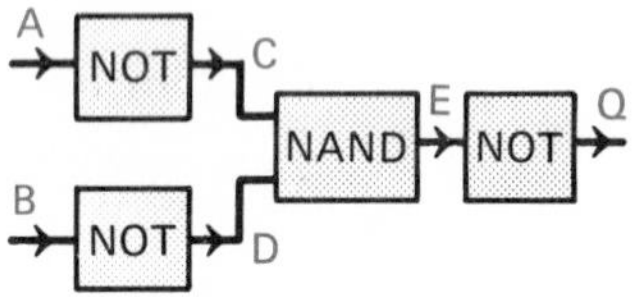

A →[NOT]→ C
B →[NOT]→ D
→[NAND]→ E →[NOT]→ Q

A	B	C	D	E	Q
0	0				
0	1				
1	0				
1	1				

Fig. 25.11

Q6
Write the truth table for the circuit in Fig. 25.12. (*Note*. It has 8 input combinations.)

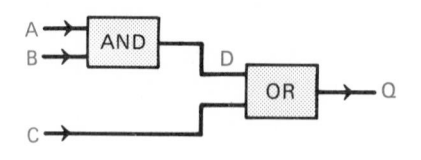

Fig. 25.12

Q7
Write the truth table for the circuit in Fig. 25.13, including the levels at C, D, E and F.

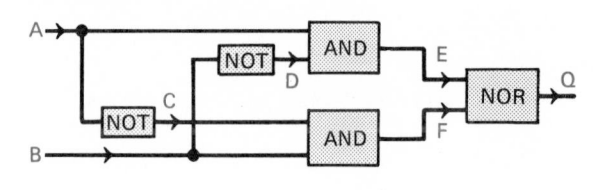

Fig. 25.13

Q8
The circuit in Fig. 25.14 is for a burglar alarm in which an electric bell rings when light falls on the LDR in a dark room.

(a) What is the voltage level at A (i.e. a '1' or a '0') when S is **(i)** closed, **(ii)** open?
(b) What is the voltage level at B (i.e. a '1' or a '0') when the LDR is **(i)** in the dark, **(ii)** in the light?

(c) Which type of basic logic gate would make Q = '1' when light fell on the LDR with S closed?
(d) Why is a transistor needed between the logic gate and the electric bell?

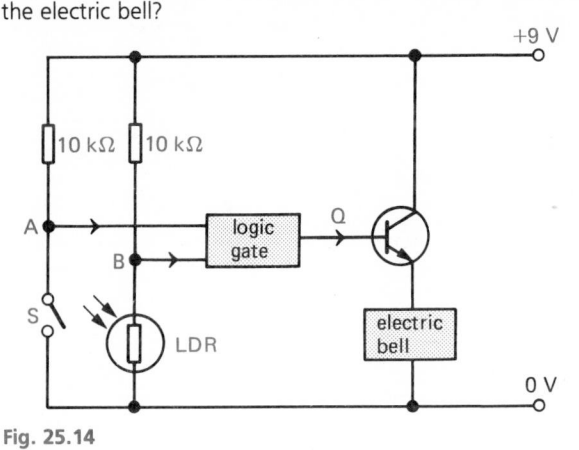

Fig. 25.14

26 Electronics and society

Electronics is having an ever-increasing impact on all our lives. Work and leisure are changing as a result of the social, economic and environmental influence of new technology. In the first industrial revolution, machines replaced muscles. In the second, now upon us, and caused by electronics, brain power is being replaced. Few areas of human activity are likely to escape.

◆ Reasons for impact

Why is electronics having such a great impact? Some of the reasons are listed below.

(i) *Mass production* of large quantities of semiconductor devices (e.g. ICs) allows them to be made very cheaply.

(ii) *Miniaturization* of components means that even complex systems can be quite compact.

(iii) *Reliability* of electronic components is a feature of well-designed circuits. There are no moving parts to wear out, no servicing is needed and systems can be robust.

(iv) *Energy consumption* and use of natural resources tends to be much less than for their non-electronic counterparts.

(v) *Speed of operation* can be millions of times greater than for other alternatives (e.g. mechanical devices).

(vi) *Transducers* of many different types are available for transferring information in and out of an electronic system.

To sum up, electronic systems tend to be cheaper, smaller, more reliable, less wasteful, much faster and can respond to a wider range of signals than other systems.

◆ Areas of impact

(a) Home. Devices such as washing machines, burglar alarms, telephones, cookers and sewing machines, Fig. 26.1a, now contain electronic components. Central heating systems and garage doors may have automatic electronic control. For home entertainment, computers, video cassette recorders (VCRs), compact disc players, TV sets with Teletext operated by remotely controlled keypads that use infrared, and electronic games, are finding their way into more and more homes.

(b) Medical services. These have benefitted greatly in recent years from the use of electronic instruments and appliances. Electrocardiograph (ECG) recorders for monitoring the heart, ultrasonic scanners for checks during pregnancy, deaf aids, heart pacemakers, artificial kidneys, limbs with electronic control and talking newspapers for the blind are some examples.

(a) Computer based sewing machine

(b) Arc-welding computer controlled robot on a car production line

(c) Computers in the office

(d) Scanning electron microscope

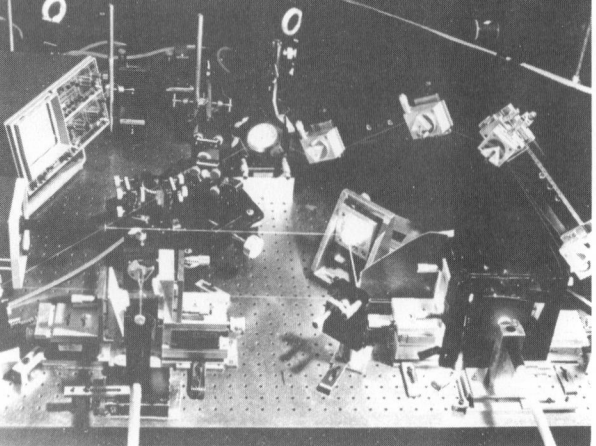
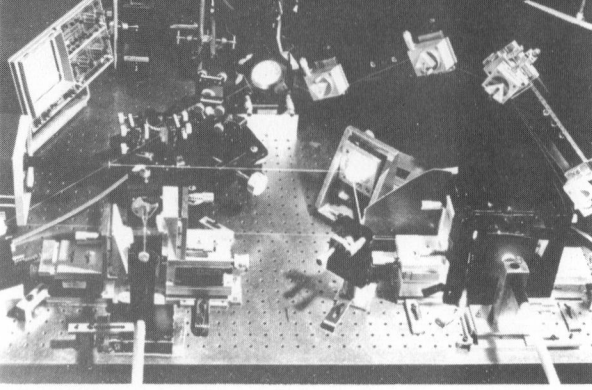

(e) Mode-locked laser pulsed light experiment

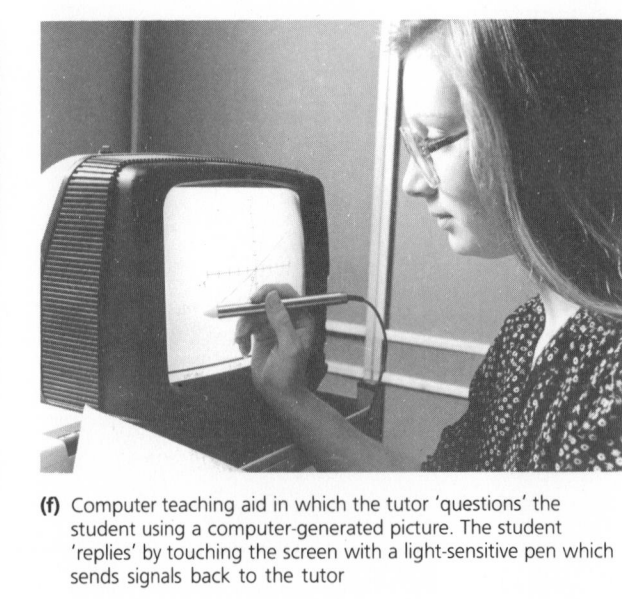

(f) Computer teaching aid in which the tutor 'questions' the student using a computer-generated picture. The student 'replies' by touching the screen with a light-sensitive pen which sends signals back to the tutor

Fig. 26.1

(c) Industry. Microprocessor-controlled equipment (Chapter 49) is taking over in industry. Robots are widely used for car assembly work to do dull, routine, dirty jobs such as welding, Fig. 26.1*b*, and paint spraying. In many cases production lines and even whole factories, e.g. sugar refineries and oil refineries, are almost entirely automated. Computer aided design (CAD) of products is increasing, even in the clothing industry. The face of industry is being changed by electronics.

(d) Offices, banks and shops. Word processors are efficient and more interesting replacements for typewriters, Fig. 26.1*c*. Mail in the form of text, numbers and pictures can be transmitted by electronic means. Cash dispensers at banks and building society offices are a great convenience for their customers. Bar codes like the one on the back cover of this book and on tins and packets are used by supermarkets for stock control in conjunction with a bar code reader (or a laser) and a data recorder, possibly connected to a computer (Chapter 45). A similar system is operated by some libraries to record the issue and return of books. Shop cash registers are almost universally electronic today.

(e) Communications. Communication satellites enable events on one side of the world to be seen and heard on the other side, as they happen. Electronic telephone exchanges like System X are the order of the day. Car telephone systems, called *cellular radio*, permit people in cars, trains and ferries to make calls on the existing telephone network, computers being used to switch them when they leave one area (cell) and enter another.

(f) Weather forecasting. Weather satellites provide forecasters with infrared pictures of large areas of the Earth. Radar too is used to detect cloud formations.

(g) Transport. The safety of many forms of transport can be improved by the use of electronic devices to give the user more information about the system, e.g. a ship or a car. Traffic signals and traffic flow are regulated in many large cities by microprocessors. Modern railway signalling systems are much more dependent on electronics. Automatic pilots are common in aircraft, as are simulators for pilot training.

(h) Emergency services. Infrared operated thermal imagers help rescue workers looking for people trapped in collapsed buildings, after disasters such as earthquakes.

(i) Scientific research. Scientific discoveries aid technology, which in turn, produces better tools and techniques for scientists to do their research. The scanning electron microscope, used to magnify and 'see' the surface of a material on a cathode ray screen, Fig. 26.1*d*, is such a tool.

Another is the pulsed laser, now spearheading investigations into very high speed transmission of digital information using optical techniques, Fig. 26.1*e*.

(j) Education. Microcomputers, pocket calculators (instead of log tables and slide rules), interactive teaching aids like the one in Fig. 26.1*f*, more courses on electronics in schools, colleges and universities (and their accompanying textbooks like this one) are just some of the innovations in education due to the impact of electronics.

(k) Leisure. For some people, leisure means participating in or attending sporting activities and here the electronic score board may be much in evidence. For others, leisure means visiting the theatre where the lighting and sound effects, in modern musicals, are programmed by a computer. For the golf enthusiast, electronic machines claim to analyse 'swings' and reduce handicaps.

◆ Consequences of impact

Most of the social and economic consequences of electronics are beneficial but a few cause problems.

(a) Improved quality of life. This results from the greater convenience and reliability of electronic systems, increased life expectancy and leisure time, and fewer dull, repetitive jobs.

(b) Better communication. The world has become a smaller place due to the speed with which news can be reported to our homes by radio and television. This, and the influence of information systems such as Teletext and Viewdata, should produce a more well-informed public.

(c) Databases. These are memories (Chapter 32) which can store huge amounts of information for rapid transmission from one place to another. For example, police can obtain by radio, details of a car they are following, in seconds. Databases raise questions, however, about invasion of privacy and security (see Chapter 45).

(d) Early obsolescence of equipment. Rapid changes of design due to technological advances mean that equipment can soon go out of date and need replacing.

(e) Employment. The demand for new equipment creates new industry and jobs (to make and maintain it), but when electronic systems replace mechanical ones, redundancy and retraining problems arise. Conditions of employment and long-term job prospects can also be affected for many people, especially certain manual and clerical workers, e.g. typists. One industrial robot replaces four factory workers.

(f) Public attitude. Modern electronics is a 'hidden' technology with parts that are enclosed in a tiny package and do not move. It is also a 'throwaway' technology in which the whole lot is discarded and replaced if a part fails — by an expert. For these reasons it may be regarded as mysterious and unfriendly since people feel they do not understand what makes it tick.

◆ The future

The only certain prediction about the future is that new technologies will be developed and these, like present ones, will continue to have a considerable influence on our lives.

Today the development of 'intelligent' Fifth Generation computers is being pursued with great vigour and optical systems, which are more efficient than electronic ones for transferring (by optical fibres), storing (by holographic memories) and processing information are starting to appear.

◇ Questions

Q1

The greengrocery department in a supermarket has a cash register with touch switches labelled as in Fig. 26.2. It is controlled by a microprocessor.

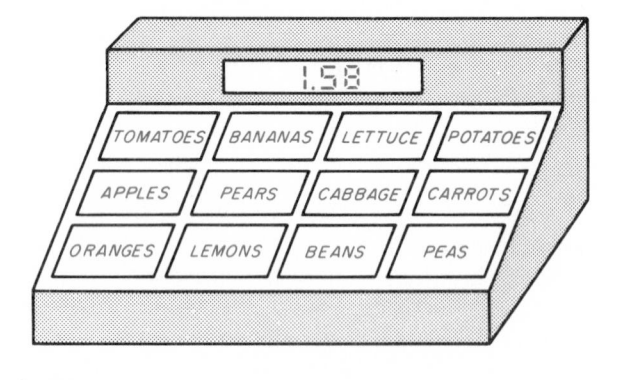

Fig. 26.2

State **(a)** *two* advantages and **(b)** *two* disadvantages of this type of cash register compared with the usual electronic keyboard type.

Q2

Give **(a)** *one* advantage and **(b)** *one* disadvantage of the *bar code* method used at some supermarkets for getting information about the stock they hold.

Q3

One microprocessor is replacing several devices in a car and taking over a wider range of tasks (e.g. checking the state of lamps, monitoring tyre pressures, etc.).

List some of the **(a)** advantages and **(b)** disadvantages of this development.

Q4

A combination lock for a safe uses electronic logic gates in the circuit of Fig. 26.3.

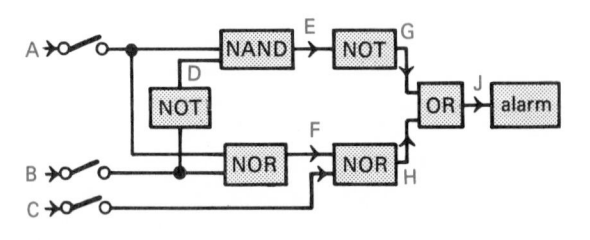

Fig. 26.3

(a) Draw up a truth table for the eight possible input combinations of the switches ('1' for on, '0' for off) showing the output states at D, E, F, G, H and J.
(b) There are six different orders of closing the switches A, B, C namely: ABC, ACB, BCA, BAC, CBA, CAB. Which order does *not* set off the alarm? (If J = '1' the alarm is activated.)

Check list **Electronics and society**

After studying *Chapter 23: Electronic systems I,* **you should be able to**

◇ state that in the systems approach, an electronic system is regarded as consisting of an input transducer, processing sub-systems and an output transducer, and can be represented by a block diagram,

◇ state that electronic switches are digital devices with input and output voltages that are either 'high' ('1') or 'low' ('0'),

◇ state that a transistor switch is an inverter,

◇ state that a transducer driver or buffer is a current amplifier,

◇ state that the output of a latch goes and stays 'high', no matter what happens afterwards at the input,

◇ draw and explain the block diagram for a burglar alarm,

◇ state that a logic gate has one output and two (or more) inputs, the output being 'high' or 'low' depending on the combination of input voltages,

◇ construct truth tables, for AND, NAND, OR, NOR and NOT gates, and

◇ draw the block diagram for a safety system for machine operators.

After studying *Chapter 24: Electronic systems II,* **you should be able to**

◇ state that an amplifier increases the voltage, current or power of the input,

◇ state that in a non-inverting amplifier, the output voltage is greater than the input voltage and of the same sign,

◇ state that in an inverting amplifier, the output voltage is greater than the input voltage but of opposite sign,

◇ state that a comparator compares two input voltages (d.c. or a.c.) and gives a digital output,

◇ state that in a summing amplifier the output voltage is the algebraic sum of the input voltages,

◇ state that in a difference amplifier the output voltage is the difference between the two input voltages (a.c. or d.c.),

◇ draw and explain the block diagram for an automatic garage door system,

◇ state that a pulse generator or astable multivibrator produces an output voltage that is a continuous square wave,

◇ state that a triggered pulse producer or delay unit or monostable multivibrator produces one output pulse lasting for a fixed time,

◇ state that a ramp generator produces a sawtooth waveform output voltage,

◇ draw and explain the block diagram for a pulsed flashing lamp,

◇ state that a counter counts the pulses at its input and produces an output in binary form,

◇ state that a decoder converts binary signals into decimal ones,

◇ draw and explain the block diagram for a digital voltmeter,

◇ state that when the stages of a system are joined together, **(a)** each stage must be able to supply the current required by the following stage and **(b)** the voltage levels and ranges of each stage must match the next stage,

◊ give examples of interfacing devices, and

◊ state the impedance matching conditions necessary for **(a)** maximum voltage and **(b)** maximum power transfer between the stages of a system.

After studying *Chapter 25: Electronic systems III*, you should be able to

◊ solve system problems stated in words using combinations of logic gates, e.g. street lights, heater control, and

◊ construct the truth table for a system from its logic diagram.

After studying *Chapter 26: Electronics and society*, you should be able to

◊ give six reasons why electronics is having an impact on society,

◊ give examples of the use of electronics in each of the following areas: home, medical services, industry, offices, banks, shops, communications, weather forecasting, transport, emergency services, scientific research, education and leisure, and

◊ state some of the positive and negative social and economic consequences of the impact of electronics.

Digital sub-systems

27 Transistor as a switch

◆ Digital sub-systems

Digital sub-systems contain switching-type circuits in which the inputs and outputs involve only two levels of voltage, referred to as 'high' and 'low'. 'High' is near the supply voltage, e.g. $+5\,V$ and is also called *logic level 1* (or just '1'). 'Low' is near $0\,V$ and is called *logic level 0* (or just '0'). The signals are electrical *pulses*, Fig. 27.1 and are the kind that occur in pocket calculators, digital watches, computers, control systems and increasingly in communications.

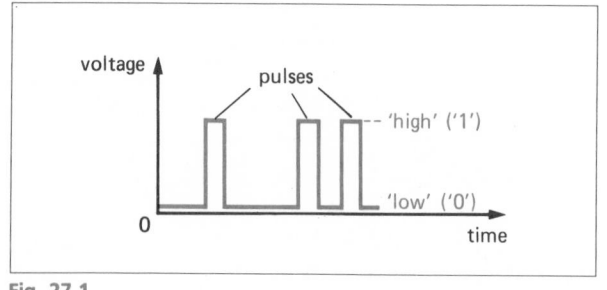

Fig. 27.1

The transistor is the basic switching device in digital sub-systems. It has many advantages over other electrically operated switches such as relays. It is small, cheap, reliable, has no moving parts, has an almost indefinite life (in well-designed circuits) and can switch millions of times a second.

Today digital sub-systems are made as *integrated circuits* and are more complex (Chapter 15) than the discrete component versions from which they developed.

◆ Transistor switch

The basic common–emitter transistor switching circuit is shown in Fig. 27.2. It has a current-limiting series resistor R_B in the base (input) circuit and a load resistor R_L in the collector (output) circuit (Chapter 15).

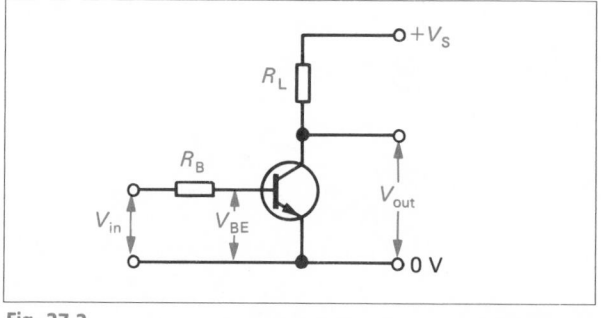

Fig. 27.2

The relationship between the output voltage V_{out} and the input voltage V_{in} can be investigated experimentally using the circuit of Fig. 27.3.

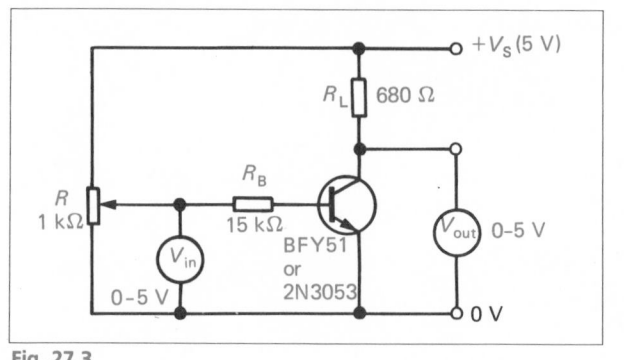

Fig. 27.3

The variable resistor R acts as a potential divider across the supply voltage V_S. If it is adjusted, V_{in} can be gradually increased from 0 to 5 V and corresponding values of V_{in} and V_{out} noted on the input and output voltmeters.

From the values obtained, a graph of V_{out} against V_{in} can be drawn, like that in Fig. 27.4. It has three parts:

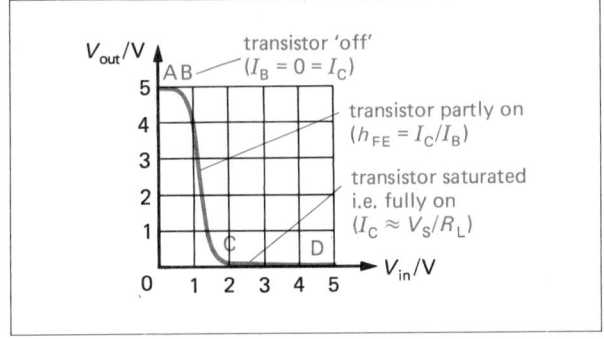

Fig. 27.4

(i) AB: V_{in} is 'low' (less than 0.6 V or so) and is too small to turn on the transistor. In this state the base current I_B is zero as is the collector current I_C; the *transistor is off*, i.e. not conducting and behaves like a very *high* resistor, i.e. a switch in the 'off' position. Since $I_C = 0$, there is no current through R_L and therefore no voltage drop across it. Hence $V_{out} = V_S$ (5 V), as the graph shows, and we can say that when

V_{in} is 'low', V_{out} is 'high'

(ii) BC: in the small range of V_{in} between about 0.6 V and 1.4 V, V_{out} falls rapidly as V_{in} increases. The transistor has been turned on by V_{in} exceeding 0.6 V and causing I_B to flow. As a result the transistor conducts. I_C passes through R_L and there is a voltage drop across it, i.e. V_{out} decreases since part of V_S is now dropped across R_L. (R_L and the transistor form a potential divider across V_S.) This part of the graph is nearly a straight line and along it

$$h_{FE} = \frac{I_C}{I_B}$$

(iii) CD: V_{in} is 'high' (greater than 1.4 V) and $V_{out} \approx 0$ V, i.e. the voltage drop across the transistor is zero and almost all V_S is dropped across R_L.

Hence

$$V_S \approx I_C \times R_L$$

Since V_S and R_L are fixed, I_C now has its maximum value given by $I_C \approx V_S/R_L$. The *transistor is fully on* and is said to be *saturated* since any further increase in I_B does not increase I_C. The transistor in this part behaves like a very

low resistance ($\approx 0\,\Omega$), i.e. like a switch that is 'on'. We can say that when

V_{in} is 'high', V_{out} is 'low'

To sum up, a transistor switch is an *inverter* or *NOT gate* and is used either in the 'off' or 'fully on' (saturated) states, i.e. on parts AB and CD of Fig. 27.4.

◆ Notes

1 Although V_{in} varies from 0 to 5 V, the voltage between the base and emitter V_{BE} (Fig. 27.2) remains almost steady at about 0.6 V. ($V_{in} - 0.6$ V) is dropped across R_B which is essential to limit I_B when V_{in} exceeds 0.6 V.

2 Numerical problems can be solved using
(a) the collector–emitter circuit equation:

$$V_S = I_C \times R_L + V_{out} \tag{1}$$

which follows from the fact that R_L and the transistor are in series with V_S, and

(b) the base–emitter circuit equation:

$$V_{in} = I_B \times R_B + V_{BE} \tag{2}$$

Since R_B and the base–emitter junction of the transistor are in series with V_{in}.

◇ Worked example

In the transistor switch circuit of Fig. 27.5 what is

(a) *the voltage V_{BE} required to turn on the (silicon) transistor*
(b) *the voltage across R_B if $V_{in} = 4$ V,*
(c) *the base current I_B in R_B,*
(d) *the voltage across R_L if the transistor is just saturated,*
(e) *the collector current I_C,*
(f) *h_{FE} for the transistor, and*
(g) *V_{out}?*

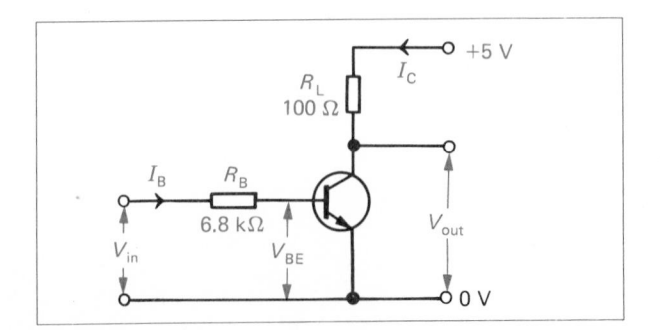

Fig. 27.5

(a) $V_{BE} \approx +0.6\,\text{V}$

(b) From equation (2) above, we get

$$\text{voltage across } R_B = I_B \times R_B = V_{in} - V_{BE}$$
$$= 4\,\text{V} - 0.6\,\text{V}$$
$$= 3.4\,\text{V}$$

(c) $I_B = \dfrac{\text{voltage across } R_B}{R_B} = \dfrac{3.4\,\text{V}}{6.8\,\text{k}\Omega}$

$\qquad = 0.5\,\text{mA}$

(d) Voltage across $R_L = 5\,\text{V}$

(e) $I_C = \dfrac{\text{voltage across } R_L}{R_L} = \dfrac{5\,\text{V}}{100\,\Omega}$

$\qquad = 0.05\,\text{A} = 50\,\text{mA}$

(f) We have

$$h_{FE} = \frac{I_C}{I_B} = \frac{50}{0.5} = 100$$

(g) $V_{out} = 0\,\text{V}$

◆ Alarm circuits

In many alarm circuits a transducer in a potential divider circuit (Chapter 12) is the source of an analogue signal (Chapter 15) that is used to switch on a transistor which then activates an alarm.

(a) Light-operated. A simple circuit which switches on a lamp L when it gets dark is shown in Fig. 27.6. R and the light dependent resistor (LDR) form a potential divider across the 6 V supply. The input is the p.d. V_{in} across the LDR and in bright light is small because the resistance of the LDR is low (e.g. 1 kΩ) compared with that of R (10 kΩ). V_{BE} is less than the 0.6 V or so required to turn on the transistor.

In the dark more of the 6 V supply is dropped across the LDR, due to its greater resistance (e.g. 1 MΩ), and less across R. V_{in} is then large enough for V_{BE} to reach 0.6 V and switch on the transistor which creates a collector current sufficient to light L. If R is replaced by a variable resistor, the light level at which L comes on can be adjusted.

When R and the LDR are interchanged, L is on in the light and off in the dark and the circuit could act as an intruder alarm.

(b) Temperature-operated. In the high-temperature alarm circuit of Fig. 27.7 a thermistor and resistor R form a potential divider across the 6 V supply. When the temperature of the thermistor rises, its resistance decreases, so increasing V_{in} and V_{BE}. When $V_{BE} \approx 0.6\,\text{V}$, the transistor switches on and collector current (too small to ring the bell directly) flows through the relay coil. The relay contacts close, enabling the bell to obtain, directly from the 6 V supply, the larger current it needs.

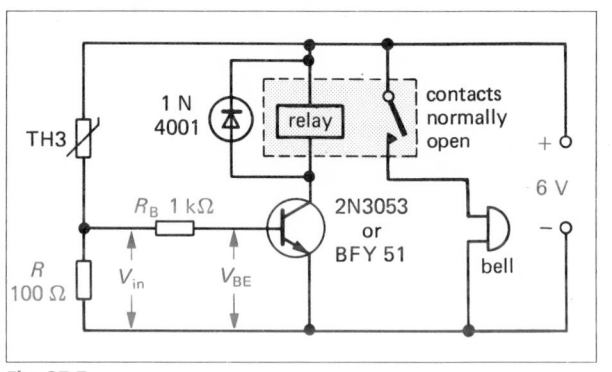

Fig. 27.7

The diode protects the transistor from damage by the large voltage induced in the relay coil (due to its inductance) when the collector current falls to zero (at switch-off). The diode is forward biased to the induced e.m.f. and, because of its low resistance, offers an easy path to it. To the power supply the diode is reverse biased and its high resistance does not short-circuit the relay coil when the transistor is on.

If the thermistor and R are interchanged, the circuit could act as a frost-warning device.

(c) Time-operated. In the circuit of Fig. 27.8, when S_1 and S_2 are closed, L is on and the transistor is off

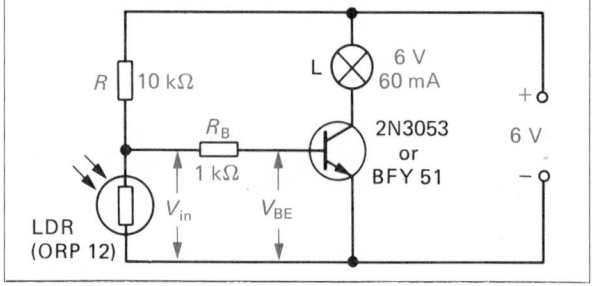

Fig. 27.6

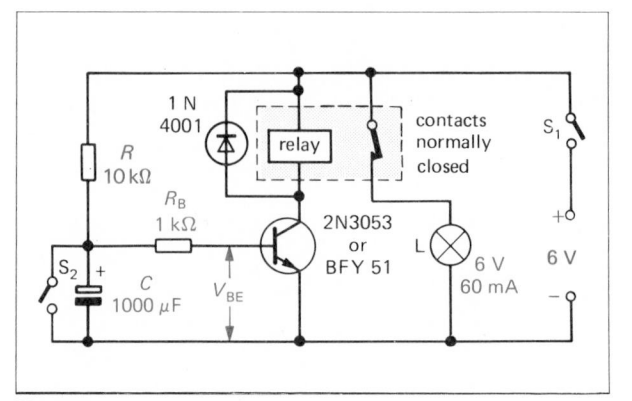

Fig. 27.8

because $V_{BE} = 0$ (due to S_2 short-circuiting C and stopping it charging up). If S_2 is opened, C starts to charge through R and, after a certain time, $V_{BE} = 0.6\,V$ causing the transistor to switch on. This operates the relay whose contacts open and switch off L. The time delay between opening S_2 and L going off depends on the time constant $T (= C \times R)$ (Chapter 10). If either C or R or both are increased in value, the time delay increases. The circuit could be used as a *timer* to control a lamp in a photographic dark room. It is reset by opening S_1 and closing S_2 to let C discharge.

(d) Sound-operated with latching. The variable resistor R in Fig. 27.9 is adjusted so that the transistor switches 'on' only when someone speaks into the microphone. The emitter current then provides the gate current which triggers the thyristor (Chapter 14) and allows current to flow through the lamp. The lamp stays on till the 6 V supply is disconnected, i.e. the thyristor acts as a latching switch.

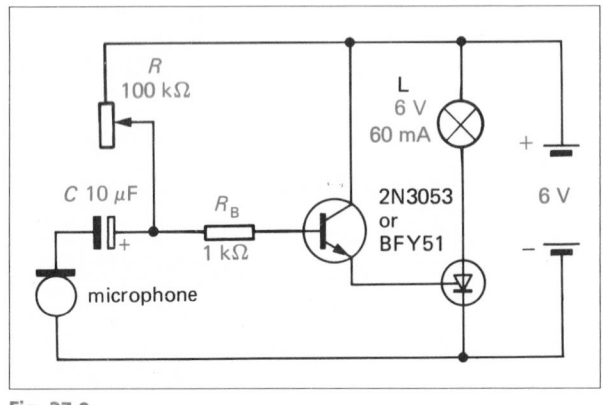

Fig. 27.9

The capacitor C stops d.c. from the battery passing via R through the microphone and upsetting the operation of the transistor. But it allows the a.c. produced in the microphone by the sound to pass to the base.

The circuit could form the basis of a sound-operated intruder alarm.

Note. A relay can also be used as a latch in a switching circuit but compared with a thyristor, it is slower, requires more current and is less reliable because its contacts can wear out.

◇ Questions

Q1

In the circuit of Fig. 27.10, what is V_{out} when **(a)** S is open **(b)** S is closed?

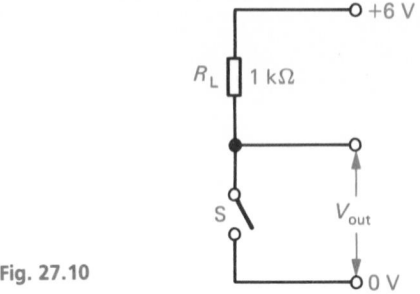

Fig. 27.10

Q2

In the switching circuit of Fig. 27.11, what is
(a) the value of V_{BE} needed to turn on the (silicon) transistor,
(b) the voltage across R_B if $V_{in} = 5\,V$,
(c) I_B,
(d) the voltage across R_L if the transistor is just saturated,
(e) I_C,
(f) h_{FE} for the transistor,
(g) V_{out}?

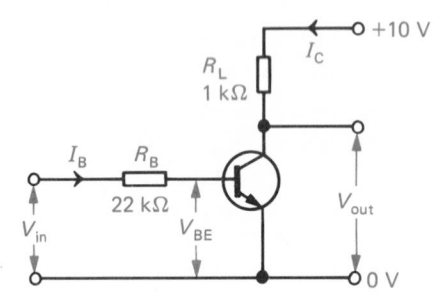

Fig. 27.11

Q3

In the circuit of Fig. 27.12
(a) When Tr is off, what is **(i)** the p.d. across R_L and **(ii)** V_{out}?
(b) When R_1 is decreased what change occurs to V_{in}?
(c) When Tr is saturated, what is **(i)** the p.d. across R_L and **(ii)** V_{out}?
(d) Why is **(i)** R_B and **(ii)** R_L necessary?

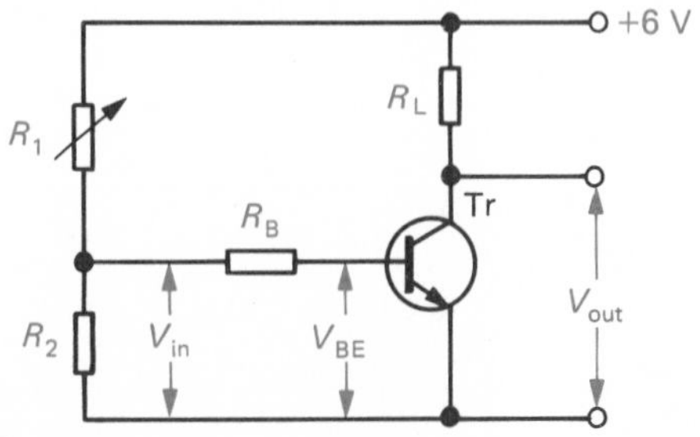

Fig. 27.12

Q4

(a) Explain why the circuit in Fig. 27.13 switches the transistor off a certain time after switch S is opened.

(b) What happens if the value of *R* is increased?

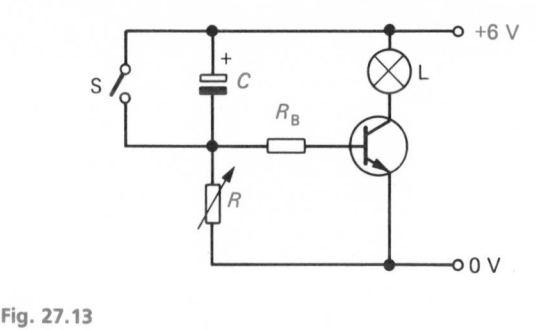

Fig. 27.13

Q5

For the circuit in Fig. 27.14

(a) state what conditions, light or dark, cause L to light, if *R* is large,

(b) explain how and why V_{in} changes when conditions change from light to dark, and

(c) state the advantage of using a variable resistor for *R*.

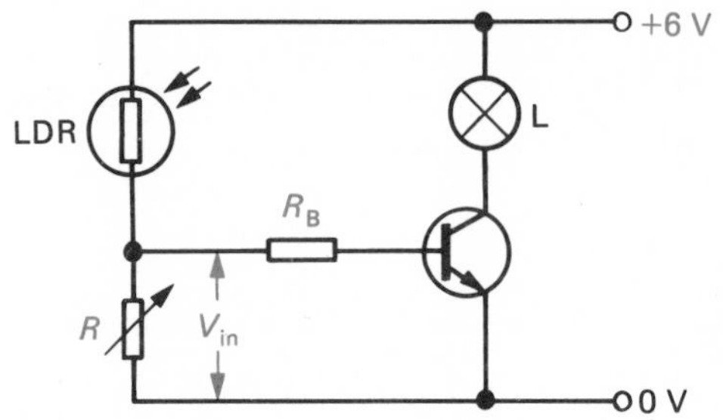

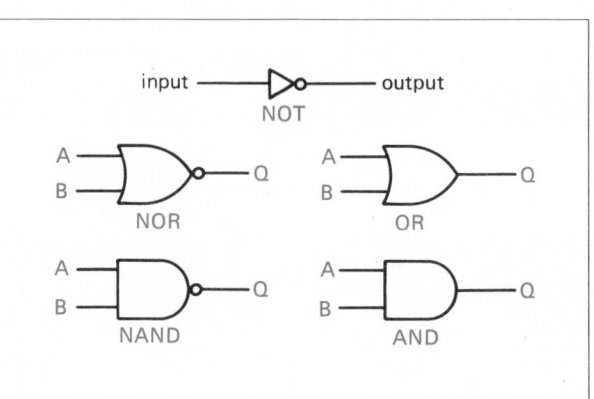

Fig. 27.14

28 Logic gates

◆ Basic gates

The truth tables for NOT, NOR, OR, NAND and AND gates were given in Chapter 23. Their properties are summarized below and their international symbols are given in Fig. 28.1. They are available as 14 or 16 pin d.i.l. ICs with several gates (often four) on the same chip and using common power supply connections.

Try to remember the following:

NOT:	output always opposite of input
NOR:	output 1 *only* when all inputs 0
OR:	output 1 *unless* all inputs 0
NAND:	output 1 *unless* all inputs 1
AND:	output 1 *only* when all inputs 1

Fig. 28.1

◆ Exclusive-OR gate (EXOR)

This is an OR gate with only two inputs which gives a 'high' output when either input is 'high' but not when both are 'high'. Unlike the ordinary OR gate (sometimes called the *inclusive*-OR gate) it excludes the case of both inputs being 'high' for a 'high' output. It is also called the *difference* gate because the output is 'high' when the inputs are different.

The symbol and truth table are shown in Fig. 28.2.

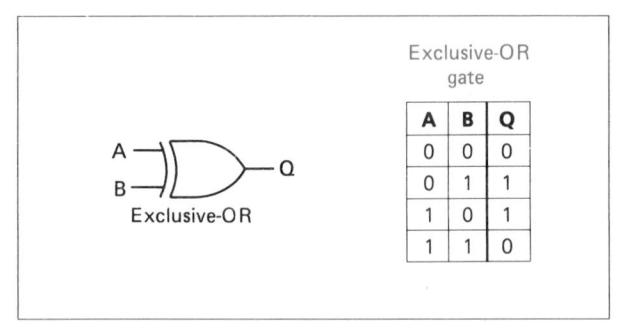

Fig. 28.2

◆ Other gates from NAND gates

Other logic gates (and circuits) can be made by combining only NAND gates (or only NOR gates), a fact which is often used in logic circuit design, as we shall see later.

The NAND gate equivalents for different gates are shown in Fig. 28.3. For example, if the inputs of a NAND

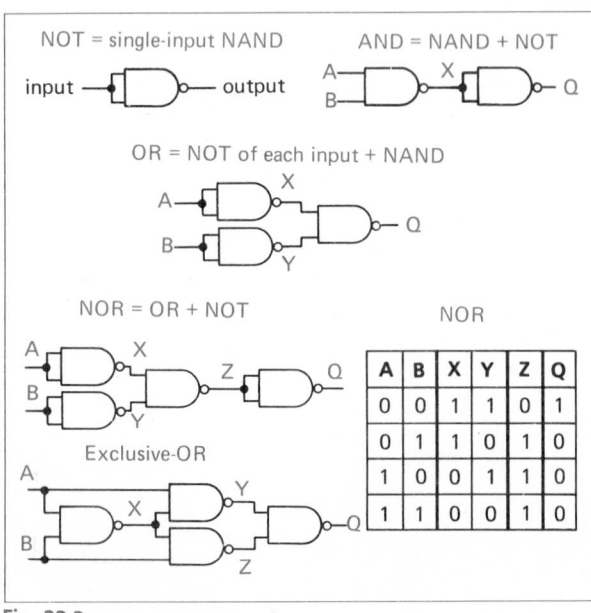

Fig. 28.3

are joined together, it behaves as a NOT since a NAND gives a '0' output if both its inputs are '1' and a '1' output if either input is '0'. You can check that the others give the correct output for the various input combinations by constructing a stage-by-stage truth table, as has been done for the NOR gate made from four NAND gates. Note and remember!

(i) NOT = single-input NAND (or NOR), made by joining all the inputs together,
(ii) AND = NAND followed by NOT,
(iii) OR = NOT of each input followed by NAND,
(iv) NOR = OR followed by NOT.

◆ Logic circuit design

The design of logic circuits was considered in Chapter 25 using the 'inspection of truth tables' method. More complex circuits can be constructed using a type of mathematics called *Boolean algebra*. Two examples follow in which the final design contains *only NAND gates*, so reducing the need to have a supply of all types of gate.

◆ Design of exclusive-OR gate (EXOR)

Lines 2 and 3 of the truth table in Fig. 28.2 show that the output Q is 1 only when:

A is 0 **AND** B is 1
OR
A is 1 **AND** B is 0

The method requires this statement to be rewritten so that both inputs appear as 1s. Therefore if A is 0, inverting A with a NOT gate makes the input (called 'not A' and written $\bar{A}$) a 1. Similarly instead of writing B as 0, we can say $\bar{B}$ (i.e. not B) is 1. The statement, which is the same as before, becomes Q is 1 when:

$\bar{A}$ is 1 **AND** B is 1
OR
A is 1 **AND** $\bar{B}$ is 1

Using the notation of Boolean algebra, we get

$$Q = \bar{A}.B + A.\bar{B} \qquad (1)$$

where a dot (.) represents the AND logic operation and a plus (+) indicates the OR operation.

Using *any* logic gates this means the circuit consists of two two-input AND gates (each with a NOT gate in one input) feeding a two-input OR gate, as in Fig. 28.4.

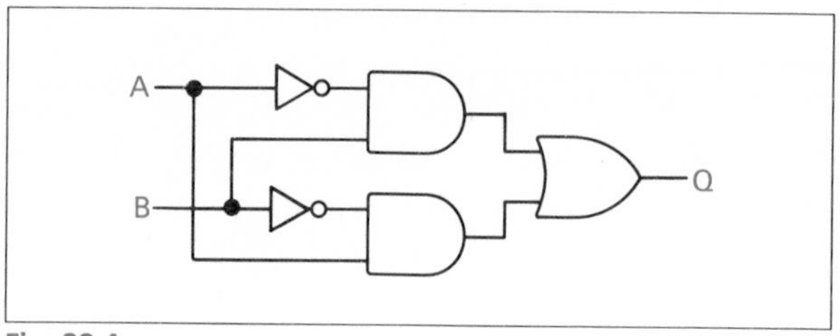

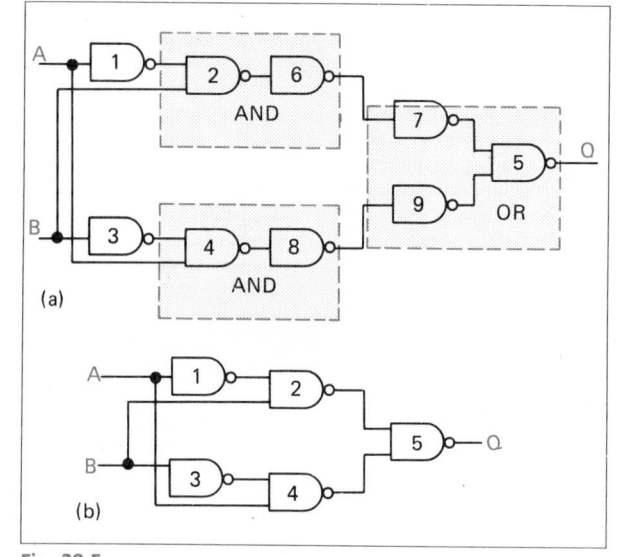

Fig. 28.4

To implement it with only NAND gates we use the facts stated earlier

NOT = one-input NAND
AND = NAND followed by NOT
OR = NOT of each input followed by NAND

The circuit becomes that of Fig. 28.5a but inverting an input twice gives the original input, i.e. the successive NOT gates 6 and 7, also 8 and 9, cancel each other, so only NAND gates 1, 2, 3, 4 and 5 are needed. The equivalent NAND gate circuit is given in Fig. 28.5b. Although different from the exclusive-OR circuit in Fig. 28.3, it performs the same logical operation. Note that $\bar{A}$ and $\bar{B}$ are obtained by inverting A and B with one-input NAND gates (1 and 3), i.e. with NOT gates.

Fig. 28.5

◆ Design of traffic lights system

The problem is to design a logic circuit with two inputs A and B and three outputs R, Y and G obeying the truth table of Table 28.1. If R, Y and G feed red, yellow and green lights (e.g. (LEDs), these would flash in the order of British traffic signals when A and B are supplied continuously by a two-bit binary code representing the numbers 0 to 3 (Chapter 29).

State	A	B	R	Y	G
0	0	0	1	0	0
1	0	1	1	1	0
2	1	0	0	0	1
3	1	1	0	1	0

Table 28.1

From the truth table we can write

(i) R is 1 when (lines 0 and 1):

A is 0 **AND** B is 0 (i.e. $\bar{A}$ is 1 **AND** $\bar{B}$ is 1)

OR

A is 0 **AND** B is 1 (i.e. $\bar{A}$ is 1 **AND** B is 1)

(ii) Y is 1 when (lines 1 and 3):

A is 0 **AND** B is 1 (i.e. $\bar{A}$ is 1 **AND** B is 1)

OR

A is 1 **AND** B is 1

(iii) G is 1 when (line 2):

A is 1 **AND** B is 0 (i.e. A is 1 **AND** $\bar{B}$ is 1)

Rewriting **(i)**, **(ii)** and **(iii)** in Boolean notation and factorizing as in ordinary algebra:

$$R = \bar{A}.\bar{B} + \bar{A}.B = \bar{A}(\bar{B} + B)$$
$$Y = \bar{A}.B + A.B = B(\bar{A} + A)$$
$$G = A.\bar{B}$$

Now if the two inputs to an OR gate are an input and its inverse (called its *complement*), one input is a 1, making the output 1 (since for an OR gate, the output is 1 unless all inputs are 0). That is $\bar{A} + A$ is 1 and $\bar{B} + B$ is 1, hence we get

$$R = \bar{A} \qquad Y = B \qquad G = A.\bar{B}$$

Thus the logic circuit has to feed R from input A via a NOT gate while Y goes to input B directly and G is supplied by the output of an AND gate having A and the complement of B as its inputs, Fig. 28.6a. Using only NAND gates, the circuit is as in Fig. 28.6b.

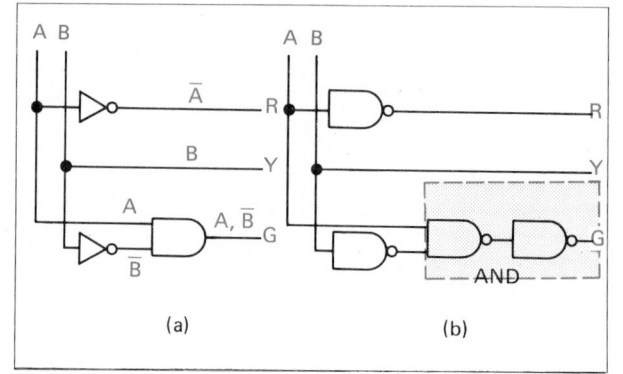

Fig. 28.6

◆ Logic gate ICs

Each IC package has several gates on the same chip. For example, a quad two-input NAND gate contains four identical NAND gates, with two inputs and one output per gate. Every gate therefore has three pins, making fourteen pins altogether on the package. This includes two for positive and negative power supply connections which are common to all four gates.

The TTL quad two-input NAND IC, 7400, is shown in Fig. 28.7a and its CMOS equivalent, the 4011B, in Fig. 28.7b. There are similar IC packages for the other logic gates, some with four or eight inputs.

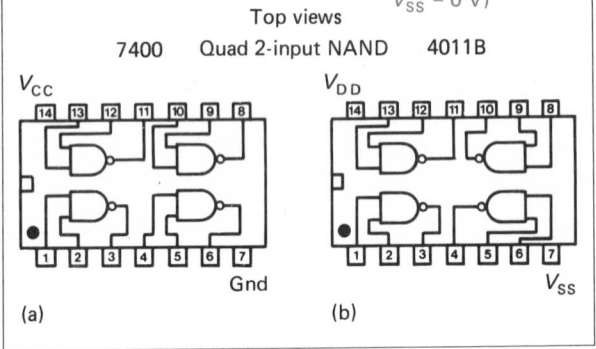

Fig. 28.7

The output current obtainable from a gate is limited to a few milliamperes. If more is required a current amplifying *buffer* must be used, e.g. a transistor.

◇ Questions

Q1
Write the truth table for the logic circuit in Fig. 28.8.

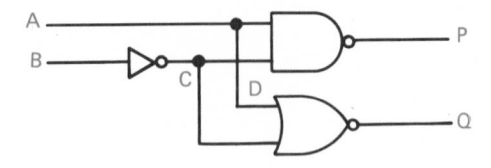

Fig. 28.8

Q2
Draw up a truth table for each of the systems **(a)** and **(b)** shown in Fig. 28.9 and say what logic function each performs.

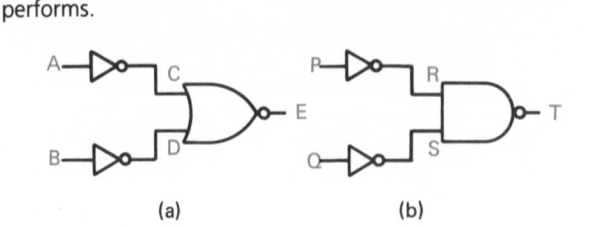

Fig. 28.9

Q3
(a) Construct a truth table for a three-input NAND gate.
(b) Draw a diagram to show how a two-input NAND gate can be used as a NOT gate.
(c) Draw a diagram to show how three two-input NAND gates can be used as an OR gate.
(d) What do the terms logic level 1 ('high') and logic level 0 ('low') actually represent when used in connection with logic gates?

Q4
By constructing their truth tables, show that the circuit in Fig. 28.10a is equivalent to a three-input AND gate, Fig. 28.10b.

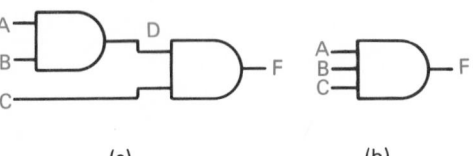

Fig. 28.10

Q5
(a) Write the truth table for a logic circuit which gives a logic 1 output with a two-bit binary input when the number 1 (decimal) is at its input.
(b) Design a logic circuit, using *any* gates, which implements **(a)**.
(c) Repeat **(b)** using NAND gates only.

29 Binary adders

◆ Codes

Normally we count on the scale of ten or decimal system using the ten digits 0 to 9. When the count exceeds 9, we place a 1 in a second column to the left of the units column to represent tens. A third column to the left of the tens column gives hundreds and so on. The values of successive columns starting from the right are 1, 10, 100, etc., or in powers of ten, 10^0, 10^1, 10^2, etc.

(a) Binary code. Counting in electronic systems is done by digital circuits on the scale of two or *binary* system. The digits 0 and 1 (called 'bits', from *bi*nary dig*its*) are used and are represented electrically by 'low' and 'high' voltages respectively. Many more columns are required since the number after 1 in binary is 10, i.e. 2 in decimal, but the digit 2 is not used in the binary system.

Successive columns in this case represent, from the right, powers of 2, i.e. 2^0, 2^1, 2^2, 2^3, etc., or in decimal 1, 2, 4, 8, etc. The table below shows how the decimal numbers from 0 to 15 are coded in the binary system; a four-bit code is required. Note that the least significant bit (l.s.b.), i.e. the 2^0 bit, is on the extreme right in each number and the most significant bit (m.s.b.) on the extreme left.

For large numbers, higher powers of two have to be used. For example:

$$decimal\ 29 = 1 \times 16 + 1 \times 8 + 1 \times 4 + 0 \times 2 + 1 \times 1$$
$$= 1 \times 2^4 + 1 \times 2^3 + 1 \times 2^2 + 0 \times 2^1 + 1 \times 2^0$$
$$= 11101\ in\ binary\ (a\ five\text{-}bit\ code)$$

Decimal		Binary				Hexadecimal
$10^1(10)$	$10^0(1)$	$2^3(8)$	$2^2(4)$	$2^1(2)$	$2^0(1)$	$16^0(1)$
0	0	0	0	0	0	0
0	1	0	0	0	1	1
0	2	0	0	1	0	2
0	3	0	0	1	1	3
0	4	0	1	0	0	4
0	5	0	1	0	1	5
0	6	0	1	1	0	6
0	7	0	1	1	1	7
0	8	1	0	0	0	8
0	9	1	0	0	1	9
1	0	1	0	1	0	A
1	1	1	0	1	1	B
1	2	1	1	0	0	C
1	3	1	1	0	1	D
1	4	1	1	1	0	E
1	5	1	1	1	1	F

(b) Hexadecimal code. One of the obvious disadvantages of binary code is the representation of even quite small numbers by a long string of bits. The hexadecimal (hex) code is more compact and therefore less liable to error. In it, the range of decimal digits, i.e. 0 to 9, is extended by adding the letters A to F for the numbers 10 to 15 respectively, as shown in the table above.

For larger numbers, successive columns from the right represent powers of sixteen (hence hexadecimal), i.e. $16^0(1)$, $16^1(16)$, $16^2(256)$, etc. For example,

decimal 16 $=$ $1 \times 16^1 +$ $0 \times 16^0 =$ 10 in hex
decimal 29 $=$ $1 \times 16^1 + 13 \times 16^0 =$ 1D in hex
decimal 407 $= 1 \times 16^2 + 9 \times 16^1 + 7 \times 16^0 = 197$ in hex

(c) Binary coded decimal (BCD). This is a popular, slightly less compact variation of binary but in practice it allows easy conversion back to decimal for display purposes. Each digit of a decimal number is coded in binary instead of coding the whole number. For example,

decimal 29 = 0010 1001 in BCD

In binary, decimal 29 requires only five bits. It is obviously essential to know which particular binary code is being used.

◆ Half-adder

Adders are electronic circuits which perform addition in binary and consist of combinations of logic gates.

(a) Adding two bits. A half-adder adds *two bits at a time* and has to deal with four cases (essentially three since two are the same). They are:

0	0	1	1
+0	+1	+0	+1
0	1	1	10

In the fourth case, 1 plus 1 equals 2, which in binary is 10, i.e. the right column is 0 and 1 is carried to the next column on the left. The circuit for a half-adder must therefore have two inputs, i.e. one for each bit to be added, and two outputs, i.e. one for the *sum* and one for the *carry*.

(b) Circuit. One way of building a half-adder from logic gates uses an exclusive-OR gate and an AND gate. From their truth tables in Fig. 29.1*a* and *b*, you can see that the output of the exclusive-OR gate is always the *sum* of the addition of two bits (being 0 for 1 + 1), while the output of the AND gate equals the *carry* of the two-bit addition (being 1 only for 1 + 1). Therefore if both bits are applied to the inputs of both gates at the same time, binary addition occurs.

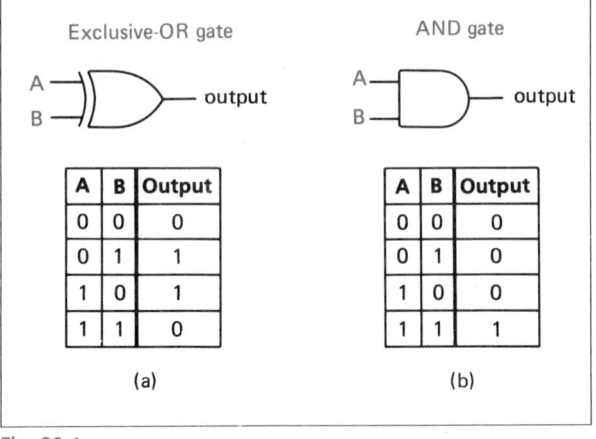

Fig. 29.1

The circuit is shown with its two inputs A and B in Fig. 29.2 along with the half-adder truth table.

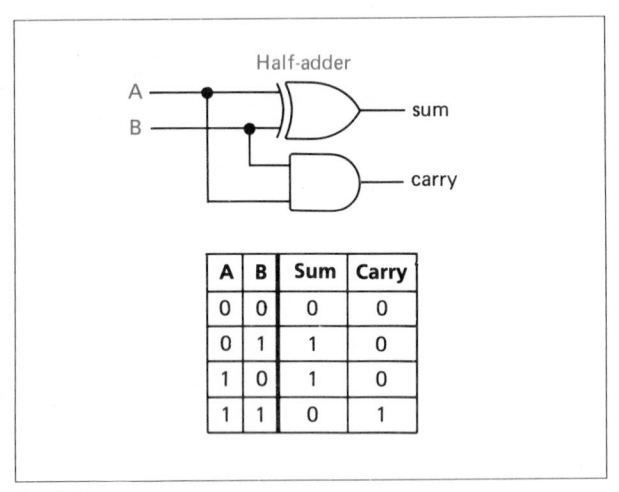

Fig. 29.2

◆ Full-adder

(a) Adding three bits. This is a necessary operation when two multi-bit numbers are added. For example, to add 3 (11 in binary) to 3 we write:

$$\begin{array}{r} 11 \\ +11 \\ \hline 110 \end{array}$$

The answer 110 (6 in decimal) is obtained as follows. In the least significant (right-hand) column we have

$1 + 1 = \text{sum } 0 + \text{carry } 1$

In the next column three bits have to be added because of the carry from the first column, giving

$1 + 1 + 1 = \text{sum } 1 + \text{carry } 1$

(b) Circuit. A full-adder circuit therefore needs three inputs, A, B and C (two for the digits and one for the carry) and two outputs (one for the *sum* and the other for the *carry*). It is realized by connecting two half-adders (HA) and an OR gate, as in Fig. 29.3*a*. We can check that it produces the correct answer by putting A = 1, B = 1 and C = 1, as in Fig. 29.3*b*.

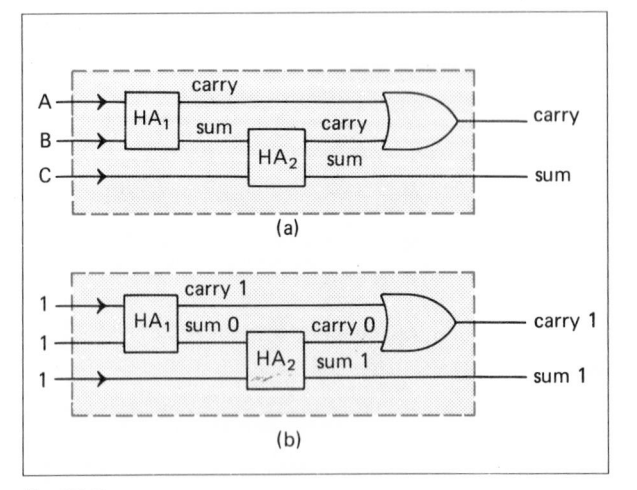

Fig. 29.3

The first half-adder HA_1 has both inputs 1 and so gives a sum of 0 and a carry of 1. HA_2 has inputs 1 and 0 and gives a sum of 1 (i.e. the sum output of the full-adder) and carry of 0. The inputs to the OR gate are 1 and 0 and, since one of the inputs is 1, the output (i.e. the carry output of the full-adder) is 1. The addition of $1 + 1 + 1$ is therefore *sum* 1 and *carry* 1.

The truth table with the other three-bit input combinations is given below. You may like to check that the circuit does produce the correct outputs for them.

Inputs			Outputs	
A	B	C	Sum	Carry
0	0	0	0	0
0	0	1	1	0
0	1	0	1	0
1	0	0	1	0
0	1	1	0	1
1	0	1	0	1
1	1	0	0	1
1	1	1	1	1

◆ Multi-bit adder

Two multi-bit binary *numbers* are added by connecting adders in parallel. For example, to add two four-bit numbers, four adders are needed, as shown in Fig. 29.4 for the addition of 1110 (decimal 14) and 0111 (decimal 7). Follow it through to see that the sum is 10101 (decimal 21). Strictly speaking the full-adder FA$_1$ need only be a half-adder since it only handles two bits.

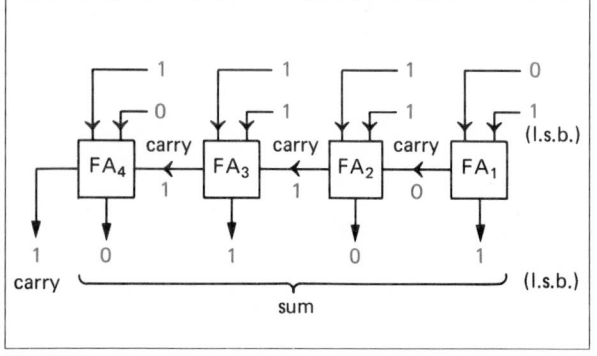

Fig. 29.4

The largest binary numbers that can be added by a four-bit adder are 1111 and 1111, i.e. 15 + 15 = 30. By connecting more full-adders to the left end of the system, the capacity increases.

In the block diagram for a *four-bit parallel adder*, shown in Fig. 29.5, the four-bit number A$_4$A$_3$A$_2$A$_1$ is added to B$_4$B$_3$B$_2$B$_1$, A$_1$ and B$_1$ being the least significant bits (l.s.b.). S$_4$S$_3$S$_2$ and S$_1$ represent the sums and C$_0$, the most significant bit (m.s.b.) of the answer, is the carry of the output.

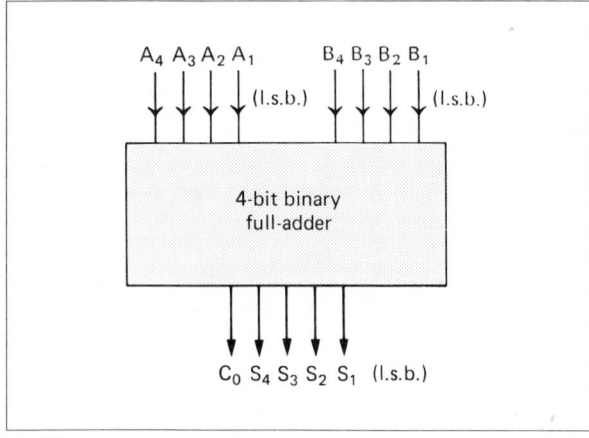

Fig. 29.5

◆ Designing adders

(a) Half adder. From lines 2 and 3 of the truth table in Fig. 29.2 we see that the SUM output S of the two bits A and B to be added, is 1 only when

A is 0 **AND** B is 1
OR
A is 1 **AND** B is 0

Following the procedure of Chapter 28 we can therefore write in Boolean notation

$$S = \bar{A}.B + A.\bar{B}$$

This is the same as equation (1) in Chapter 28, i.e. S is given by an exclusive-OR gate.

Also, from line 4 of the truth table, the CARRY output C is 1 only when:

A is 1 **AND** B is 1

That is, C = A.B.

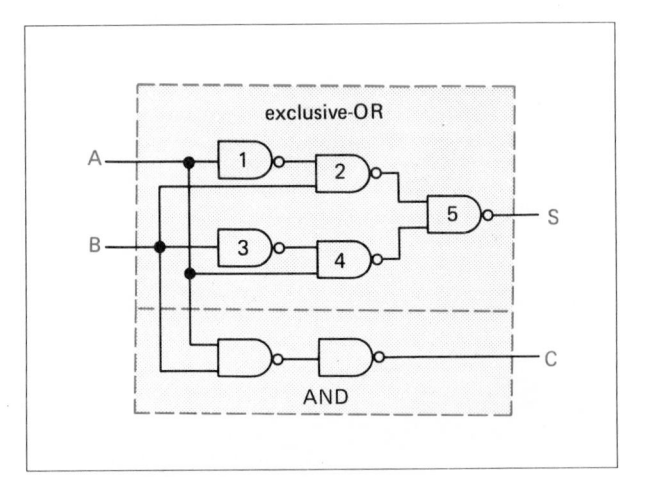

Fig. 29.6

This is implemented by a two-input AND gate. The NAND equivalent of the complete half-adder circuit is given in Fig. 29.6.

(b) Full-adder. A full-adder for adding three bits can be made from two half-adders and an OR gate (as in Fig. 29.3*a*). It can be designed from first principles using the truth table in Fig. 29.4.

The Boolean expression from the SUM output is (from lines 2, 3, 4 and 8)

$$SUM = \bar{A}.\bar{B}.C + \bar{A}.B.\bar{C} + A.\bar{B}.\bar{C} + A.B.C$$

The circuit in Fig. 29.7 gives this output. It uses four three-input AND gates (with some inputs inverted) and a four-input OR gate. The simplified equivalent NAND

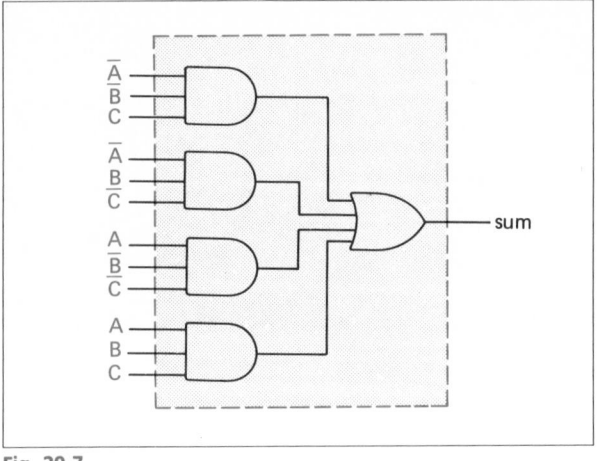

Fig. 29.7

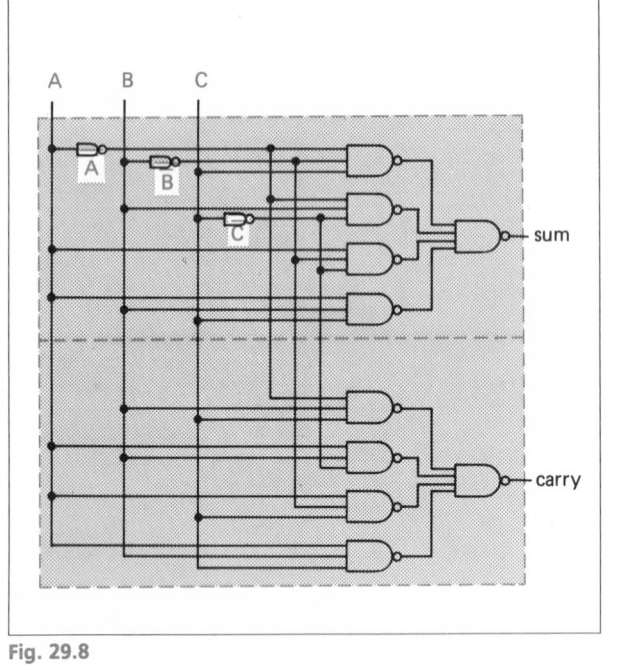

Fig. 29.8

gate circuit is shown on the top half of Fig. 29.8; the cases in which there are two successive NOT gates have been omitted.

Similarly the Boolean expression for the CARRY output is obtained from lines 5, 6, 7 and 8 of the truth table and is

$$CARRY = \overline{A}.B.C. + A.B.\overline{C} + A.\overline{B}.C. + A.B.C$$

It can also be implemented using four AND gates and an OR gate. The lower half of Fig. 29.8 gives the simplified NAND gate equivalent: the whole circuit is for a full-adder using only NAND gates.

◇ **Questions**

Q1
Make the following code conversions:
(a) decimal numbers 4, 13, 21, 38, 64 to binary,
(b) binary numbers 111, 11001, 101010, 110010 to decimal,
(c) decimal numbers 6, 11, 15, 31, 83, 300 to hexadecimal,
(d) hexadecimal numbers 3, A, D, 1E, 1A5 to decimal,
(e) decimal numbers 9, 17, 28, 370, 645 to BCD.

Q2
Add the following pairs of binary numbers and check your answers by converting the binary numbers to decimal:
(a) 10 + 01, **(b)** 11 + 10, **(c)** 101 + 011, **(d)** 1011 + 0111.

30 Bistables

◆ Bistable multivibrators

The *bistable* or *flip-flop* is a switching circuit with two outputs, one of which is 'high' when the other is 'low' and vice versa.' The outputs, denoted by Q and $\bar{Q}$ (pronounced 'not' Q), are *complementary*. In one state Q = 1 and $\bar{Q}$ = 0 and in the other Q = 0 and $\bar{Q}$ = 1.

Each of the two states is a stable one (hence bistable) which is retained (or stored or remembered) until the bistable is 'triggered', causing one output to 'flop' from 1 to 0 and the other to 'flip' from 0 to 1.

Bistables, of which there are several different types, are used as latches, in counters (Chapter 31), registers and memories (Chapter 32).

◆ R–S bistable

The R–S bistable has two inputs, R (for RESET) and S (for SET), Fig. 30.1.

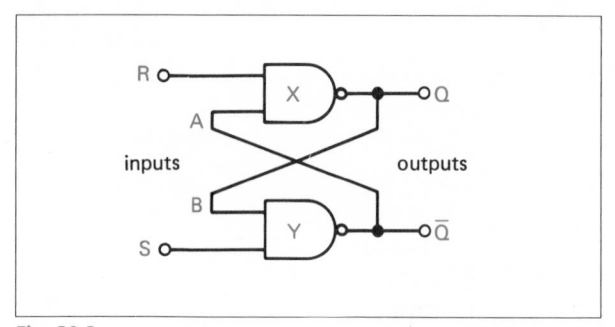

Fig. 30.1

It can be made from two two-input NAND gates, connected as in Fig. 30.2, so that there is feedback from each output to one input (not R or S) of the other NAND gate.

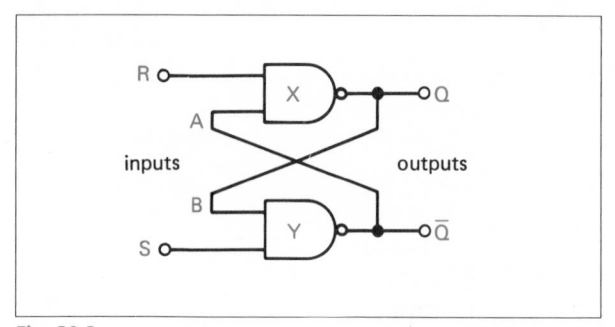

Fig. 30.2

(a) Set state. If R = 0 and S = 1, NAND gate X has at least one of its inputs at logic 0, therefore its output Q must be at logic 1 (since the output of a NAND is always 1 unless all its inputs are 1s). Q is fed back to input B and

so both inputs to NAND gate Y are 1s, i.e. S = 1 and B = 1; hence output $\bar{Q}$ = 0.

If R becomes 1 with S still 1, gate X inputs are now R = 1 and A = 0 (since $\bar{Q}$ = 0), i.e. one input is 0 and so Q stays at 1. The circuit has thus *latched* the state Q = 1, $\bar{Q}$ = 0.

(b) Reset state. In this second stable state Q = 0 and $\bar{Q}$ = 1. It is given by R = 1 and S = 0. Since gate Y has one of its inputs at 0, its output $\bar{Q}$ = 1. $\bar{Q}$ is fed back to input A and so both inputs to X are 1s, i.e. R = 1 and A = 1; hence output Q = 0.

If S becomes 1 with R still 1, Q stays at 0, showing that the reset state has been *latched*.

The truth table is shown below.

State	R	S	Q	$\bar{Q}$
Set	0	1	1	0
	1	1	1	0
Reset	1	0	0	1
	1	1	0	1

Note. When S = 1 and R = 1, Q and $\bar{Q}$ can be either 1 or 0 depending on the state before this input condition existed. The previous output state is retained as shown by the second and fourth rows of the truth table.

◆ D-type bistable

The symbol for a D-type bistable is given in Fig. 30.3.

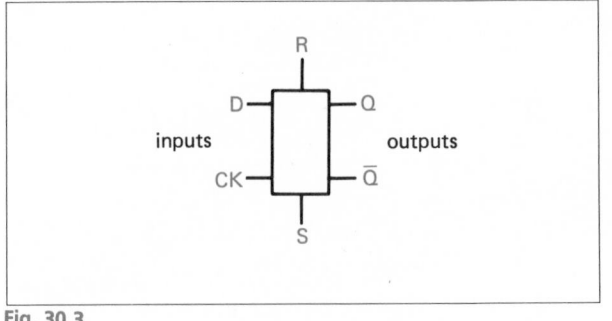

Fig. 30.3

The D input is the one to which a bit of *data* (i.e. a 0 or a 1) is applied for 'processing' by the bistable. The CK (clock) input has *clocking* or *triggering* pulses applied to it and these control exactly *when* the D input is processed. S is the *set* input allowing Q to be set to 1 and R is the *reset* input by which Q can be made 0.

Triggering is necessary in large digital systems where there are hundreds of interconnected bistables and we have to ensure that they all change state at the same time, i.e. are synchronized. As a result, the outputs Q and $\bar{Q}$ do not respond immediately to changes at the input. They wait till a clock pulse is received at the CK input.

In most modern bistables triggering occurs during the *rise* of the clock pulse from 0 to 1. For a D-type bistable this means that the data (a 0 or a 1) at the D input passes to the Q output on the *rising edge* of the clock pulse. For example, in Fig. 30.4, if initially D = 1 and Q = 0 (therefore $\bar{Q}$ = 1), then on the rising edge AB of the first clock pulse, the D input, i.e. a 1, is transferred to the Q output making Q = 1 (and $\bar{Q}$ = 0). When the D input changes to 0, Q does not become 0 until another clock pulse rising edge occurs, i.e. along CD.

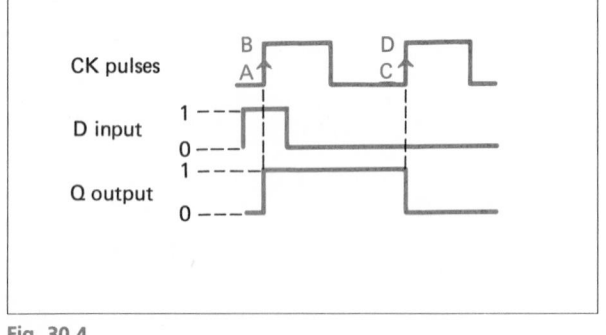

Fig. 30.4

To sum up. The Q output 'latches' on to the D input (and stores it as a 1 or 0) *at the instant a clock pulse changes its level from 0 to 1.* During the rest of the clock pulse, if the D input changes, it does not affect the Q output. A D-type bistable is a one-bit data latch.

◆ Clocks and triggering

(a) Clocks. Clock pulses are supplied by some sort of pulse generator. It may be a crystal controlled oscillator (Chapter 46) with a very steady repetition frequency, e.g. 10 MHz, or an astable multivibrator (Chapter 33) or a mechanical switch turning a d.c. supply on and off. The pulses should have fast rise and fall times, i.e. be 'good' square waves, and any switches should be debounced (see below).

(b) Triggering. There are two types of triggering or clocking operation. In *level* triggering, bistables change state when the logic level of the clock pulse is 1 or 0. The R–S bistable described earlier is level triggered.

In *edge* triggering a *change* in voltage level causes switching, usually on the rise of the clock pulse from

logic level 0 to logic level 1. The D-type bistable considered before is rising-edge triggered.

In general, edge triggering is more satisfactory than level triggering because in the former, the output changes occur at an *exact* instant during the clock pulse. Any further changes do not affect the output until the next clock pulse rise. In level triggering, output changes can occur at any time while CK is 1, whereas in edge triggering, the precise time of data capture is known.

◆ Latch

A latching circuit consisting of inter-connected D-type bistables is used to obtain a steady reading on what would otherwise by a rapidly changing numerical display. For example, pulses coming at a high rate from a counter would, without a latch, be seen as a blur.

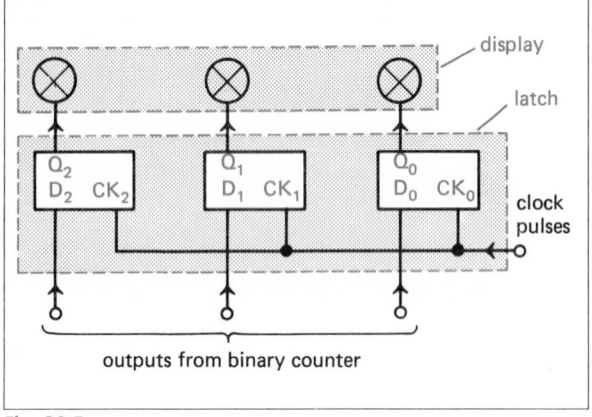

Fig. 30.5

A simple circuit for a three-light display is shown in Fig. 30.5. When the latch receives an appropriate clock pulse, the outputs from the three-bit binary counter (Chapter 31) are passed from the D inputs on the bistables to their respective Q outputs. They are held there until the next count enters the latch. In the meantime, the counter can carry on counting.

A latch is used in a digital voltmeter (Chapter 24) and is basically a store or 'memory'.

◆ T-type bistable

If the $\bar{Q}$ output on a D-type bistable is connected to the D input as in Fig. 30.6a, successive clock pulses make the flip-flop 'toggle'. If the first clock pulse leaves Q = 1 and $\bar{Q}$ = 0 (because D = 1), then feedback (from $\bar{Q}$ to D) makes D = 0 and during the second clock pulse D is transferred to Q, so now Q = 0 and $\bar{Q}$ = 1. D now becomes 1 and the third clock pulse makes Q = 1 and $\bar{Q}$ = 0 again and so on, i.e. toggling occurs.

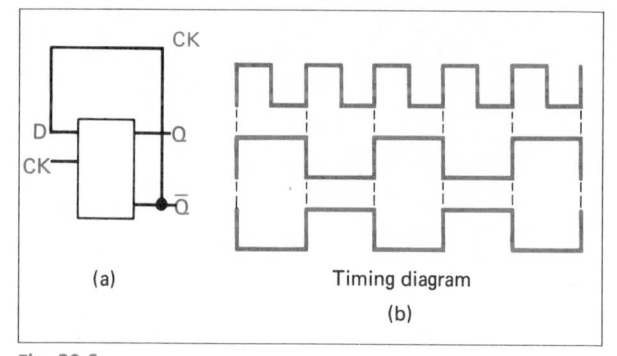

Fig. 30.6

Hence, Q = 1 *once* every two clock pulses, that is, the output has *half* the frequency of the clock pulses, as shown in the timing diagram of Fig. 30.6*b*, and is *dividing the clock frequency by two*. T-type bistables are used as divide-by-two circuits in binary counters.

◆ Debouncing a switch

If a mechanical switch, for example on a keyboard, is used to change the state of a bistable (or any other logic system), more than one electrical pulse may be produced due to the metal contacts of the switch not staying together at first but bouncing against each other rapidly and creating extra unwanted pulses, Fig. 30.7*a*. The effect of this 'contact bounce' can be eliminated by using an RS bistable in the debouncing circuit of Fig. 30.7*b* to 'clean up' the switch action.

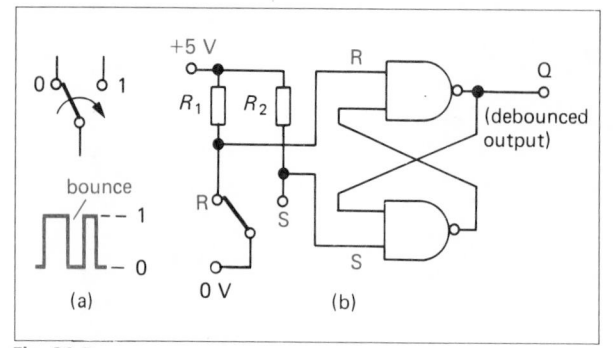

Fig. 30.7

When the switch is in the position shown, R is connected to 0 V and is at logic 0 while S is at logic 1 due to its connection via R_2 to supply positive. Hence Q = 1 (from the truth table in Fig. 30.3). If the switch is then operated to make the circuit at the other contact and

Switch position		R	S	Q
R o⟋ o S	making contact at R	0	1	1
R o ⟍ o S	moving to make contact at S	1	1	1
R o ⟍ o S	making contact at S	1	0	0
R o ⟍ o S	bounces back from contact at S	1	1	0
R o ⟍ o S	remakes contact at S	1	0	0

Fig. 30.8

'bounces' once, the logic levels at R and S for different positions are given in Fig. 30.8. The last three lines show that Q stays at logic 0 despite the bounce.

◆ Schmitt trigger

A Schmitt trigger is a type of bistabe whose output switches very rapidly from one state to the other. It is available in IC form as an inverter or NOT gate (also NAND), and has several uses.

(a) Rise- and fall-time improver. For reliable operation many logic circuits (e.g. TTL) require input pulses with very fast rise and fall times, i.e. good square waves. When logic gates switch between 0 and 1 and vice versa, they behave as high-gain amplifiers (i.e. they operate in a way that transistors do on part BC of their V_{out}–V_{in} graph in Fig. 27.4, as we shall see in Chapter 35). They are then most likely to become unstable and produce spurious (extra) signals. It is therefore essential for gates to spend only a short time in this critical region.

A Schmitt trigger can convert a slowly changing analogue input from a potential divider like that in Fig. 30.9 (with an LDR, a thermistor or a capacitor between A and B), into one with a fast rise-time, i.e. a digital input, for application to the AND gate.

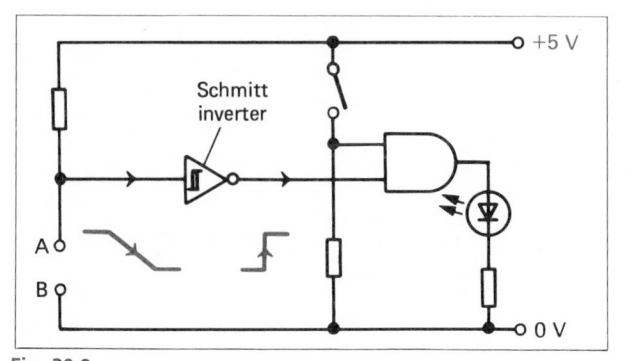

Fig. 30.9

(b) Noise eliminator. Schmitt triggers are also useful for cleaning up 'noisy' inputs, i.e. inputs that have picked up unwanted voltages or currents which appear as spikes on the waveform, Fig. 30.10. This is most likely to happen when gates are switching and is a further reason for having pulses with fast rise and fall times.

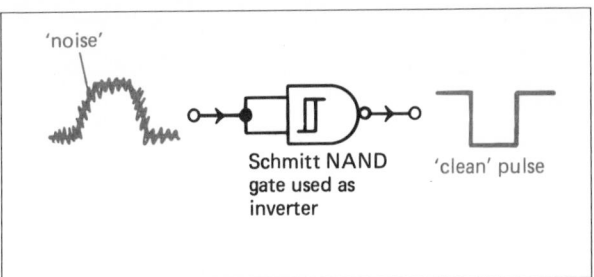

Fig. 30.10

(c) Pulse generator. A circuit for a wide range, square wave pulse generator using a TTL 7413 Schmitt trigger four-input NAND IC (as an inverter) is shown in Fig. 30.11. It can be used as a clock for simple logic systems. The output frequency f is given by

$$f \approx \frac{2000}{C}\,\text{Hz}$$

where C is in μF. R can be varied in the range 330 Ω to 470 Ω as a fine frequency control.

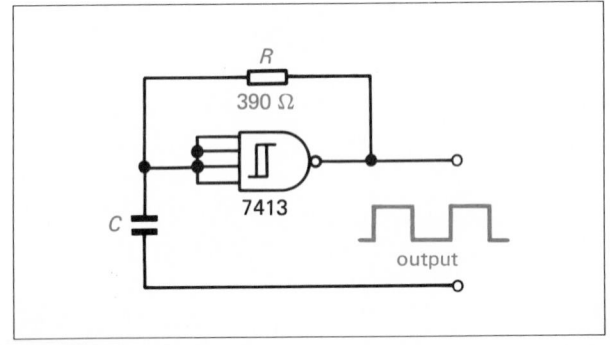

Fig. 30.11

(d) Other uses. Schmitt triggers can be used to debounce switches and to convert a sine wave input into a good square wave output (see Chapter 34 question 15). They may also replace conventional gates, but cost more.

(e) Switching action. The action is shown by the graph in Fig. 30.12. The value of the input voltage V_{in} which triggers the circuit and makes the output V_{out} jump from the 'low' to the 'high' state is called the *upper trip point* (UTP), here 2 V. The change from the 'high' to the 'low' state occurs at a lower value of V_{in},

called the *lower trip point* (LTP), here 1 V. Values of V_{in} between the UTP and the LTP are in the 'dead' band and are ignored.

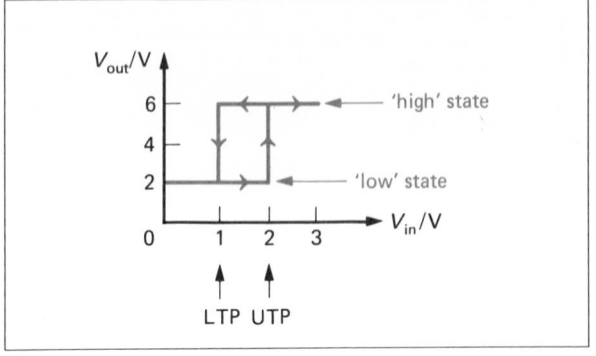

Fig. 30.12

◆ Bistable ICs

The TTL 7474 and the CMOS 4013B ICs each consist of two independent D-type flip-flops. Both are rising-edge triggered and have set and reset inputs, Fig. 30.13a, b.

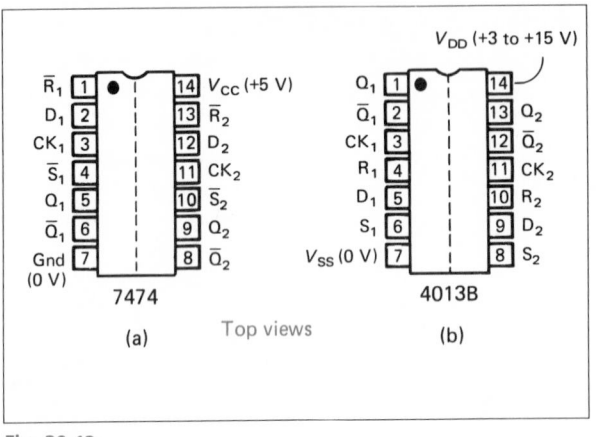

Fig. 30.13

◇ Questions

Q1
Clock pulses of frequency 2 Hz are applied to the CK input of a D-type flip-flop connected to toggle. What is the frequency of the output pulses?

Q2
(a) State *one* use for an R–S bistable.
(b) State *three* uses for a Schmitt trigger.

Q3
The block diagram in Fig. 30.14a is for a D-type bistable.

(a) What do D, CK, Q and $\bar{Q}$ represent?
(b) Explain the term bistable.
(C) Initially if Q = 0, what is $\bar{Q}$?
(d) The pulse in Fig. 30.14b is fed to CK. If D = 1 what is Q *just after the rising edge* AB of the pulse?
(e) What is Q *just after the falling edge* CD of the pulse?

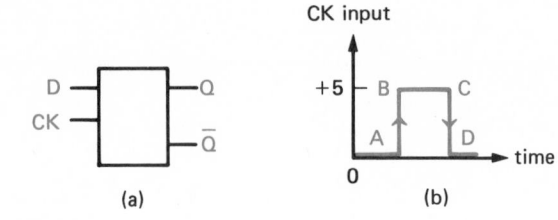

Fig. 30.14

31 Counters and decoders

Electronic counters consists of bistables connected so that they *toggle* (Chapter 30), i.e. behave as T-type bistables, when the pulses to be counted are applied to their clock (CK) input. Counting is done in binary code, the *binary digits* (bits) 1 and 0 being represented by the 'high' and 'low' states of the bistable's Q output.

◆ Binary up-counter

(a) Action. A simple four-bit binary up-counter is shown in Fig. 31.1 using four toggling D-type flip-flops (i.e. with $\bar{Q}$ joined to D in each case).

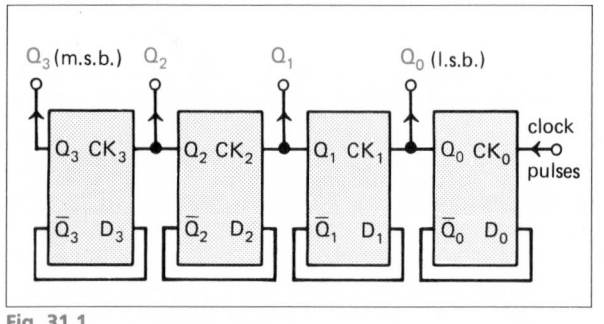

Fig. 31.1

The Q output of each one feeds the clock (CK) input of the next. The total count is given in *binary* at any time by the states of

$Q_0 = 2^0 = 1 =$ least significant bit (l.s.b.)
$Q_1 = 2^1 = 2$
$Q_2 = 2^2 = 4$
$Q_3 = 2^3 = 8 =$ most significant bit (m.s.b.)

It progresses *up* from 0000 (0 in decimal) to 1111 (15 in decimal), as shown in the following table, before reset-

ting to 0000. For example, after 9 clock pulses, the states are

$$\frac{Q_3(8)\ Q_2(4)\ Q_1(2)\ Q_0(1)}{1\quad\ \ 0\quad\ \ 0\quad\ \ 1} = \frac{\text{Decimal}}{9}$$

If LEDs were connected to the Q outputs and 0 V, those joined to Q_3 and Q_0 would be alight.

For counts above 15, two or more four-bit binary counters (each an IC) can be connected in series.

Number of clock pulse	Output			
	Q_3	Q_2	Q_1	Q_0
0	0	0	0	0
1	0	0	0	1
2	0	0	1	0
3	0	0	1	1
4	0	1	0	0
5	0	1	0	1
6	0	1	1	0
7	0	1	1	1
8	1	0	0	0
9	1	0	0	1
10	1	0	1	0
11	1	0	1	1
12	1	1	0	0
13	1	1	0	1
14	1	1	1	0
15	1	1	1	1

(b) Modulo. The modulo of a counter is the number of output states it goes through before resetting to zero. A counter with three flip-flops counts from 0 to $(2^3 - 1) = 8 - 1 = 7$; it has eight different output states representing the decimal numbers 0 to 7 and is a modulo-8 counter.

(c) Frequency divider. In a modulo-8 counter one output pulse appears at Q_2 every eighth clock pulse. That is, if f is the frequency of a regular train of clock pulses, the frequency of the pulses from Q_2 is $f/8$. Q_2 is 0 for four clock pulses and 1 for the next four pulses, as Fig. 31.2 shows.

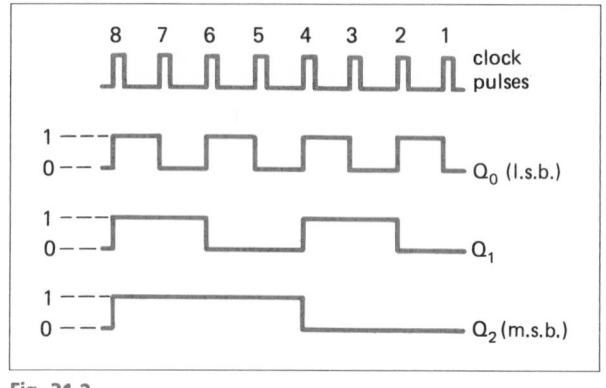

Fig. 31.2

This follows because the flip-flops are toggling and, as was explained in Chapter 30 for the T-type bistable, each one produces pulses at its Q output which have *half* the frequency of those at its CK input. Therefore, in a modulo-8 counter with three flip-flops, the frequency of the pulses at successive Q outputs are (if the clock pulses have frequency f) $f/2$ at the first, $\frac{1}{2} \times f/2 = f/4$ at the second and $\frac{1}{2} \times f/4 = f/8$ at the third. For example if $f = 32\,Hz$, the pulses at the Q output of the third flip-flop would be $32/8 = 4\,Hz$.

A modulo-8 counter is a 'divide-by-8' circuit as well. Counters are used as dividers in digital watches.

◆ Binary down-counter

In a down-counter the count decreases by one for each clock pulse. To convert a three-bit up-counter into a down-counter, the $\bar{Q}$ output (instead of the Q) of each flip-flop is coupled to the CK input of the next, as in Fig. 31.3. The count is still given by the Q outputs.

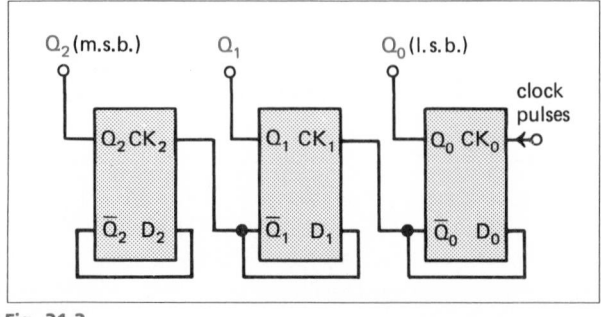

Fig. 31.3

◆ BCD counter

A binary coded decimal (BCD) counter counts from 0 to 9 in binary before resetting. It is a modulo-10 counter, made by modifying a four-bit binary up-counter as in Fig. 31.4.

When the count is 1010 (decimal 10), $Q_3 = 1$, $Q_2 = 0$, $Q_1 = 1$ and $Q_0 = 0$, and since both inputs to the AND gate are 1s (i.e. Q_3 and Q_1), its ouput is 1 and this resets all the flip-flops to 0 (otherwise it would be a modulo-16 counter counting from 0 to 15).

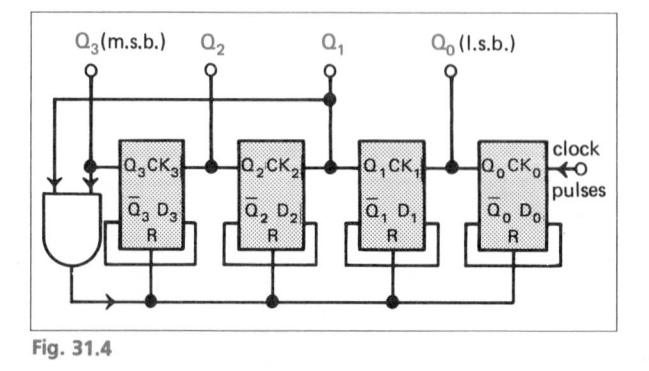

Fig. 31.4

The circuit could also be used to detect a certain number in a count.

◆ BCD decoder

A BCD decoder receives the four outputs from a four-bit binary counter, at its four inputs. It has to convert them into a form which makes a decimal display possible. A seven-segment LED display consists of seven small LEDs, which produce the numbers 0 to 9 when various combinations of the seven segments light up. The BCD decoder therefore has to create, from its four inputs (A, B, C, D), seven outputs (a, b, c, d, e, f, g), each one capable of driving one LED segment, Fig. 31.5.

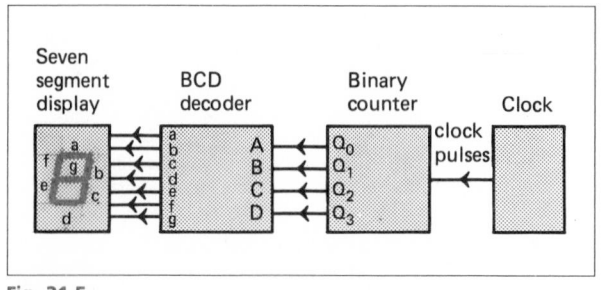

Fig. 31.5

As an example of the decoding action suppose $D = 0$, $C = 0$, $B = 1$ and $A = 1$; the BCD input is thus 0011 (3 in decimal). The five outputs a, b, c, d, g needed to light the five LED segments making a '3' all go 'high', i.e. a, b, c, d, g.

To hold the count on the display steady at any instant, a four-bit latch would be connected between the counter and the decoder (see Fig. 24.12 for the digital voltmeter).

◆ Displays

(a) LED. Each segment in a seven-segment LED display has an anode lead at which current enters and a cathode lead at which it leaves. All seven cathodes (or anodes) are joined together to form a common cathode (or anode). Such displays are often designed to work on 5 V d.c. with a current limiting resistor (e.g. 330 Ω on 5 V) in series with each segment, A segment in a common cathode type requires a 1 to light it up; in a common anode type a 0 must be fed to it.

(b) LCD. In a seven-segment liquid crystal display, the segments go 'dark' when a p.d. is applied across them. It has a silvered background which reflects back incident light and it is against this continuously visible background (except in darkness when it has to be illuminated) that the numbers show up as dark segments.

LCDs are much used in digital watches where their very small current needs (typically 5 μA for all segments on) prolongs battery life.

◆ Counter and decoder ICs

Binary and BCD counters are available as TTL and CMOS IC packages and also BCD decoders.

◇ Questions

Q1
(a) How many output states are there in a counter which has **(i)** 1, **(ii)** 2, **(iii)** 3, **(iv)** 4 and **(v)** 5 bistables?
(b) What is the highest decimal number each counter in **(a)** can count before resetting?

Q2
(a) What is meant by the modulo of a counter?
(b) How many flip-flops are needed to build counters of modulo **(i)** 2, **(ii)** 5, **(iii)** 7, **(iv)** 10 and **(v)** 30?
(c) If f is the frequency of the clock pulses applied to a modulo-10 counter, what is the frequency of the output pulses from the last flip-flop?

Q3
The logic levels of the outputs from a BCD decoder to a seven-segment LED display are shown in Fig. 31.6.

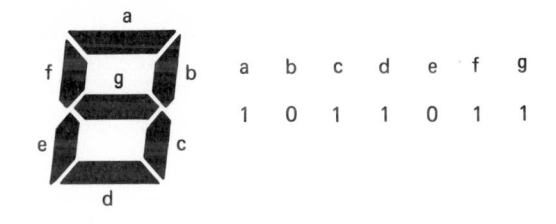

a	b	c	d	e	f	g
1	0	1	1	0	1	1

Fig. 31.6

What does the display read?

32 Memories and registers

◆ Memories

(a) Organization. A memory stores *data*, i.e. the information to be processed, in binary code, and the *program* (note the spelling) *of instructions* to be carried out. An IC semiconductor memory consists of an array of flip-flops that behave as latches, called memory cells, each storing one bit of data at its Q output — as 1 if Q = 1 and a 0 if Q = 0. The array is organized so that the bits are in groups or 'words' of typically 1, 4, 8 or 16 bits.

Every word has its own location or *address* in the memory which is identified by a certain binary number. The first word is at address zero, the second at one, the third at two and so on. The table below shows part of the contents of a sixteen word, four-bit memory, i.e. it has sixteen addresses each storing a four-bit word. For example, in the local with address 1110 (decimal 14), the data stored is the four-bit word 0011 (decimal 3).

Address					Data				
Decimal	Binary				Binary				Decimal
	m.s.b.			l.s.b.	m.s.b.			l.s.b.	m.s.b. l.s.b.
0	0	0	0	0	0	1	0	1	5
1	0	0	0	1	1	1	0	0	12
2	0	0	1	0	0	1	1	0	6
3	0	0	1	1	1	0	0	1	9
14	1	1	1	0	0	0	1	1	3
15	1	1	1	1	0	1	1	1	7

In a *random access memory* all words can be located equally quickly, i.e. access is random and it is not necessary to start at address zero.

(b) Types. There are two main types — Read Only Memories, i.e. ROMs, and Read and Write Memories which are confusingly called RAMs (because they allow random access, as ROMs also do). A RAM not only lets the data at any address be 'read' but it can also have new data 'written' in. Whereas a RAM loses the data stored almost as soon as the power to it is switched off, i.e. it is a *volatile* memory, a ROM does not, i.e. it is *nonvolatile*. ROMs are used for permanent storage of fixed data such as the program in a computer. RAMs are required when data has to be changed.

The programmable ROM or PROM lets the user 'burn' the pattern of bits, i.e. the program, into a ROM by applying a high voltage which fuses a link in the circuit. The disadvantage of this type is that it does not allow changes or corrections to be made later. When alter-

ations are necessary, for instance during the development of a program, an erasable PROM or EPROM is used in which the program is stored electrically and is erased by exposure to ultraviolet radiation before re-programming.

(c) Structure. The simplified structure of a sixteen word four-bit RAM is shown by the block diagram of Fig. 32.1. It consists mainly of an array of four-bit latches (Chapter 30), an address decoder and some control logic.

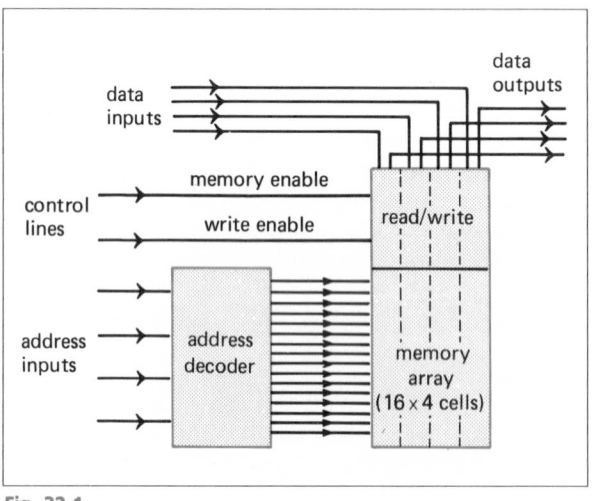

Fig. 32.1

To 'write' a word into a particular address the four-bit binary number of the address is applied to the address inputs and the word (also in binary) is set up at the data inputs. When *write enable* and *memory enable* are at the appropriate logic levels the word is stored automatically at the correct address in the memory array, as located by the address decoder.

To 'read' a word stored at a certain address, the address code is applied as before and the word appears at the data outputs if write enable and memory enable are at the required logic levels.

(d) Storage capacity. A sixteen word four-bit memory has a storage capacity of $16 \times 4 = 64$ bits (it has 64 memory cells) and is limited to four-bit words.

An eight-bit word is called a *byte*. In computer language the symbol K (capital K) is used to represent 1024 (2^{10}). For example, a memory with a capacity of 4 K bits stores $4 \times 1024 = 4096$ bits, i.e. 512 words if it is organized in bytes or 1024 four-bit words. Do not confuse K with k (small k), which stands for kilo, i.e. 1000.

◆ RAM 40114B IC

This is a sixteen word four-bit CMOS random access memory IC whose pin connections are given in Fig. 32.2.

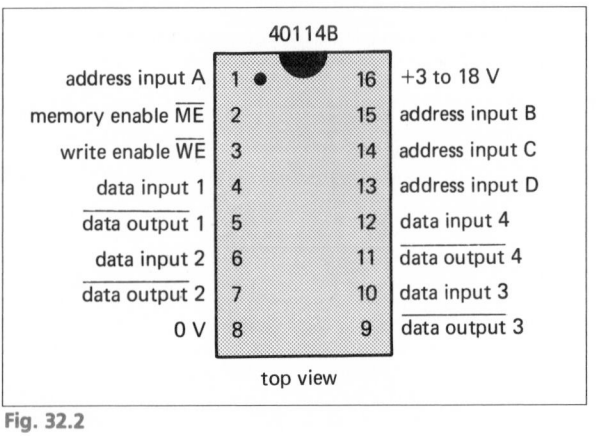

Fig. 32.2

The least significant bits (l.s.b.) are handled by address input A, data input 1 and data output 1. The most significant bits (m.s.b.) are dealt with by address input D, data input 4 and data output 4.

To 'write' data in, $\overline{ME}$ and $\overline{WE}$ must both be 'low' (0).

To 'read' data in a selected address, $\overline{ME}$ should be 0 and $\overline{WE}$ 1. The *complement* of the required 'word' then appears at the data outputs. The true 'word' can be obtained at the data outputs if when the word is 'written' in, it is first inverted by having an inverter in each data input line. The truth table summarizing the behaviour of the IC is given below. (The bar over $\overline{ME}$ shows that the memory reads *or* writes, i.e. is enabled, when its input is 0. Similarly, the bar over $\overline{WE}$ shows that it stores data, i.e. writes it into the memory, only when its input is 0.)

ME	WE	Operation	Output
0	0	Writes, i.e. stores 4-bit word at inputs	Tristated
0	1	Reads, i.e. feeds 4-bit word to outputs	Complement of selected word
1	0	Disabled, i.e. neither reads nor writes	Tristated
1	1	Disabled, i.e. neither reads nor writes	Tristated

When the output is *tristated* it is electrically isolated from the *data bus* (see Chapter 45), i.e. the connections from the output to other parts of the system.

Some memories (e.g. RAM 7065) can write and read data from a bidirectional data bus, i.e. inputs also act as outputs.

◆ Shift registers

A shift register is a memory which stores a binary number and shifts it out when required. It consists of several D-type flip-flops, one for each bit (0 or 1) in the number. The bits may be fed in and out serially, i.e. one after the other, or in parallel, i.e. all together. Shift registers are used, for example, in calculators to store two binary numbers before they are added.

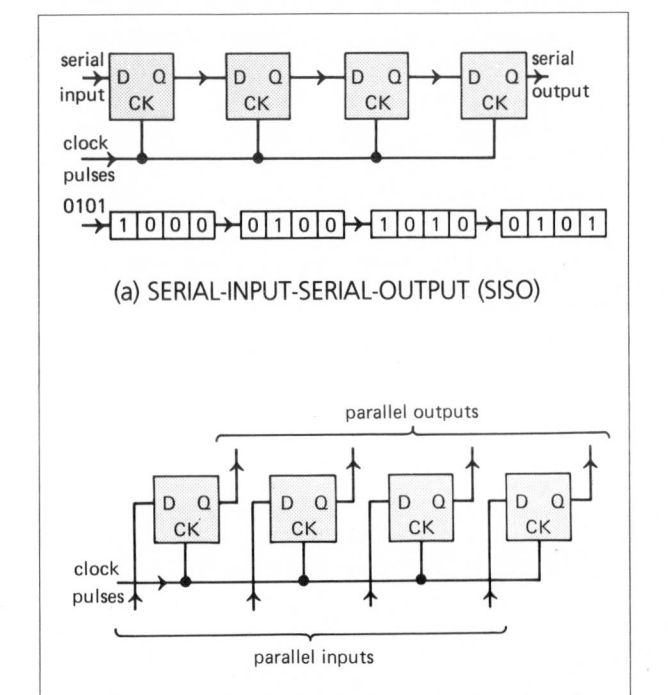

Fig. 32.3

In the four-bit serial-input-serial-output (SISO) type of Fig. 32.3*a*, clocked D-type flip-flops are used, the Q output of each one being applied to the D input of the next. The bits are loaded one at a time, usually from the left, and move one flip-flop to the right every clock pulse. Four pulses are needed to enter a four-bit number such as 0101 and another four to move it out serially.

In the parallel-input-parallel-output (PIPO) type of Fig. 32.3*b*, all bits enter their D inputs simultaneously and are transferred together to their respective Q outputs (where they are stored) by the same clock pulse. They can then be shifted out in parallel, so allowing data to be loaded and unloaded more quickly than in the SISO type.

Two other types are serial-input-parallel-output (SIPO) and parallel-input-serial-output (PISO).

◇ Questions

Q1
The circuit in Fig. 32.4 is for a simple memory which can store one four-bit 'word'.
(a) Which are the inputs?
(b) Which are the outputs?
(c) What is the 'word' stored at present?

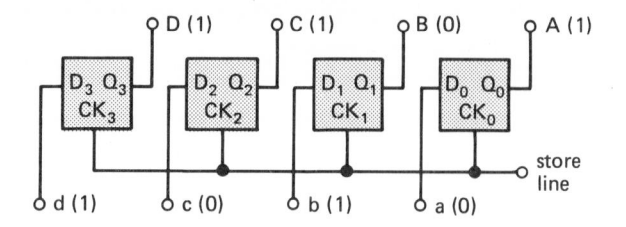

Fig. 32.4

Q2
(a) Explain: data, bit, word, address, write, read, random access, volatile, byte.
(b) Distinguish between **(i)** a ROM and a RAM, **(ii)** a PROM and an EPROM.
(c) What is the storage capacity of a sixty-four word eight-bit memory in **(i)** bits, **(ii)** bytes?

Q3
(a) What does a shift register do?
(b) How many clock pulses are needed to shift an eight-bit binary number into an eight flip-flop serial shift register?

33 Astables and monostables

◆ Timers

Many electronic systems require *timers* to control their operations. Astable and monostable multivibrators can be used for this purpose.

Multivibrators (of which bistables are also examples) have two output states — 'high' and 'low'. An *astable* is stable in neither state (hence 'astable' meaning 'not stable'), but switches from one state to the other automatically, at a rate determined by the circuit components. It generates a continuous stream of pulses, often square wave, and is an *oscillator* or *pulse generator* (Chapter 24).

A *monostable* has one stable state and one unstable state. Normally it is in its stable state but can be switched to the other state by applying a trigger pulse, where it stays for a certain time before returning to the stable state. It is a *triggered pulse producer* (Chapter 24) which produces a single pulse.

The popular 555 timer IC, Fig. 33.1, can be used in either role.

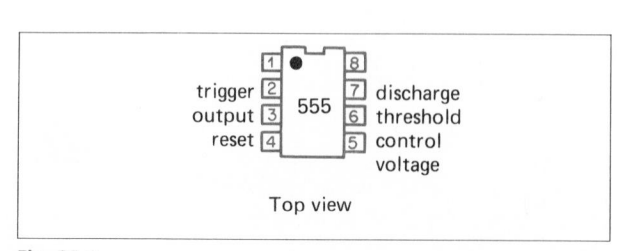

Fig. 33.1

◆ 555 timer IC

This works off any d.c. supply from 3 V to 15 V and with a maximum output current of 200 mA it can drive a loudspeaker directly.

(a) Monostable operation. The basic arrangement is shown in Fig. 33.2a. R_1 and C_1 are external components whose values fix the time T of the single output voltage

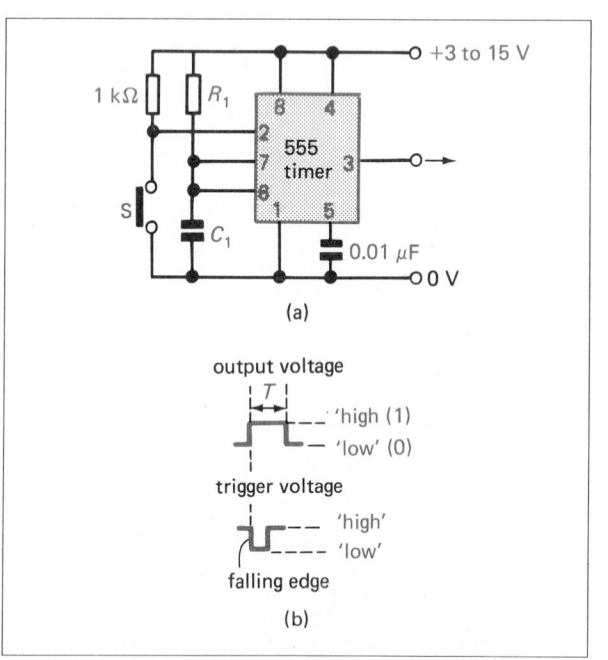

Fig. 33.2

pulse produced when S is pressed and released, Fig. 33.2*b*. The monostable is triggered by the falling edge of the input voltage pulse.

It can be shown that *T* is given in seconds by

$$T = 1.1 R_1 C_1 \approx R_1 C_1$$

if R_1 is in MΩ and C_1 in μF. For example, if $R_1 = 1$ MΩ and $C_1 = 10$ μF, $T \approx 1 \times 10 \approx 10$ s.

(b) Astable operation. In the circuit of Fig. 33.3*a*, R_1, R_2 and C_1 are external components whose values decide the frequency of the stream of square wave pulses produced automatically at the output.

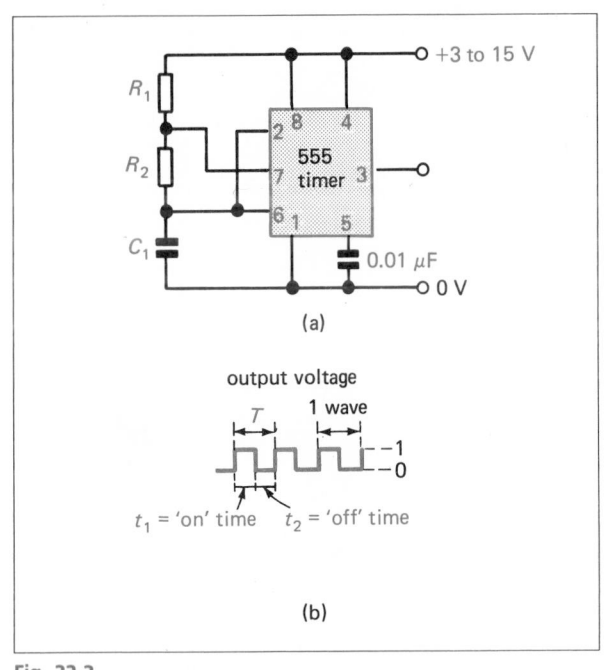

(a)

output voltage

(b)

Fig. 33.3

The period *T* of the square wave is given by

$$T = 0.7(R_1 + 2R_2) C_1$$

where *T* is in seconds if R_1 and R_2 are in MΩ and C_1 in μF.

If R_2 is much greater than R_1, then

$$T \approx 0.7(2R_2)C_1 \approx 1.4R_2C_1$$

Since $f = 1/T$, it follows that

$$f \approx \frac{1}{1.4R_2C_1} \approx \frac{0.7}{R_2C_1}$$

For example, if $R_2 = 1$ MΩ and $C_1 = 1$ μF, then $f \approx 0.7$ Hz which is about 1 square wave per second. The *maximum operating frequency* is about 500 kHz (given by small values of R_1, R_2 and C_1) and the minimum frequency one cycle in several hours (depending only on the leakage of C_1).

The *duty cycle* or *mark-to-space ratio* (Chapter 7) is given by

$$\text{duty cycle} = \frac{\text{'on' time when output is '1'}}{\text{'off' time when output is '0'}}$$

$$= \frac{t_1}{t_2} \text{ (see Fig. 33.3}b\text{)}$$

It can be shown that

$$t_1 \approx 0.7(R_1 + R_2) C_1 \text{ and } t_2 = 0.7R_2C_1$$

Hence t_1 always exceed t_2 unless R_1 is very small compared with R_2, in which case $t_1 \approx t_2$ and a true square wave is obtained, i.e. duty cycle = 1. Note that

$$T = t_1 + t_2 \approx 0.7(R_1 + R_2)C_1 + 0.7R_2C_1$$

$$\approx 0.7(R_1 + R_2 + R_2)C_1 \approx 0.7(R_1 + 2R_2)C_1$$

(c) Frequency modulation. The control voltage connection (pin 5 on the IC) is usually connected to 0 V via a 0.01 μF capacitor. However, if a voltage (between ⅓ and ⅔ of the supply voltage) is applied to it, the frequency of the astable output can be varied independently of R_1, R_2 and C_1. The process is called *frequency modulation*.

◆ Uses of astables and monostables

(a) Dark-room timer. A simple use for a monostable is to bring on a light for a certain time in a dark-room.

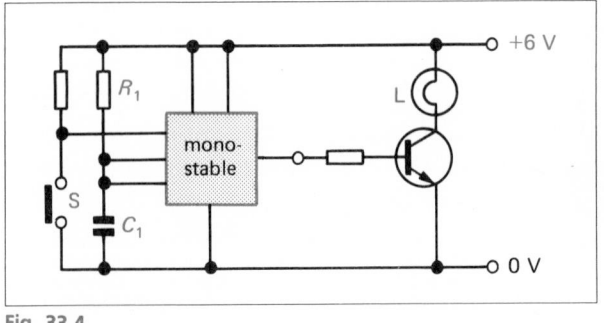

Fig. 33.4

In the circuit of Fig. 33.4, which shows the principle, when S is pressed and released, the output from the monostable is connected to a transistor switch which controls the filament lamp.

(b) Pulsed flashing lamp. The block diagram for this system, which uses a monostable and an astable, was given in Chapter 24, Fig. 24.10. One 555 timer connected as a monostable can act as the *triggered pulse producer* and another, connected as an astable, provides the *pulse generator*.

(c) Traffic lights. The logic circuit for controlling a set of traffic lights was worked out in Chapter 28, Fig. 28.7. An astable can be used as a *clock* to trigger a two-bit binary counter, and together they produce the sequence of four different states required for the lights to come on in the correct order, Fig 33.5.

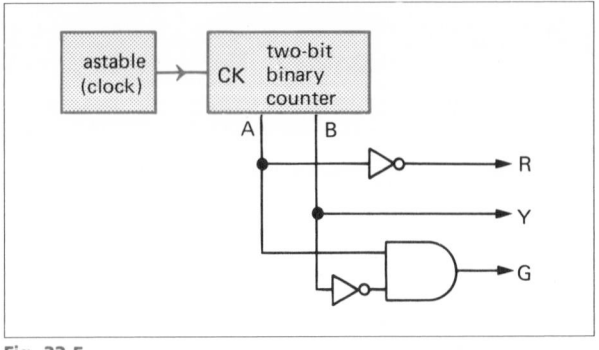

Fig. 33.5

In this application the astable is used as a continuous *sequence generator*.

(d) Counter, decoder and display. In the block diagram of the system in Fig. 31.5, the clock controlling the binary counter could be an astable.

(e) Electronic organ. An astable is used to generate the different notes in an electronic organ.

◇ Questions

Q1
(a) What is meant by saying that a multivibrator has stable states?
(b) How many stable states has **(i)** a monostable, **(ii)** an astable, and **(iii)** a bistable?

Q2
Draw two circuits to show how you would connect a LED to the output and power supply of a monostable so that the LED lights when the output is **(a)** 'high', **(b)** 'low'.

Q3
The graph in Fig. 33.6 shows how the output voltage from an astable varies with time.
(a) What is the period of the output?
(b) What is the frequency of the output?
(c) What is the value of the duty cycle?

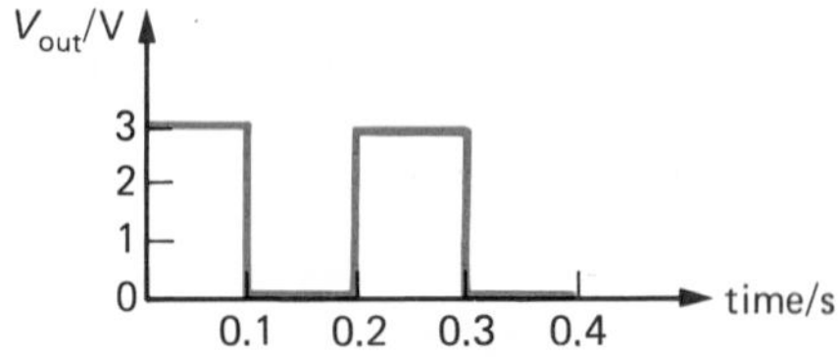

Fig. 33.6

Q4
The astable output in Fig. 33.3 has a frequency of 1 Hz and has a LED with a suitable series resistor connected between it and the 0 V line. R_2 is much greater than R_1.
(a) What would you see the LED doing?
(b) What happens to the LED if the value of R_2 is halved?
(c) What happens to the LED if the value of C_1 is doubled?

34 Additional questions

◇ Core level

Transistor as a switch

Q1
In the circuit of Fig. 34.1 what is
(a) the resistance of Tr if it is saturated,
(b) I_C when Tr is saturated,
(c) I_L when Tr is saturated,
(d) I_L when Tr is off (not conducting)?

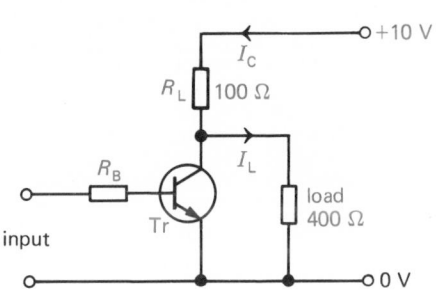

Fig. 34.1

Q2
The circuit in Fig. 34.2 is used to switch on a lamp when the temperature falls.
(a) How does the resistance of the thermistor change when the temperature falls?
(b) When the temperature falls how does the voltage change across (i) R, (ii) the thermistor?
(c) What must be the value of V_{BE} before the transistor (silicon) starts to switch on L?
(d) What is the advantage of having R variable?

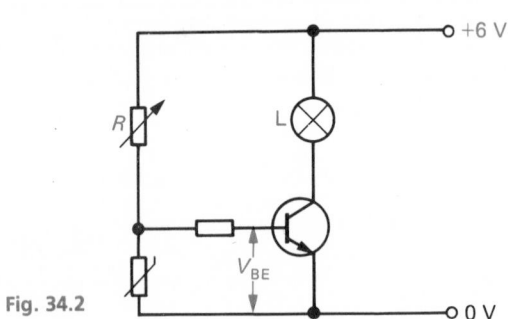

Fig. 34.2

Logic gates

Q3
Draw up a truth table for the logic circuit in Fig. 34.3, including levels at C and D.

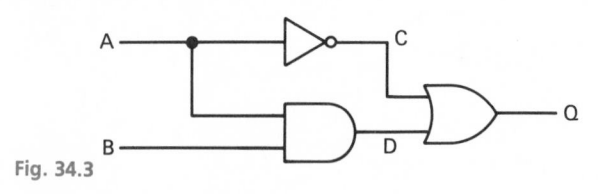

Fig. 34.3

Q4
Logic probes consisting of a LED in series with a 330 Ω resistor are shown in Fig. 34.4a, b, checking the outputs Q of logic gates.
For each case state whether the LED lights up when Q is '1' or '0'.

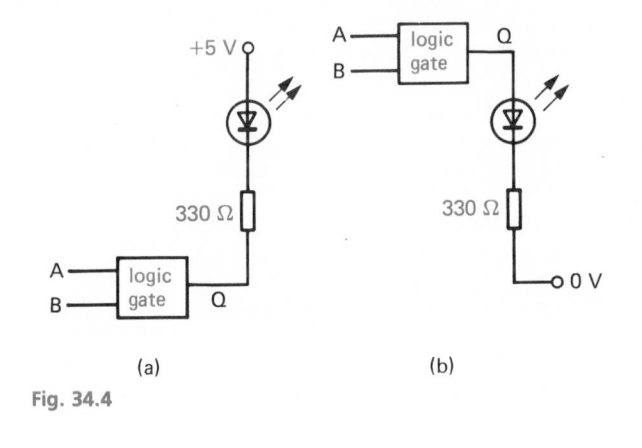

(a)　　　　　　　　(b)

Fig. 34.4

Bistables

Q5
Copy Fig. 34.5 which refers to a D-type bistable operating on the *rising edges* of clock pulses. Draw under it the waveform for the Q output.

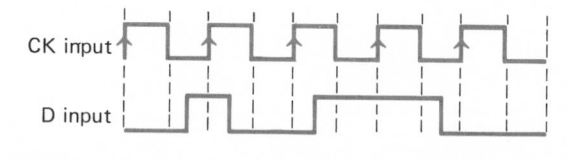

Fig. 34.5

Q6
The block diagram for a model traffic lights system is shown in Fig. 34.6a. Under it are the waveforms of two complementary square wave outputs, A and B, from a pulse generator, Fig. 34.6b, c.
(a) Copy the waveforms and draw below them the waveforms for (i) the output from the D-type flip-flop, if it

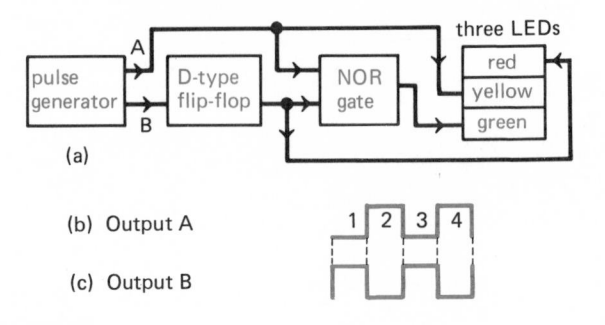

(a)

(b) Output A

(c) Output B

Fig. 34.6

changes the state of its output on the *rising edge* of an input pulse, and **(ii)** the output from the NOR gate
(b) If the LEDs light up when they receive a logic 1 signal, draw up a truth table for the first four stages of the sequence in which they light.

Counters and decoders

Q7
(a) What is the function of the circuit in Fig. 34.7?
(b) If the pulse producer produces one square pulse each time S is pressed, what is the state of the LEDs after it is pressed *five* times, if initially all are off?
(c) If the pulse producer is replaced by a pulse generator of frequency 80 Hz, what is the frequency of the pulses at **(i)** Q_0, **(ii)** Q_1, **(iii)** Q_2?

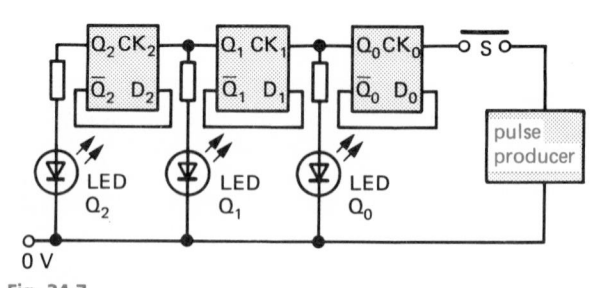

Fig. 34.7

Q8
State *one* advantage and *one* disdavantage of **(a)** LCDs, **(b)** LED displays.

Memories and registers

Q9
(a) Explain the statement 'a bistable has memory'.
(b) How many bistable memory cells are needed to store four four-bit 'words'?

Astables and monostables

Q10
What happens to the pitch of the note from the loudspeaker in the astable circuit of Fig. 34.8 when the amount of light falling on the LDR **(a)** increases, **(b)** decreases?

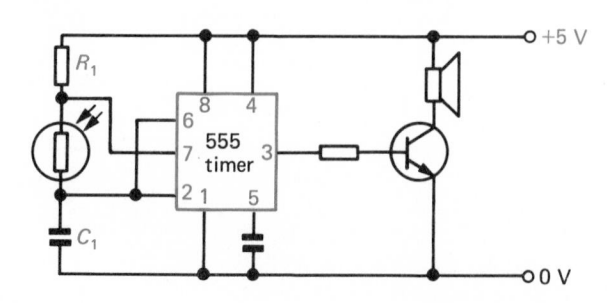

Fig. 34.8

◇ Further level

Transistor as a switch

Q11
The circuit in Fig. 34.9 allows a mains lamp to be on for a certain time.
(a) Which transistor(s) is (are) 'on' if S_1 and S_2 are closed?
(b) Is the mains lamp on or off if S_1 and S_2 are closed? Why?
(c) What happens if S_1 is opened?
(d) How can the time for which the lamp is on be changed?
(e) What is the purpose of D?
(f) What is the purpose of R_B?
(g) How could the circuit be changed to allow the lamp to come on some time *after* opening S_1?

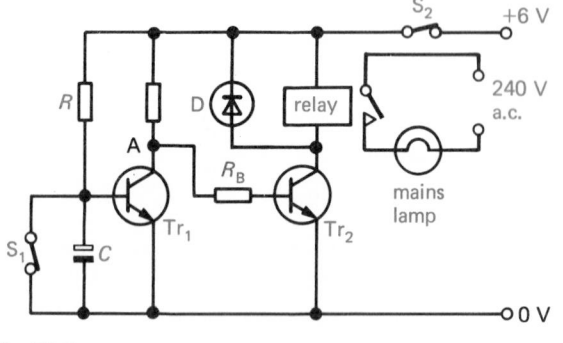

Fig. 34.9

Logic gates

Q12
In the system of logic gates in Fig. 34.10 the LED lights up when certain switches are closed.
(a) Draw up a truth table for the system.
(b) What is the logic level at Q when the LED lights?
(c) What is the voltage of A when S_1 is **(i)** open, **(ii)** closed?
(d) State the combination of switches which, when pressed, light the LED.

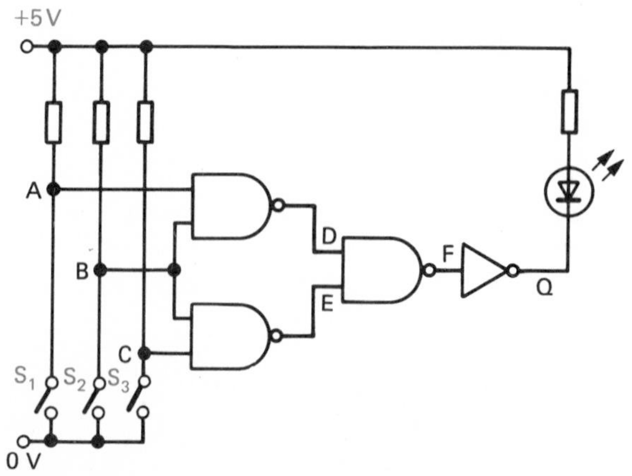

Fig. 34.10

Binary adders

Q13
(a) Construct a truth table for the half-adder shown in Fig. 34.11.
(b) If output S stands for 'sum' and output C for 'carry', use the truth table to say what a half-adder does.

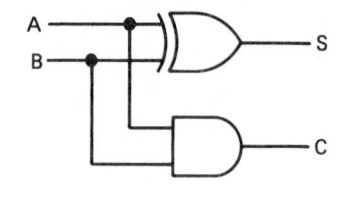

Fig. 34.11

Bistables

Q14
(a) What is the circuit in Fig. 34.12 called?
(b) Which letters are **(i)** inputs, **(ii)** outputs?
(c) If $S = 1$ and $R = 0$ what is the state of **(i)** Q, **(ii)** $\bar{Q}$?
(d) If R is now made 1 and S stays at 1, what is the state of **(i)** Q, **(ii)** $\bar{Q}$?

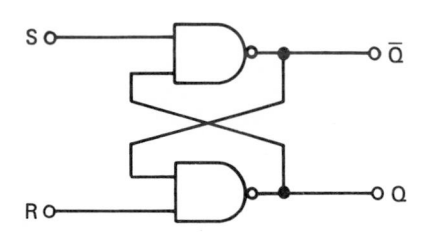

Fig. 34.12

Q15
(a) Draw the characteristic of a Schmitt trigger which has a UTP = 3 V, a LTP = 2 V, a 'high' state = 9 V and a 'low' state = 3 V.
(b) Sketch the output voltage waveform from the Schmitt trigger of **(a)** if the input is a sine wave of peak value 5 V.

Counters and decoders

Q16
Draw the block diagram for a modulo-6 binary up-counter which resets every sixth clock pulse.

Memories and registers

Q17
The truth table for a sixteen word four-bit RAM IC is given in Fig. 34.13 with its symbol.
(a) What do the letters **(i)** ME and **(ii)** WE mean?
(b) What is meant by the term 'disabled'?
(c) State the procedure you would follow to store the four-bit word 1100 at the memory location with address 0010.
(d) State the procedure you would follow to read the word stored at address 1010.

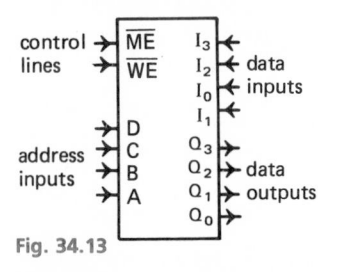

ME	WE	Operation
0	0	writes
0	1	reads
1	0	disabled
1	1	disabled

Fig. 34.13

Astables and monostables

Q18
The circuit in Fig. 34.14 shows an astable pulse generator made from a 555 timer.

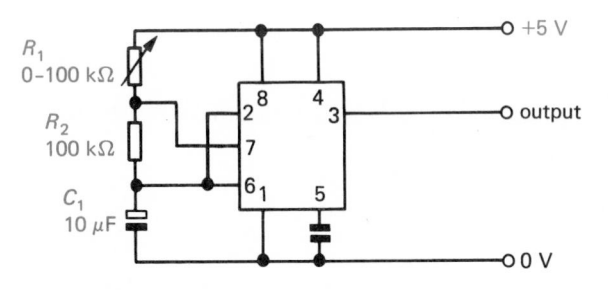

Fig. 34.14

R_1 is a variable resistor. C_1 charges through R_1 and R_2 in series and during this time t_1, the output is 'high'. C_1 discharges through R_2 only and for this time t_2, the output is 'low'. t_1 and t_2 are given in seconds by

$$t_1 = 0.7(R_1 + R_2)C_1 \text{ and } t_2 = 0.7R_2C_1$$

where R_1 and R_2 are in MΩ (or Ω) and C_1 is in μF (or F).
(a) Copy and complete the table below when R_1 has values of 0, 50 kΩ and 100 kΩ. $T = t_1 + t_2$.

R_1 (kΩ)	R_2 (kΩ)	t_1 (s)	t_2 (s)	T (s)	t_1/t_2
0	100				
50	100				
100	100				

(b) What is T called?
(c) What is t_1/t_2 called?
(d) Which value of t_1/t_2 gives *true* square waves?
(e) Draw a graph of output voltage against time when $R_1 = R_2 = 100$ kΩ; label both axes in the correct units.

Check list Digital sub-systems

After studying *Chapter 27: Transistor as a switch*, you should be able to

◇ state that digital sub-systems are ICs containing switching-type circuits in which the outputs and inputs are either 'high' (logic level 1) or 'low' (logic level 0),

◇ state the advantages of the transistor as a switch over other electrical switches, and draw the basic circuit for it,

◇ draw a circuit to investigate the relationship between V_{out} and V_{in} for a transistor switch and sketch the graph showing it,

◇ state that when V_{in} is 'low', V_{out} is 'high' and when V_{in} is 'high', V_{out} is 'low',

◇ state that there is a small range of values of V_{in} over which V_{out} changes from 'high' to 'low',

◇ state that when V_{out} is 'high', the transistor is 'off' (non-conducting) and when V_{out} is 'low', the transistor is 'fully on' (conducting and saturated),

◇ state that when a transistor is used as a switch it is either 'off' or 'fully on',

◇ solve numerical problems on the transistor switch circuit,

◇ explain the operation of light-operated, temperature-operated, time-operated and sound-operated circuits which switch on a transistor, and

◇ appreciate how a thyristor can be used in a latching circuit and compare its properties with those of a relay.

After studying *Chapter 28: Logic gates*, you should be able to

◇ recall the truth tables of NOT, NOR, OR, NAND, AND and exclusive-OR (EXOR) gates and draw their international symbols,

◇ recall how NOT, NOR, OR and AND gates can be made from NAND gates only, and

◇ design an exclusive-OR gate and a traffic lights system using Boolean algebra.

After studying *Chapter 29: Binary adders*, you should be able to

◇ make code conversions from decimal to binary, hexadecimal, BCD and vice versa,

◇ state what a half-adder does, recognize its circuit, and construct a truth table for it,

◇ state what a full-adder does and construct a truth table for it,

◇ add two four-bit binary numbers, and

◇ design a circuit for **(a)** a half-adder and **(b)** a full-adder, using Boolean algebra.

After studying *Chapter 30: Bistables*, you should be able to

◇ state that a bistable or flip-flop is a switching circuit with two stable states and changes state when triggered,

◇ recognize and explain the action of an R–S bistable and draw up a truth table showing the outputs for given input sequences,

◇ recognize the symbol for a D-type bistable and state that it is a data latch,

◇ state that in a D-type bistable data is transferred from the data input to the output on the rising edge of a clock pulse and draw a timing diagram,

◇ recognize and describe the action of a number of D-type bistables connected as a latch,

◇ understand the toggling action of a T-type bistable and state that it is a divide-by-two circuit,

◇ explain how a switch can be debounced using an R–S flip-flop,

◇ state that the output of a Schmitt trigger switches very rapidly from one state to the other,

◇ state some uses of Schmitt triggers, and

◇ draw a graph to show the switching action of a Schmitt trigger.

After studying Chapter 31: Counters and decoders, you should be able to

◇ recognize and describe the action of a circuit consisting of a number of toggling D-type bistables connected as a binary up-counter or a frequency divider,

◇ state that the modulo of a counter is the number of output states it goes through before resetting to zero,

◇ recognize and describe the action of a binary down-counter,

◇ state that a BCD counter counts from 0 to 9 before resetting,

◇ draw the circuits for counters of different modulo using an AND gate and reset,

◇ state that a BCD decoder converts a four-bit binary count at its input into seven outputs to drive a seven-segment display,

◇ state which outputs from a BCD decoder are needed to light up any number from 0 to 9 on a seven-segment display, and

◇ state the advantages and disadvantages of LCD and LED displays.

After studying Chapter 32: Memories and registers, you should be able to

◇ state what a memory does,

◇ explain the terms data, address, word, bit and byte,

◇ state that there are two main types of memory — RAM and ROM, and distinguish between them,

◇ draw a block diagram for a sixteen word four-bit RAM, and state that basically it consists of sixteen four-bit latches,

◇ state the procedure for writing a word into and reading a word out of a memory,

◇ explain what is meant by a tristated output, and

◇ state what a shift register does and identify the different types.

After studying Chapter 33: Astables and monostables, you should be able to

◇ state that an astable multivibrator produces a continuous train of 'square' waves, i.e. it is a pulse generator, and has no stable states,

◇ state that a monostable multivibrator produces a single pulse of a certain duration when triggered, i.e. it is a triggered pulse producer, and has one stable state,

◇ use a 555 timer IC in monostable and astable modes,

◇ use a graph of astable output voltage against time to work out the period and frequency of the wave,

◇ use the formulae for the 555 timer relating period (and frequency) to circuit values in both monostable ($T \approx R_1C_1$) and astable ($T \approx 1.4R_2C_1$) modes,

◇ explain the term duty cycle and state how it is changed, and

◇ give examples of the use of astables and monostables.

Analogue sub-systems

35 Transistor as an amplifier

◆ Analogue sub-systems

In analogue sub-systems the signals being processed are electrical representations (analogues) of physical quantities which can vary continuously with time, taking on *all* values between a certain maximum and a certain minimum, Fig. 35.1. The information they carry, e.g. the loudness and pitch of a sound, is in the amplitude and shape of their waveform. Many contain *amplifier-type* or *linear* circuits in which the input and output are directly proportional (e.g. doubling the input doubles the output). Many audio and radio sub-systems are analogue types.

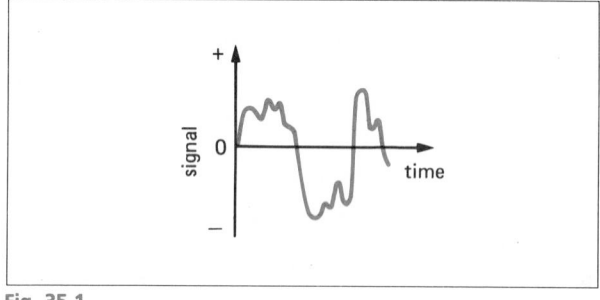

Fig. 35.1

◆ Amplifiers

In general, the job of an amplifier is to produce an output which is an enlarged copy of the input. Amplification of one or more of the input voltage, current and power occurs. In the last case, the extra power at the output is provided by an external source, e.g. a battery. The following terms are used in connection with an amplifier:

$$\text{voltage gain } (G_V) = \frac{\text{output votage } (V_{out})}{\text{input voltage } (V_{in})}$$

$$\text{power gain } (G_P) = \frac{\text{power out } (P_{out})}{\text{power in } (P_{in})}$$

The current gain (h_{FE}) has already been defined (Chapter 15).

Amplifiers are classified according to the job they do, i.e. voltage, current or power amplification, and the frequency range they cover. An *audio frequency* (AF) amplifier amplifies a.c. signals in the audio frequency range (20 Hz to 20 kHz). *Radio frequency* (RF) amplifiers operate above 20 kHz.

The *bandwidth* of an amplifier is the range of frequencies within which the gain G does not fall below 0.7 of its maximum value G_{max}. For example, the amplifier with the gain–frequency graph in Fig. 35.2 has a bandwidth of below 10 Hz to above 10 kHz, and all frequencies between are amplified more or less equally.

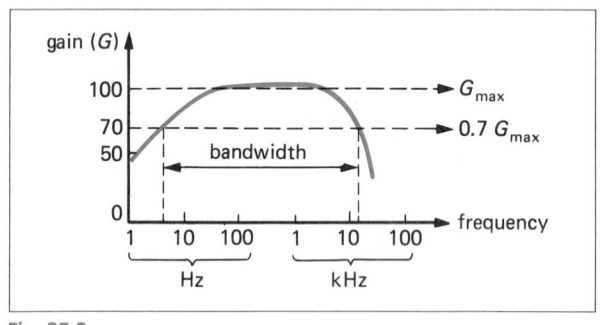

Fig. 35.2

◆ Transistor voltage amplifier

The transistor is the basic amplifying device in analogue sub-systems.

(a) Action. The amplifying action can be seen using the graph of V_{out} against V_{in}, obtained in Chapter 27,

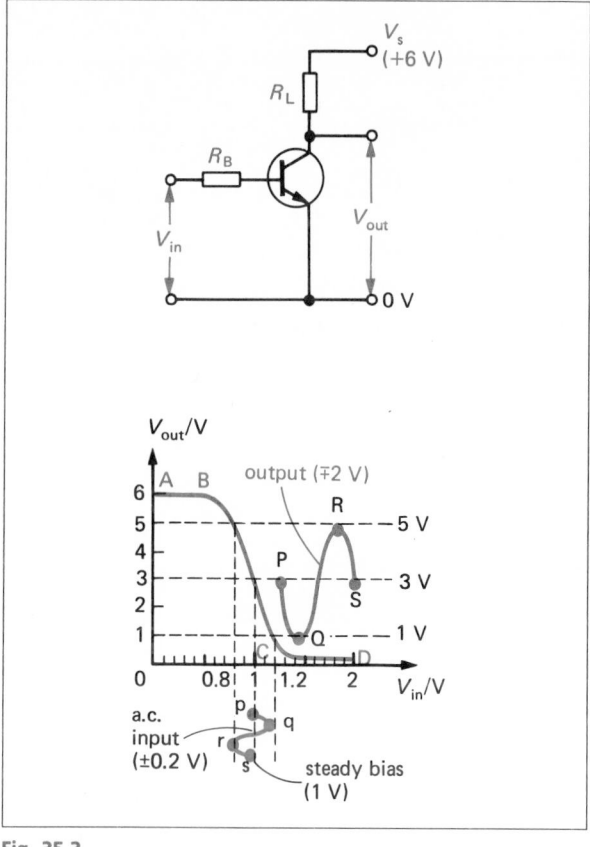

Fig. 35.3

Fig. 27.4 when the transistor switch was considered. It is shown again here with the basic transistor circuit, Fig. 35.3.

Normally V_{in} would be a.c.; suppose it has waveform pqrs. We see from the graph that when $V_{in} = 1$ V (point p on input waveform), $V_{out} = 3$ V (point P on output waveform). When $V_{in} = 1.2$ V (point q), $V_{out} = 1$ V (point Q). When $V_{in} = 0.8$ V (point r), $V_{out} = 5$ V (point R) and

when $V_{in} = 1$ V again (point s), $V_{out} = 3$ V (point S). PQRS is therefore the waveform of V_{out}.

V_{in}/V	0.8	1.0	1.2
V_{out}/V	5	3	1

From the results, summarized in the table above, we see that if V_{in} changes from 0.8 V to 1.0 V, V_{out} changes from 5 V to 3 V. That is, a change of 0.2 V in V_{in} produces a change of 2 V in V_{out}. PQRS represents an a.c. voltage with a peak value that is 10 times greater than that of the a.c. input, i.e. amplification has occurred.

The voltage gain G_V for this a.c. signal is given by

$$G_V = \frac{\text{a.c. output voltage}}{\text{a.c. input voltage}} = \frac{2}{0.2} = 10$$

(b) Bias. As an amplifier, a transistor usually works on the straight part BC of its V_{out}–V_{in} graph. If it doesn't, the output waveform PQRS is not an *exact* magnified copy of the input waveform pqrs. To ensure that it does, a steady voltage (and current) is also applied to the base — called the *bias* voltage (or current) — so that with no a.c. input, $V_{out} \approx \frac{1}{2}V_s$. This allows V_{out} to vary over its maximum possible range from, in theory, 0 V to V_s, when there is an a.c. input.

In the case we are considering, a steady bias of 1 V applied to the base makes $V_{out} = 3$ V. An a.c. input of ± 0.2 V on top of this bias causes the base voltage to wobble *up* and *down* between 0.8 V and 1.2 V. As a result, V_{out} wobbles *down* and *up* in step from 5 V to 1 V, i.e. by ∓ 2 V, as we have seen.

(c) Distortion. If the steady bias voltage and current are too low or too high or the a.c. input is too large, the output waveform is not an exact copy of the input waveform, i.e. distortion occurs. These effects are shown in the graphs of Fig. 35.4a,b,c.

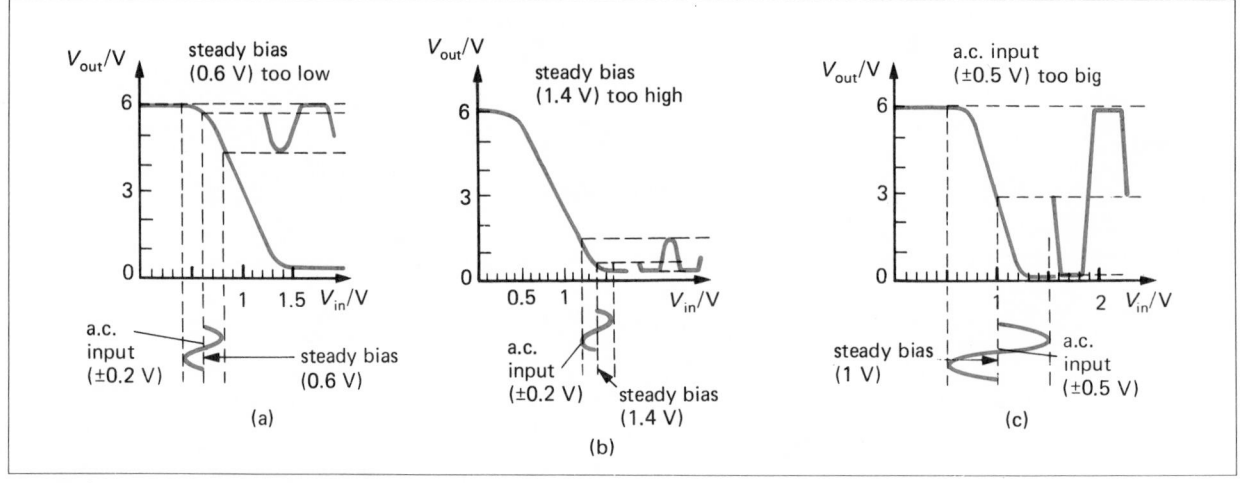

Fig. 35.4

◆ Common–emitter a.c. amplifier circuit

In the three voltage amplifier circuits that follow, the transistor is in common–emitter connection (Chapter 15) but the steady bias arrangements are different for each one.

(a) Supply-to-base bias, Fig. 35.5. The bias is obtained via resistor R_B connected to the + of the power supply. With no a.c. input, a steady d.c. base current I_B passes from V_s through R_B into the base and back via the emitter to 0 V. The value of R_B can be calculated if we know I_C, h_{FE}, V_{BE} and V_s.

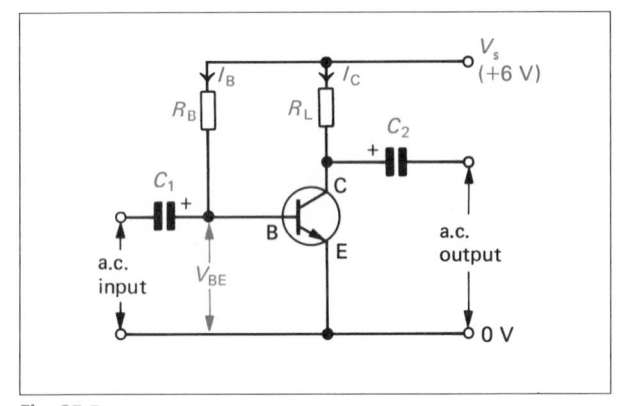

Fig. 35.5

Suppose $I_C = 2$ mA, $h_{FE} = 100$, $V_{BE} = 0.6$ V (the turn-on voltage) and $V_s = 6$ V.

We have from the definition of h_{FE} (Chapter 15) that $h_{FE} = I_C / I_B$, hence

$$I_B = \frac{I_C}{h_{FE}} = \frac{3\,mA}{100} = 0.03\,mA$$

Since R_B and the base–emitter of the transistor form a potential divider across V_s, we can say

voltage across $R_B + V_{BE} = V_s$

That is

voltage across $R_B = V_s - V_{BE}$
$$= 6 - 0.6 = 5.4\,V$$

But

voltage across $R_B = I_B \times R_B$

therefore $I_B \times R_B = 5.4$ V

therefore $R_B = \dfrac{5.4\,V}{I_B} = \dfrac{5.4\,V}{0.03\,mA} = \dfrac{540}{3} = 180\,k\Omega$

C_1 allows a.c. signals to pass in the input but stops any d.c. that might upset the bias arrangements. Similarly

coupling capacitor C_2 allows a.c. in the output to pass to the next stage but blocks d.c.

(b) Collector-to-base bias. In this method the value of R_B in the circuit of Fig. 35.3 is roughly *halved*, say to 100 kΩ from 180 kΩ, and connected between collector and base as in Fig. 35.6. It can then be shown that should the temperature of the transistor rise for any reason (e.g. due to the heating effect of I_C), the base bias current automatically tries to restore the original working conditions. It is a self-stabilizing circuit.

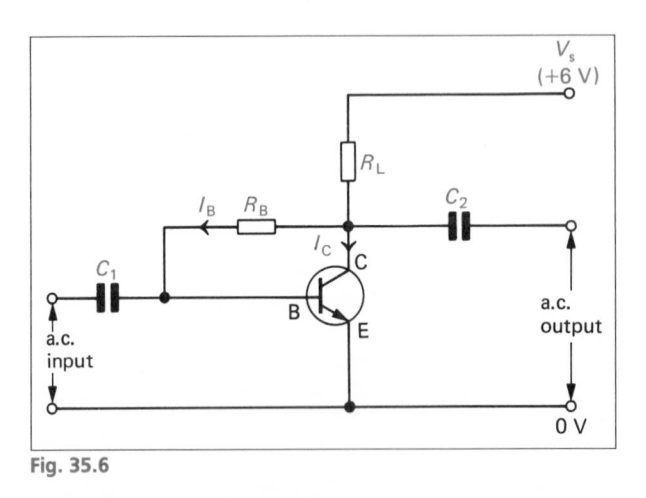

Fig. 35.6

(c) Potential divider bias. Even better stabilization is obtained if the steady bias is obtained from a potential divider as in Fig. 35.7. The junction of R_1 and R_2 fixes the base voltage at a value sufficient to turn on the

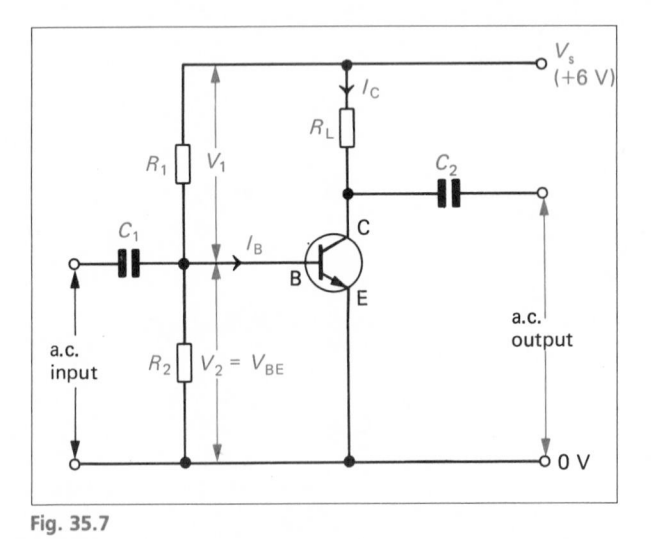

Fig. 35.7

transistor, i.e. so that $V_1/V_2 = R_1/R_2 \approx 5.4$ V/0.6 V (since $V_1 + V_2 = V_s = 6$ V). The values of R_1 and R_2 are chosen so that the current through them is about ten times greater than the steady base bias current I_B. If I_B changes, $V_2 = V_{BE}$ is then hardly affected (Chapter 5).

◆ Measuring the gain and bandwidth of an amplifier

Any of the above three common–emitter amplifier circuits can be used. An a.c. input of 10 mV, 50 Hz sine wave is taken from a *signal generator* (Chapter 19). The a.c. output from the amplifier is connected to the Y-input terminals and an *oscilloscope* (Chapter 18), which is adjusted so that the output waveform is an undistorted sine wave.

The peak-to-peak value V_{out} of the output waveform is measured on the screen graticule. The a.c. input is disconnected from the amplifier and connected to the oscilloscope and its peak-to-peak value V_{in} measured. The *voltage gain* G_V is then given by

$$G_V = \frac{V_{out}}{V_{in}}$$

To find the *bandwidth* the above procedure is repeated for different frequencies up to 100 kHz and a graph drawn of G_V against frequency using a frequency scale that increases by powers of ten as in Fig. 35.2, to accommodate the wide range of values.

◆ Emitter-follower

A common emitter transistor amplifier has a low to medium input impedance and, as a result, draws current from whatever provides its input. It is not suitable for amplifying the signal from an input transducer such as a crystal microphone which cannot supply much current.

An *emitter-follower* can be used in such cases because, as well as having a high current gain (like the common emitter amplifier), it also has a high input impedance and so takes only a tiny input current. It can therefore act as a *buffer* or *current amplifier* to meet the interfacing conditions that must be satisfied when the stages of a system are joined together (Chapter 24).

The basic circuit for a.c. signals is given in Fig. 35.8. The input voltage V_{in} is applied across the potential divider formed by the small resistance of the base–emitter in series with the much larger resistance of the load R_L in the emitter circuit. Since the output voltage V_{out} is developed across R_L, it follows that V_{out} is *less* than V_{in} by the small voltage V_{BE} (i.e. the turn-on voltage). Therefore

$$V_{out} = V_{in} - V_{BE} = V_{in} - 0.6\,\text{V}$$

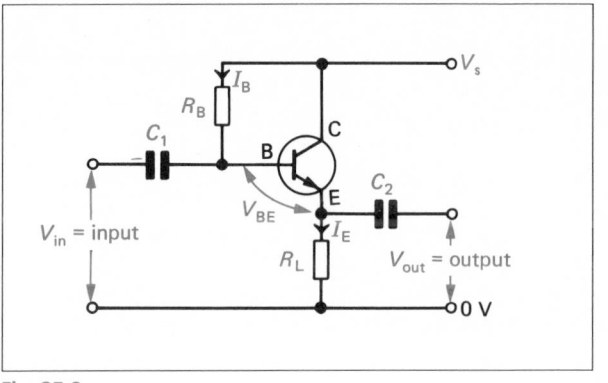

Fig. 35.8

The voltage gain $G_V = V_{out}/V_{in}$ is thus just less than 1. The current gain h_{FE} is however high and is given by

$$h_{FE} \approx \frac{I_E}{I_B}$$

since $I_E \approx I_C$.

◇ Questions

Q1
The circuit for a very simple amplifier is shown in Fig. 35.9. State
(a) the type of transistor used,
(b) where you would connect a power supply (give polarities), and
(c) where you would connect a microphone.

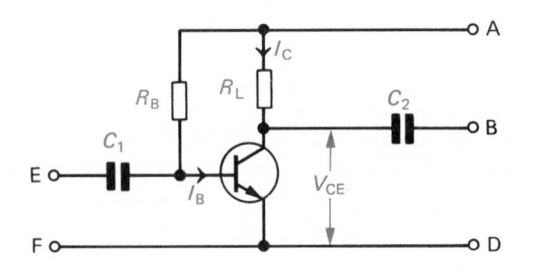

Fig. 35.9

Q2
(a) Why must a transistor amplifier be biased?
(b) Name *three* types of bias circuit.

Q3
In the circuit of Fig. 35.5 if $V_s = +9\,\text{V}$, $I_C = 2\,\text{mA}$ and $h_{FE} = 100$ for the transistor, calculate **(a)** I_B and **(b)** R_B if $V_{BE} = 0.6\,\text{V}$.

36 Operational amplifiers I

◆ About op amps

Operational amplifiers or op amps were the first analogue sub-systems to be made as ICs. They have many uses, two of the most important being
(i) as high gain voltage amplifiers of d.c. and a.c., and
(ii) as switches.

In this chapter, **(i)** will be considered. A typical op amp, like the popular 741 shown in Fig. 36.1, contains about twenty transistors as well as resistors and small capacitors on the silicon chip.

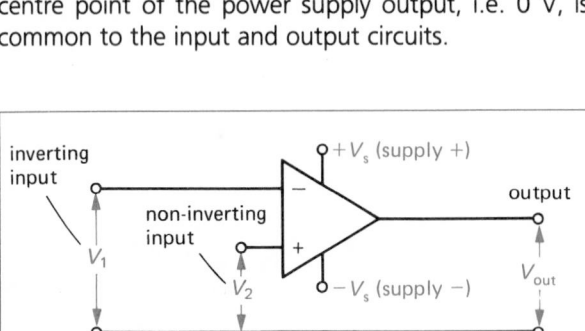

Fig. 36.1

(a) Description. It has one output and two inputs, called the *inverting input* (marked −) and the *non-inverting input* (marked +), as shown on its symbol in Fig. 36.2. A dual power supply is required giving equal positive and negative d.c. voltages $+V_s$, 0 and $-V_s$, where, for example, $+V_s = +15$ V and $-V_s = -15$ V. The centre point of the power supply output, i.e. 0 V, is common to the input and output circuits.

Fig. 36.2

Do not confuse the + and − input signs with those for the power supply polarities, which for clarity, are often left off circuit diagrams.

(b) Action. The polarity of a voltage applied to the inverting input is reversed at the output, i.e. a positive

voltage becomes an amplified negative voltage and vice versa. At the non-inverting input a positive voltage gives an amplified positive voltage and similarly with a negative voltage. Therefore
(i) if $V_2 > V_1$, i.e. the non-inverting input is greater than the inverting input, then V_{out} is *positive*. This occurs if, for example, $V_1 = 0$ V and V_2 is a small *positive* voltage. That is V_{out} has the same polarity as V_2, i.e. the output is not inverted.
(ii) if $V_1 > V_2$, i.e. the inverting input is greater than the non-inverting input, then V_{out} is *negative*. This happens when, for example, $V_2 = 0$ V and V_1 is a small *positive* voltage. That is, V_{out} has the opposite polarity to V_1, i.e. the output is inverted.
(iii) if $V_1 = V_2$, $V_{out} = 0$.

Basically an op amp is a *differential* voltage amplifier, i.e. it amplifies the difference between V_1 and V_2.

(c) Input and output impedances. An op amp has a *very high input impedance*, typically 1 MΩ to 10^6 MΩ. This means that the current it draws from the device or circuit supplying it is minute (negligible for our purposes) and the input voltage is passed on to it with little loss (Chapter 24: impedance matching).

It also has a *very low output impedance*, commonly 100 Ω, which means its output voltage is transferred efficiently to any load greater than a few kilohms.

(d) Comparison with transistor amplifier. Op amps are smaller, cheaper and more reliable than discrete component transistor amplifiers (Chapter 35).

◆ Negative feedback

When an op amp is used as an amplifier, part of the amplified output is fed back to the *inverting* input, Fig. 36.3. It therefore produces a voltage at the output which is of opposite polarity to the one from which the feedback was taken. As a result, the output and so the gain of the amplifier is reduced, i.e. the feedback is

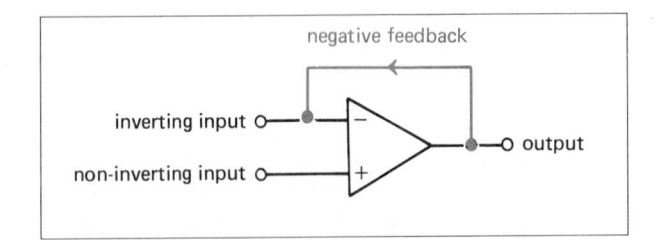

Fig. 36.3

negative. (Feedback applied to the non-inverting input would be positive and would increase the output.)

Although negative feedback reduces the gain of an amplifier and makes more stages of amplification necessary, it has several very desirable results.
(i) The gain is accurately predictable.
(ii) The frequency response is better, i.e. a wider range of frequencies is amplified by the same amount; so increasing the bandwidth.
(iii) Distortion of the output is reduced.
(iv) The amplifier is more stable.

◆ Inverting amplifier

In the basic circuit of Fig. 36.4 for an inverting voltage amplifier, the non-inverting (+) input is connected to 0 V and the input voltage V_{in} (d.c. or a.c.) to be amplified, is applied via resistor R_{in} to the inverting (−) input. The output voltage V_{out} is therefore of the *opposite* polarity to V_{in}. The *feedback resistor* R_F, by feeding back a certain fraction (depending on the value of R_F) of the output to the *inverting* input, ensures that the feedback is negative.

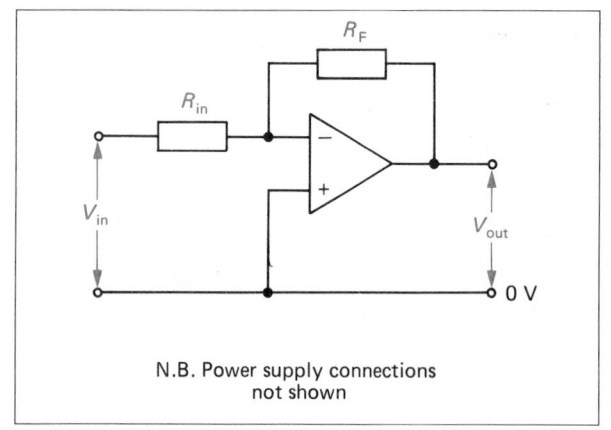

Fig. 36.4

(a) Voltage gain. It can be proved that the voltage gain G_V is given by

$$G_V = \frac{V_{out}}{V_{in}} = -\frac{R_F}{R_{in}} \qquad (1)$$

For example, if $R_F = 100\,k\Omega$ and $R_{in} = 10\,k\Omega$, then $G_V = -100/10 = -10$. The negative sign shows that V_{out} is negative if V_{in} is positive and vice versa.

From equation (1) we see that G_V depends only on the values of the two resistors R_F and R_{in} (which can be known accurately) and not on the particular op amp used.

(b) $V_{out} - V_{in}$ **graph**. If various positive and negative d.c. input voltages V_{in} are applied from the potential divider in the circuit of Fig. 36.5, the corresponding values of V_{out} can be obtained.

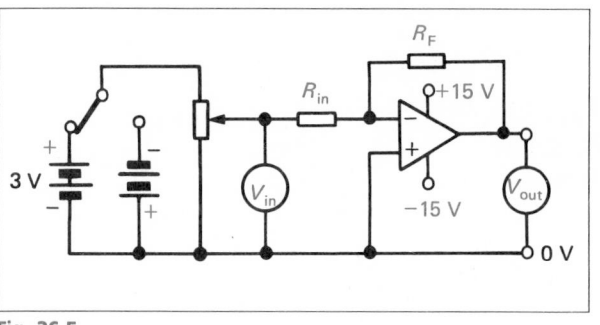

Fig. 36.5

A graph of V_{out} against V_{in} can then be plotted, like that in Fig. 36.6, which is typical for an op amp on a ± 15 V supply.

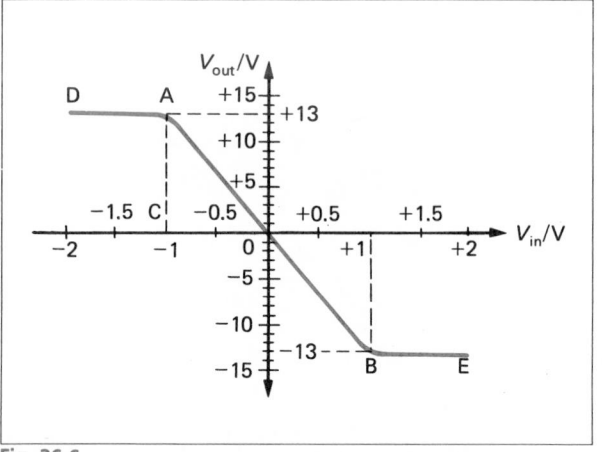

Fig. 36.6

We see from it that the amplifier has a *linear* response (i.e. V_{out} is directly proportional to V_{in}) only for values of V_{in} in the range + 1 V to − 1 V, that is on part A0B of the graph. In that region the *voltage gain* is given by

$$G_V = \frac{V_{out}}{V_{in}} = \frac{AC}{0C} = \frac{+13\,V}{-1\,V} = -13$$

The maximum positive and negative values of V_{out} cannot exceed the positive and negative values respectively of the supply, i.e. + 15 V or − 15 V on a ± 15 V supply. In practice they are less, here ± 13 V, whatever the value of V_{in}. Along DA and BE the op amp is said to be *saturated*.

It can be shown that the *input impedance* of the amplifier is R_{in} and since this can be changed to suit circuit conditions, it makes a versatile amplifier.

(c) a.c. amplifier. When used as an a.c. amplifier, coupling capacitors C_1 and C_2 can be included (to block any unwanted d.c. which might cause overloading), as shown in Fig. 36.7.

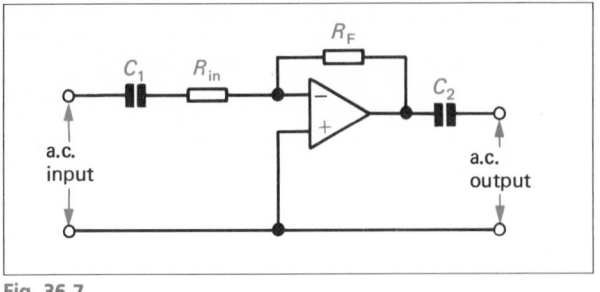

Fig. 36.7

If the input is in the linear range, Fig. 36.8a, the amplified, inverted output will be a copy of it, Fig. 36.8b. However, if the input is large enough to saturate the op amp, the output is distorted with 'clipped' peaks, Fig. 36.8c.

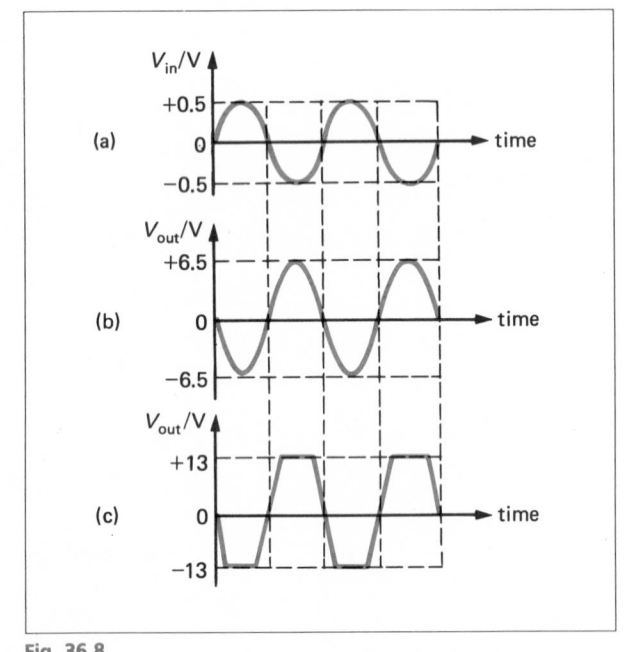

Fig. 36.8

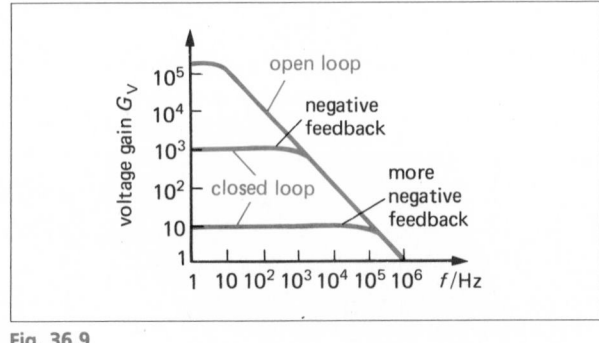

Fig. 36.9

(d) Gain and bandwidth. The voltage gain G_V can be measured at various frequencies using a signal generator and an oscilloscope, as for the transistor amplifier in Chapter 35, and a graph of G_V against frequency plotted.

G_V also varies with the amount of negative feedback. On *open loop*, with no feedback, the gain is very high, e.g. 100 000 (10^5), but on *closed loop* as the feedback is increased (by reducing R_F), G_V decreases but the bandwidth increases, as Fig. 36.9 shows.

◆ Non-inverting amplifier

The input voltage V_{in} (a.c. or d.c.) is applied to the non-inverting (+) input of the op amp. This produces an output voltage V_{out} of the *same* polarity as the input, Fig. 36.10.

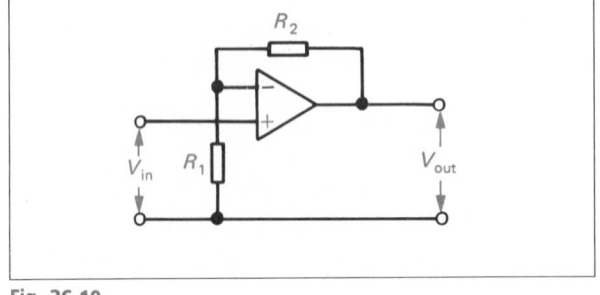

Fig. 36.10

Negative feedback is obtained by feeding back to the inverting (−) input, the fraction of V_{out} developed across R_1 in the potential divider formed by R_2 and R_1 across V_{out}.

(a) Voltage gain. It can be shown that this is given by

$$G_V = \frac{R_1 + R_2}{R_1} = 1 + \frac{R_2}{R_1} \tag{2}$$

For example, if $R_2 = 100$ kΩ and $R_1 = 10$ kΩ, then $G_V = (100 + 10)/10 = 110/10 = 11$. As with the inverting amplifier, G_V depends only on R_1 and R_2.

The *input impedance* is much higher (typically 50 MΩ) than that of the inverting amplifier and is unaffected if G_V is altered by changing R_1 or R_2. The circuit gives good matching when the input is supplied by a high impedance source such as a crystal microphone.

(b) Voltage-follower. This is a special case of the non-inverting amplifier in which *all* of the output is fed back to the inverting (−) input, Fig. 36.11. It follows that $R_2 = 0$ and R_1 is infinite, making $G_V = 1$ from equation (2). Hence $V_{out} = V_{in}$ but the circuit has an extremely high input impedance and a low output impedance. Its main use is (like the emitter-follower, Chapter 35), as a *buffer* amplifier, giving current amplification, to match a high impedance source to a low impedance load. For example, it is used as the input stage of an analogue voltmeter (Chapter 17) where the highest possible input impedance is required (so as not to disturb the circuit under test) and the output voltage is measured by a relatively low impedance meter.

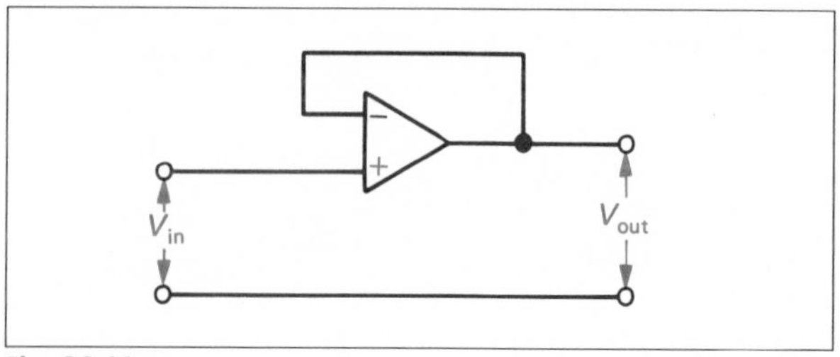

Fig. 36.11

◆ Summing amplifier

When connected as a multi-input inverting amplifier, an op amp can be used to add a number of voltages (d.c. or a.c.). Such circuits are employed as 'mixers' in audio applications to combine the outputs of microphones, electric guitars, pick-ups, special effects, etc.

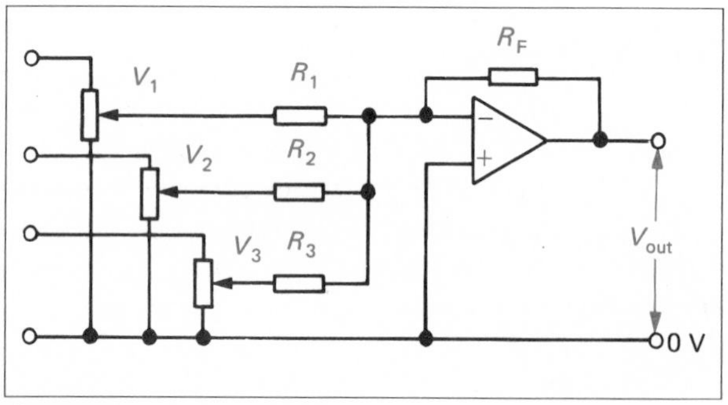

Fig. 36.12

In the circuit of Fig. 36.12 three input voltages V_1, V_2 and V_3 are applied via input resistors R_1, R_2 and R_3 respectively. The feedback resistor is R_F. It can be shown that

$$V_{out} = -R_F\left(\frac{V_1}{R_1} + \frac{V_2}{R_2} + \frac{V_3}{R_3}\right)$$

If $R_F = R_1 = R_2 = R_3$ then

$$V_{out} = -(V_1 + V_2 + V_3)$$

The output voltage is thus the *sum* of three input voltages but is of opposite polarity. For example, if $V_1 = 1$ V, $V_2 = 2$ V and $V_3 = 3$ V, $V_{out} = -(1 + 2 + 3) = -6$ V.

◇ Questions

Q1
In the circuit of Fig. 36.4 the power supply to the op amp is ±9 V and the input voltage $V_{in} = +1$ V.
(a) If $R_F = 20$ kΩ and $R_{in} = 10$ kΩ what is **(i)** the voltage gain G_V and **(ii)** the output voltage V_{out}?
(b) If $R_F = 200$ kΩ and $R_{in} = 10$ kΩ what is V_{out}?

Q2
The graph of V_{out} against V_{in} for the voltage amplifier of Fig. 36.13a is shown in Fig. 36.13b. The op amp works on ±5 V.

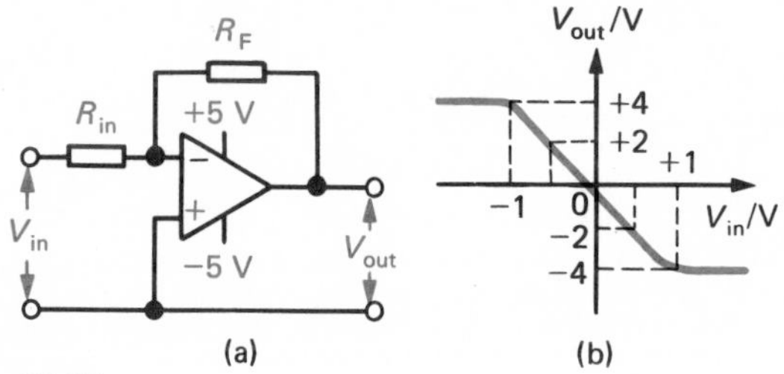

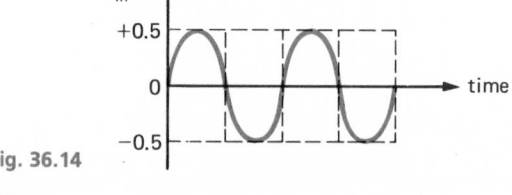

(a)   (b)

Fig. 36.13

(a) For what range of V_{in} is the response linear?
(b) What is the value of G_V in this range?
(c) If $R_F = 20$ kΩ what will be the value of R_{in} to give this value of G_V?
(d) If an a.c. input of 0.5 V peak is applied to the input, find from the graph the peak a.c. output voltage.
(e) If Fig. 36.14 shows the waveform of the a.c. input in **(d)**, sketch the corresponding output waveform, showing values.
(f) Repeat **(e)** for an a.c. input of peak value 2 V.

Fig. 36.14

Q3
In the circuit of Fig. 36.10 the power supply to the op amp is ±9 V and the input voltage $V_{in} = +1$ V.
(a) If $R_2 = 20$ kΩ and $R_1 = 10$ kΩ what is **(i)** the voltage gain G_V and **(ii)** the output voltage V_{out}?
(b) If $R_2 = 200$ kΩ and $R_1 = 10$ kΩ what is V_{out}?

Q4
In the circuit of Fig. 36.15 the power supply is ±15 V, $R_F = 30$ kΩ and $R_1 = R_2 = 15$ kΩ. Calculate V_{out} when
(a) $V_1 = +1.0$ V and $V_2 = +4$ V, and
(b) $V_1 = +1.0$ V and $V_2 = -4$ V.

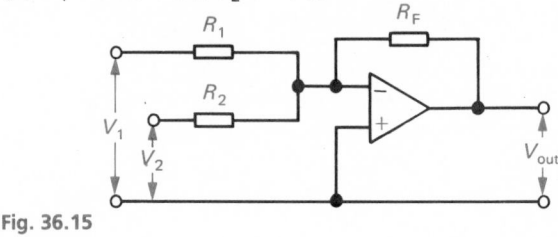

Fig. 36.15

37 Operational amplifiers II

◆ Comparator

When both inputs of an op amp are used at the same time, the output voltage V_{out} is the *difference* between the inverting (−) input voltage V_1 and the non-inverting (+) input voltage V_2, Fig. 37.1.

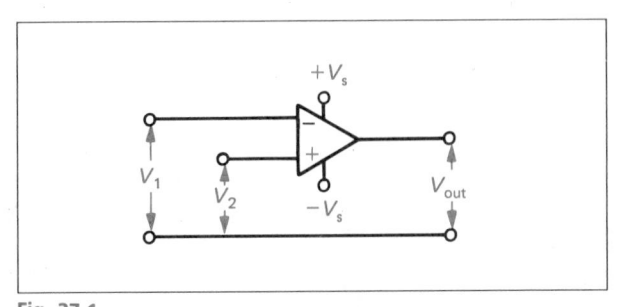

Fig. 37.1

But, because of its very high voltage gain on open loop, i.e. without negative feedback (Chapter 36), if the difference between V_1 and V_2 is greater than about 0.1 mV, the op amp saturates. V_{out} then has a constant value (for all differences more than 0.1 mV) close to either the positive (+V_s) or the negative (−V_s) of the power supply voltage, depending on whether V_2 is greater or less than V_1.

For example, V_{out} might be ±13 V on a ±15 V supply or ±8 V on a ±9 V supply.

The rule to remember is

if $V_2 > V_1$, V_{out} is positive (close to +V_s)
and
if $V_2 < V_1$, V_{out} is negative (close to −V_s)

This follows because the output is inverted from V_1, but not from V_2.

An op amp *compares* the voltages at its inputs. Its output shows which input is greater and detects any small change in the difference between them, by switching from 'high' to 'low' or vice versa. It gives a digital output.

◆ Alarm circuits

These were described earlier using a transistor as a switch (Chapter 27). An op amp in its comparator role can also be used and has certain advantages. First, switching is more sensitive (i.e. it occurs for smaller changes in the conditions that set off the alarm) and

second, it can be easier to change the reference voltage (i.e. the voltage at which switching occurs).

Two arrangements are considered below.

(a) Single rail supply. In the light-operated alarm circuit of Fig. 37.2, the inputs V_1 and V_2 are supplied by potential dividers (which use just the positive supply rail, hence 'single rail supply'), and the op amp compares them.

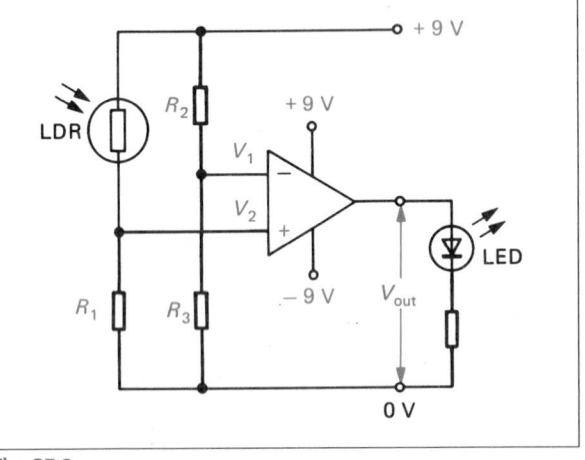

Fig. 37.2

In the dark, the resistance of the LDR is much greater than R_1, making V_2 (the voltage across R_1) less than V_1, the reference voltage (set by the ratio of R_2 to R_3), the difference being sufficient to saturate the op amp. Since V_1 (at the inverting input) is positive, V_{out} will be negative and close to −9 V.

If light falls on the LDR, its resistance decreases and causes V_2 to increase.

When V_2 (at the non-inverting input) exceeds V_1, the op amp switches to its other saturated state with V_{out} being close to +9 V. This positive voltage lights the LED (i.e. the alarm).

In effect, in this circuit the op amp changes a continuously varying *analogue* voltage (V_2) into a two-state *digital* one (V_{out}). It is a one-bit analogue to digital converter (Chapter 47).

(b) Dual rail supply. In the temperature-operated alarm circuit of Fig. 37.3, the thermistor TH and the variable resistor R form a potential divider across the ±15 V supply (i.e. across both positive and negative supply rails, hence 'dual rail supply').

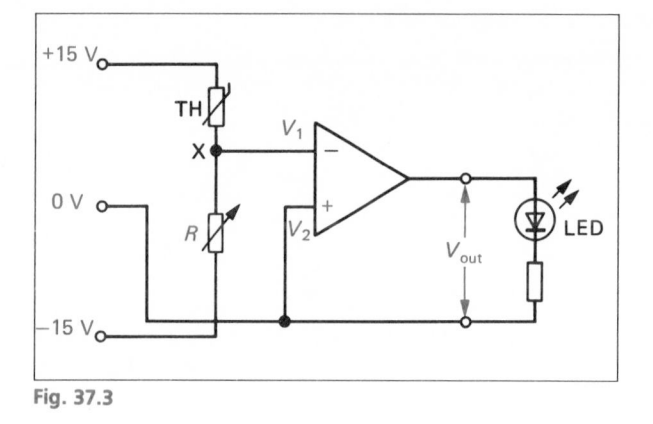

Fig. 37.3

The op amp compares the voltage V_1 at the potential divider junction X with V_2, which is 0 V.

If the temperature of TH *falls*, when it is low enough, its resistance becomes greater than that of R. More of the 30 V across the potential divider is then dropped across TH and the voltage at X goes negative, i.e. less than 0 V. Therefore $V_2 > V_1$, making V_{out} switch from near -15 V to near $+15$ V and lighting the LED. The temperature at which this occurs can be varied by altering R.

◆ Integrator

An op amp integrator is at the heart of a ramp generator for producing a voltage with a sawtooth waveform (Chapter 24). The circuit is the same as for the op amp inverting amplifier but feedback occurs via a capacitor C, connected as in Fig. 37.4, rather than via a resistor.

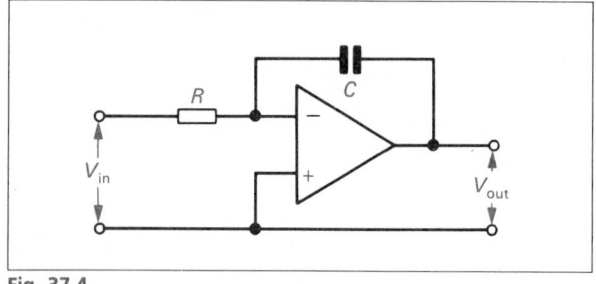

Fig. 37.4

If a *steady* input voltage V_{in} is applied through resistor R, it can be shown that after time T (in seconds), the output voltage V_{out} is given by

$$V_{out} = -\frac{1}{CR} \cdot V_{in}t$$

where C is in μF and R in MΩ. The negative sign shows that since the inverting input is used, V_{out} is negative if V_{in} is positive and vice versa.

For example, if $C = 1$ μF and $R = 1$ MΩ then

$$V_{out} = -V_{in} \cdot t$$

If $V_{in} = -3$ V, Fig. 37.5*a*, V_{out} *rises steadily* by $+3$ V per second. On a ± 15 V power supply, V_{out} is close to $+15$ V after 5 seconds, when the op amp saturates, Fig. 37.5*b*.

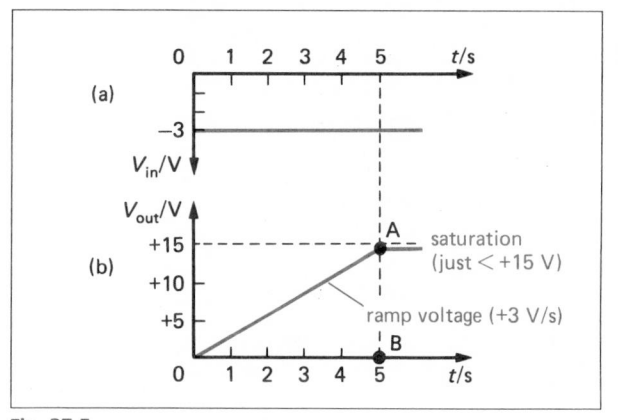

Fig. 37.5

V_{in} is thus 'added up' or integrated over a time t to give V_{out} a *ramp* voltage waveform whose *slope equals* $-V_{in}$ (when $CR = 1$s). For example, in Fig. 37.5*b*, the slope of the ramp is given by

$$\frac{AB}{OB} \approx +\frac{15\,V}{5\,s} \approx +3\,V/s$$

If $V_{in} = -6$ V, the slope would be twice as great and the op amp would saturate in half the time, i.e. 2.5 s.

To reset V_{out} to zero when it reaches its maximum value (due to the op amp saturating), a transistor is connected across C as in Fig. 37.6*a*.

When the transistor receives a reset pulse it switches on, short-circuits C and causes V_{out} to fall rapidly to 0 V. After each reset pulse, the transistor switches off, allowing V_{out} to rise again and produce a sawtooth waveform voltage like that in Fig. 37.6*b*.

A ramp generator is used in a digital voltmeter, as shown in the block diagram of Fig. 24.12.

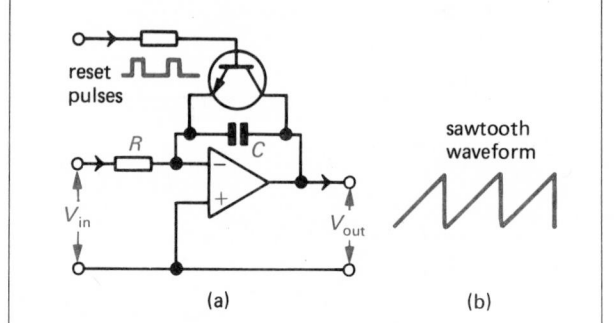

Fig. 37.6

◇ Questions

Q1

The light-operated switch in Fig. 37.7 uses an op amp as a voltage comparator.

(a) How must V_1 and V_2 compare if the op amp output is to be negative in daylight?

(b) In darkness what happens to **(i)** the LDR, **(ii)** V_2 compared with V_1, **(iii)** the output of the op amp, **(iv)** Tr, **(v)** the relay?

(c) How would you alter the circuit to make the relay be off in the dark and switch on in daylight?

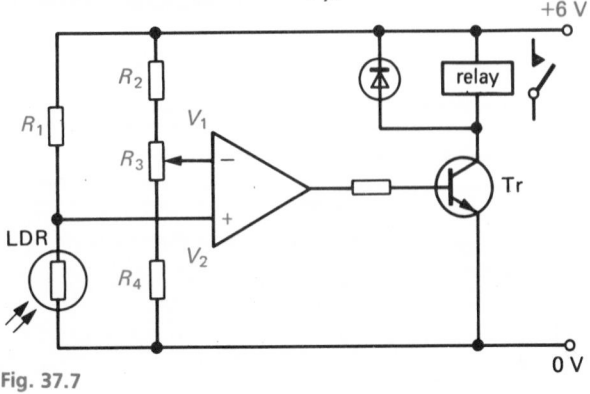

Fig. 37.7

Q2

(a) In the circuit of Fig. 37.8 is V_{out} positive or negative when S is **(i)** closed, **(ii)** open? (*Hint.* Consider the value of V_1 in each case.)

(b) What happens if R is increased?

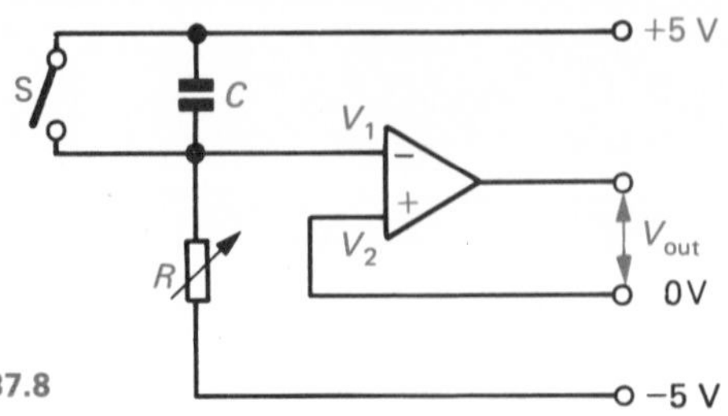

Fig. 37.8

Q3

In the circuit of Fig. 37.4 if $CR = 1$ s and $V_{in} = +5$ V

(a) does V_{out} rise or fall and at what rate, and

(b) if the op amp power supply is ± 15 V, what is the maximum value of V_{out} and when is it reached?

38 Additional questions

◇ Core level

Q1

The circuit in Fig. 38.1 is for a simple a.c. amplifier with a 6 V power supply. A small sine wave voltage is applied to its input. The output, shown in Fig. 38.2, is observed on an oscilloscope under different circuit conditions.

Which graph shows the output expected when

(a) the collector voltage at C is **(i)** +3 V, **(ii)** +1 V, **(iii)** +5 V,

(b) the input overloads the amplifier?

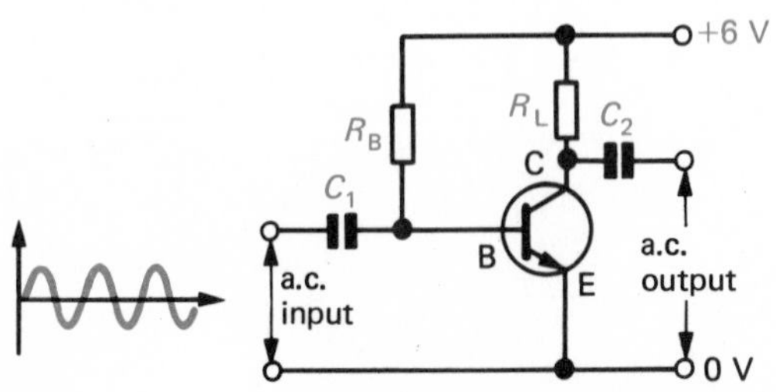

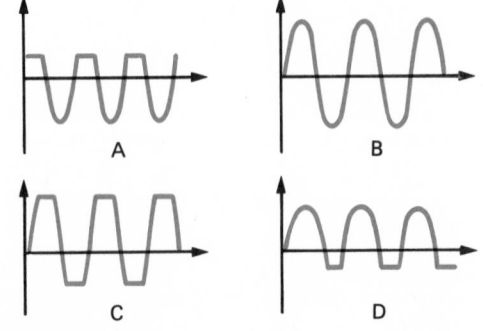

Fig. 38.1

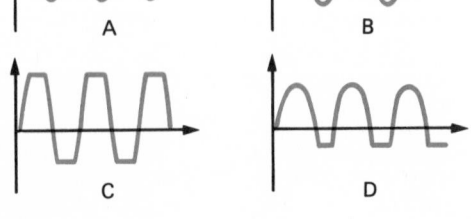

Fig. 38.2

Q2

The symbol for an op amp is shown in Fig. 38.3.

(a) What are **(i)** A, **(ii)** B and **(iii)** C?

(b) What is the purpose of the terminals marked + 15 V and − 15 V?

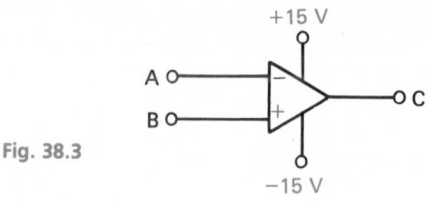

Fig. 38.3

Q3

The basic circuit for an *inverting* voltage amplifier using an op amp is shown Fig. 38.4.

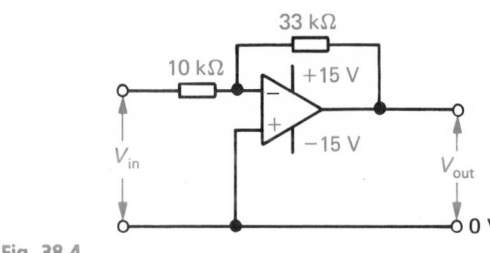

Fig. 38.4

(a) What is meant by the term *inverting amplifier*?

(b) What is the voltage gain of the amplifier?

(c) What are the values of *p*, *q*, *r* and *s* in the table below?

V_{in}/V	V_{out}/V
p	0
+2	q
r	−9.9
−5	s

(d) The waveform of a voltage which is fed into the amplifier is shown in Fig. 38.5. Copy it and draw below it the waveform of the output voltage showing its peak values.

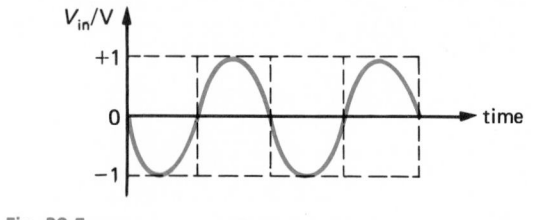

Fig. 38.5

Q4

In the circuit of Fig. 38.6*a* an LDR forms one part of a potential divider connected to the inverting input of an op amp comparator. The response of the LDR to different light intensities (measured in *lux*) is shown in Fig. 38.6*b*.

(a) What must be the value of R_1 for the voltage at the point X to be 2 V?

(b) What is the resistance of the LDR when the light intensity is 10 lux?

(c) If V_{out} is to change state when the light intensity on the LDR falls below 10 lux, what must be the resistance of R_2?

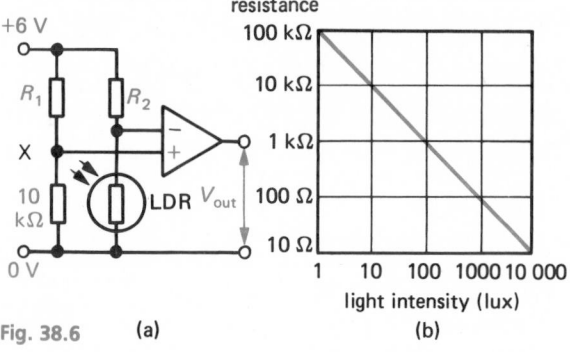

Fig. 38.6   (a)   (b)

◇ Further level

Q5

The op amp in Fig. 38.7 works on a ±9 V supply.

(a) Is it an inverting or a non-inverting amplifier?

(b) What is its voltage gain?

(c) If an a.c. of peak value ± 100 mV is applied to the input, what will be the peak output voltage?

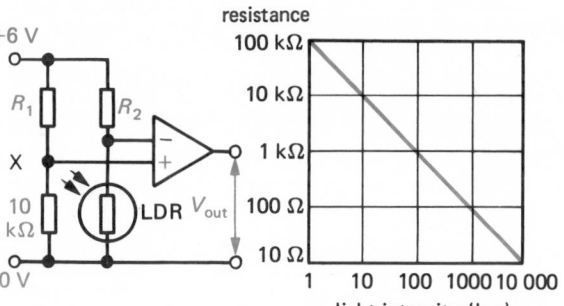

Fig. 38.7

Q6

The circuit in Fig. 38.8 switches on a heater when the temperature in a greenhouse falls below a certain value, say 0°C, which can be altered. Explain how it works.

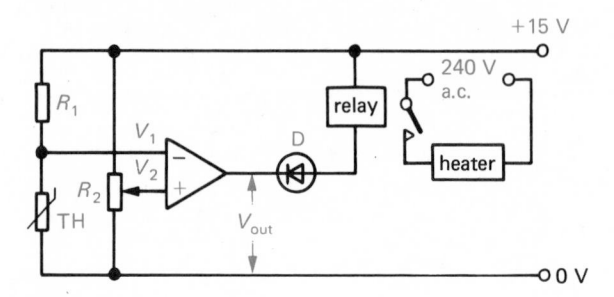

Fig. 38.8

Q7

The circuit in Fig. 38.9 is used in audio work on a ±15 V power supply.

(a) What is it called?

(b) Calculate the voltage gain of each of the two input channels.

(c) Calculate the peak values of V_{out} if those for V_1 and V_2 are ±1 V and ±3 V respectively

(d) What is the function of P and Q?

(e) What are the functions of C_1 and C_2?

Q8

The circuit in Fig. 38.10 is a delay switch which turns a LED *off* a certain time *after* S is pressed and released.

(a) Calculate V_2.

(b) What is V_1 when S is **(i)** closed, **(ii)** open?

(c) What is V_{out} when S is **(i)** closed, **(ii)** open?

(d) For what range of values of V_1 is the LED on?

(e) If a capacitor takes a time $T = CR$ seconds (where C is in μF and R in MΩ) to charge up to ⅔ of its final voltage (see Fig. 10.7*b* and here 6 V), how long is the LED on after S is released?

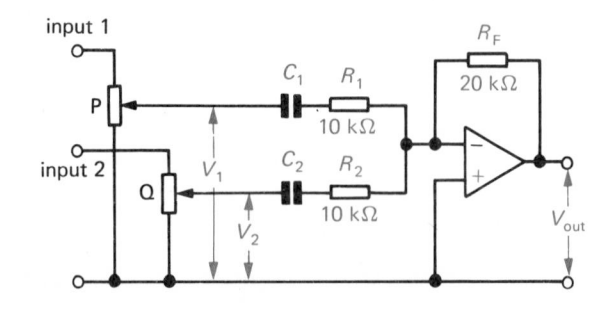

Fig. 38.9

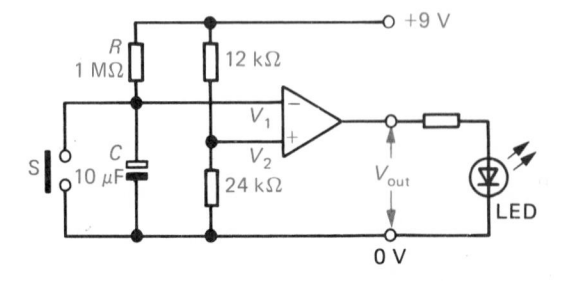

Fig. 38.10

Check list
Analogue sub-systems

After studying *Chapter 35: Transistor as an amplifier*, you should be able to

◇ state that analogue sub-systems process signals that are electrical representations (analogues) of physical quantities which can vary continuously with time, taking on all values between a certain maximum and a certain minimum,

◇ define the terms voltage gain, power gain and bandwidth relating to an amplifier,

◇ work out the voltage gain of an amplifier from a graph showing the variation of V_{out} with V_{in},

◇ explain why a transistor amplifier needs bias applied to the base,

◇ draw and recognize V_{out} waveforms caused by bias which is too low or too high or by overloading the input,

◇ draw and recognize the common-emitter a.c. amplifier circuits which use supply-to-base bias, collector-to-base bias and potential divider bias,

◇ calculate the value of the biasing resistor for the supply-to-base bias resistor knowing V_{BE}, h_{FE}, I_C and V_s,

◇ state that coupling capacitors in the input and output preserve biasing conditions while allowing a.c. signals to pass,

◇ describe how the voltage gain and bandwidth of a transistor amplifier can be measured, and

◇ state that an emitter-follower has a high input impedance and current gain and is used as a buffer or current amplifier to join the stages of a system together.

After studying *Chapter 36: Operational amplifiers I*, you should be able to

◇ state that an op amp is a very high gain IC amplifier which has two inputs, called the inverting ($-$) and non-inverting ($+$), and one output and normally operates on a dual power supply,

◇ state that the polarity of a voltage is reversed at the inverting input but not at the non-inverting input,

◇ state that negative feedback decreases the gain of an amplifier and is applied to the inverting input,

◇ state the advantages of negative feedback,

◇ recognize the circuit of an inverting voltage amplifier,

◇ state and use the relationship for the voltage gain of an inverting amplifier, i.e. $G_V = -R_F/R_{in}$,

◇ draw the circuit diagram to show how the $V_{out} - V_{in}$ graph of an inverting amplifier can be obtained,

◇ state that an inverting amplifier has a linear response for a limited range of input voltages, outside which the op amp saturates and V_{out} has a value near the positive or negative of the supply,

◇ recognize the circuit for an inverting a.c. amplifier and draw input and output waveforms for it within and beyond the linear input range,

◇ state that the bandwidth increases as the gain decreases,

◇ recognize the circuit for a non-inverting voltage amplifier,

◇ state and use the relationship for the voltage gain of a non-inverting amplifier, i.e. $G_V = 1 + R_2/R_1$,

◇ sketch input and output waveforms for an a.c. non-inverting voltage amplifier within and beyond the linear range,

◇ recall the properties and use of a voltage follower,

◇ recognize the circuit of a summing amplifier, and

◇ state and use the equation for a summing amplifier,

$$V_{out} = -R_F \left(\frac{V_1}{R_1} + \frac{V_2}{R_2} + \frac{V_3}{R_3} \right)$$

After studying *Chapter 37: Operational amplifiers II*, you should be able to

◇ recognize the op amp comparator circuit and state that if the non-inverting input V_2 is greater than the inverting input V_1, the output V_{out} will be close to the positive supply voltage, and if $V_1 > V_2$, V_{out} will be close to the negative supply voltage,

◇ recognize single rail and dual rail supply alarm circuits and explain how they work, and

◇ recognize the op amp integrator circuit and state that the slope of the ramp output voltage $V_{out} = -V_{in} \, t/(CR)$.

Communication systems

39 Information and electronics

◆ Information technology

Information technology (IT) is concerned with the ability of *computers* to store and process vast amounts of information in split seconds and of *telecommunications* to transmit it almost instantaneously. *Microelectronics* enables the equipment required to be made incredibly small and cheaply. IT is cropping up in every aspect of our lives, bringing changes, as profound as those of the Industrial Revolution, that will affect our homes, shops, offices, factories and schools as well as our health and leisure.

Links are being established allowing information to be sent anywhere in much the same way as telephones enable us to speak to each other now. In the broadest sense, information includes the messages, programmes and other 'traffic' carried by telephones, radio, television, as well as by computer signals and the various data processing devices used by banks, insurance companies and other business and government organizations. Today, information is seen, like minerals and energy, as a basic resource which is becoming more easily and widely accessible. Its control, however, raises important issues.

Some scientists are wondering whether with the possible development of ultra-intelligent machines, we may be seeing the next major step in the evolution of the universe. They argue that just as over three billion years ago, some very exotic molecules appeared on earth which produced life by entering into a new combination of matter, energy and information, so may life evolve into something else in the future, heralded by the advances now occurring in IT.

◆ Representing information

Information can be represented electrically in two ways.

(a) Digital method. In this method electricity is switched on and off and the information is in the form of electrical pulses. For example, in the simple circuit of Fig. 39.1a, data can be sent by the 'dots' and 'dashes' of the Morse code by closing the switch for a short or a longer time. In Fig. 39.1b the letter A (·–) is shown.

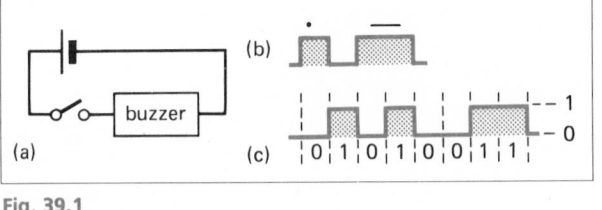

Fig. 39.1

Computers use the simpler binary code with 1 and 0 represented by 'high' and 'low' voltages respectively. They can only handle numbers (i.e. 1 and 0) and so a pattern of 1s and 0s has to be agreed for each of the 26 letters of the alphabet if words are also to be processed.

A five-bit code has 2^5 (32) variations, i.e. from 00000 to 11111, which would be enough. However, many digital systems used eight-bit words, i.e. bytes. The *American Standard Code for Information Interchange (ASCII)* is an eight-bit code that allows $2^8 = 256$ characters to be coded in binary. This is adequate for all letters of the alphabet (capitals and small), the numbers 0 to 9, punctuation marks and other symbols. Fig. 39.1c shows one eight-bit pulse, it represents the letter capital S in ASCII code.

(b) Analogue method. In this case the flow of electricity is *regulated* (not switched) and a continuous range of voltages (or currents) between 0 and some maximum is possible, Fig. 39.2a. The actual value at any instant stands for a number.

A crystal microphone produces a voltage which is the analogue of information (in the form of sound). A carbon microphone gives current as the analogue of information.

◆ Advantages of digital signals

Information in digital form has certain important advantages over that in analogue form, despite the fact that most input devices (e.g. microphones, pick-ups, thermistors) produce analogue signals. There are two main reasons for this.

(i) Digital signals can be transmitted over long distances without error because of their ability to cope with 'noise'. All signals are weakened as they travel and also pick up electrical 'noise', i.e. stray, unwanted voltages or currents which distort the waveform and cause 'hiss' and 'hum' in loudspeakers. (For example, the random motion of the carbon granules in a telephone mouthpiece generates noise, as does the sparking of a car ignition system.) See Chapter 30, Fig. 30.11.

Analogue signals require amplification (and correction) at suitable intervals, but the noise is amplified as well and may 'drown' the signal if it is weak. Digital signals on the other hand can be regenerated as 'clean' pulses, free from noise, Fig. 39.2a, b, c, since it is only necessary to detect the presence or absence of a pulse (i.e. whether it is a 1 or a 0) and not its shape.

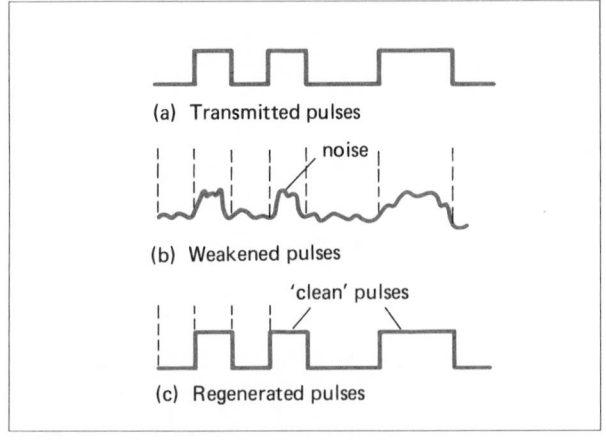

(a) Transmitted pulses

noise

(b) Weakened pulses

'clean' pulses

(c) Regenerated pulses

Fig. 39.2

(ii) Digital signals fit in with modern technology and can be used with both telecommunications and data-

processing equipment. Digital systems are easier to design and build (mostly from logic gates) and can be integrated on a single silicon chip.

◆ Analogue-to-digital conversion

With the increasing popularity of digital signals this operation is frequently necessary. It is performed by an analogue-to-digital converter (Chapter 47) in a process called *pulse code modulation* (PCM) which involves 'sampling' its value regularly.

Suppose the analogue voltage has the waveform shown in Fig. 39.3a. It is divided into a number of equally-spaced voltage levels (six in this case) and measurements taken at equal intervals to find the level at each time. Every level is represented in binary code by a number which has a characteristic series of on-off electrical pulses, i.e. a particular digital bit-pattern. A three-bit code can represent up to eight levels (0 to 7), as in Fig. 39.3b; four bits will allow sixteen levels to be coded.

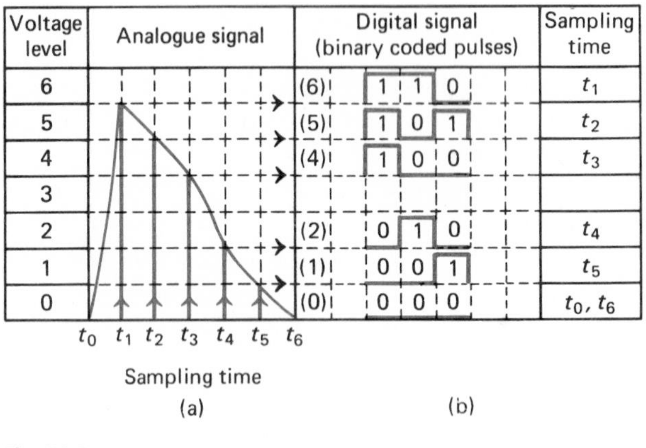

Voltage level	Analogue signal	Digital signal (binary coded pulses)			Sampling time
6		(6)	1 1	0	t_1
5		(5)	1 0	1	t_2
4		(4)	1 0	0	t_3
3					
2		(2)	0 1	0	t_4
1		(1)	0 0	1	t_5
0		(0)	0 0	0	t_0, t_6

t_0 t_1 t_2 t_3 t_4 t_5 t_6

Sampling time

(a)　　　　　　　(b)

Fig. 39.3

The accuracy of the representation increases with the number of voltage levels and the sampling frequency. The latter has to be greater than the highest frequency of the analogue signal to be sampled, since this frequency is sampled least often. The highest frequency needed for intelligible speech in a telephone is about 4000 Hz and a sampling frequency of 8000 Hz is chosen, i.e. samples are taken at 125 μs intervals, each sample lasting for 2 to 3 μs. An eight-bit code (giving $2^8 = 256$ levels) is used and so the number of bits that have to be transmitted is $8000 \times 8 = 64\,000$, i.e. the *bit-rate* is 64 kbits/s and is given by

bit-rate = sampling frequency × no of bits in code

For good quality music where frequencies up to about 20 000 Hz must be transmitted, the sampling frequency is 32 000 Hz and a sixteen-bit code ($2^{16}=65\,536$ levels) is used. The bit-rate required is $32\,000 \times 16 = 512$ kbits/s. For television signals, which carry much more information, a bit-rate of $70\,000\,000 = 70$ Mbits/s is needed. (See question 9, Chapter 44.)

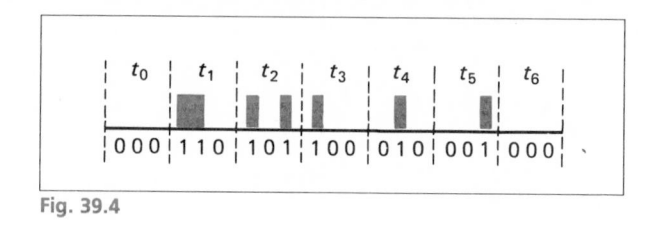

Fig. 39.4

The analogue voltage shown in Fig. 39.3*a* would be represented in digital form by the train of pulses in Fig. 39.4 using a three-bit code.

◆ Transmission of information

Electrical signals representing 'information' from a microphone, a TV camera, a computer, etc., can be sent from place to place using either cables or radio waves. Information in the form of audio frequency (AF) signals may be transmitted directly by a cable but in general, and certainly in radio and TV, they require a 'carrier'. This has a higher frequency than the information signal, its amplitude is constant and its waveform sinusoidal.

The general plan of any communication system is shown in Fig. 39.5. Signals from the *information source* are added to the carrier in the *modulator* by the process of 'modulation'. The modulated signal is sent along a 'channel' in the 'propagating medium' (i.e. cable or radio wave) by the *transmitter*.

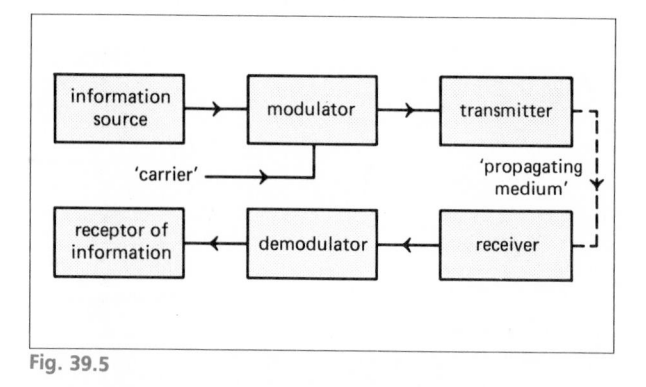

Fig. 39.5

At the receiving end, the *receiver* may have to select (and perhaps amplify) the modulated signal before the *demodulator* extracts from it the information signal for delivery to the *receptor of information*.

◆ Types of modulation

(a) Amplitude modulation (AM). The information signal from, for example, a microphone, is used to vary the *amplitude* of the carrier so that it follows the wave shape of the information signal, Fig. 39.6.

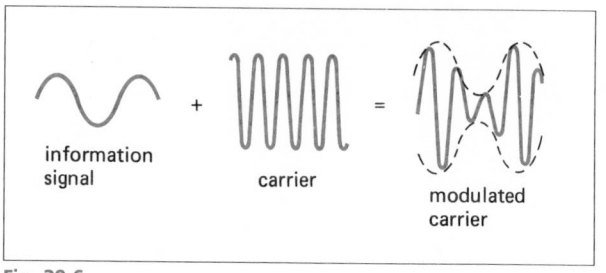

Fig. 39.6

(b) Frequency modulation (FM). In this case the information signal varies the *frequency* of the carrier, which increases if the signal is positive and decreases if it is negative. The effect, much exaggerated, is shown in Fig. 39.7.

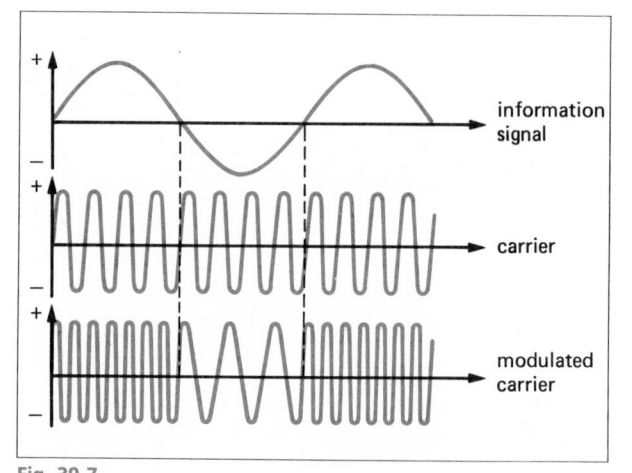

Fig. 39.7

(c) Pulse code modulation (PCM). The carrier is not transmitted continuously but is modulated to form a pattern of *pulses* which, as explained earlier, represents in binary code, regular samples of the amplitude of the information signal.

◆ Bandwidth

The term is used in two ways.

(a) Bandwidth of a signal. This is the range of frequencies a signal occupies. For intelligible speech it is 3700 Hz (e.g. 300 to 4000 Hz as in the telephone system), for high quality music it is from 20 Hz to 20 kHz or so and for television signals about 8 MHz.

The bandwidth of a modulated signal is due to the fact that when modulated, other frequencies, called *side frequencies*, are created on either side of the carrier (which is a single frequency). In AM, if the carrier frequency is f_c and a modulating frequency f_m, two new frequencies of $f_c - f_m$ and $f_c + f_m$ are produced, one below f_c and the other above it, Fig. 39.8a.

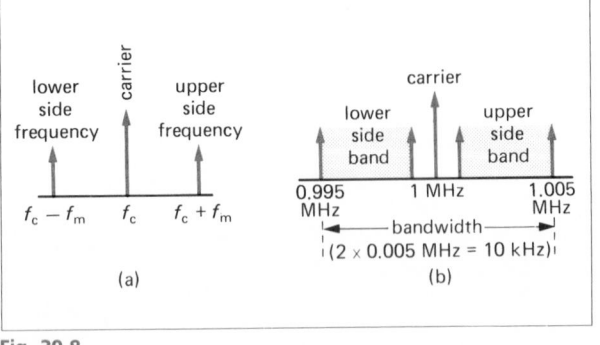

Fig. 39.8

If, as usually occurs in practice, the carrier is modulated by a range of AFs, each AF gives rise to a pair of side frequencies. The result is a band of frequencies, called the *lower* and *upper sidebands*, stretching below and above the carrier by the value of the highest modulating frequency. For example, if $f_c = 1$ MHz and the highest $f_m = 5$ kHz $= 0.005$ MHz, then $f_c - f_m = 0.995$ MHz and $f_c + f_m = 1.005$ MHz, Fig. 39.8b. The bandwidth of a carrier modulated by AF signals up to 5 kHz is thus 10 kHz. Sidebands also arise in FM.

(b) Bandwidth of a channel. This is the range of frequencies a communication channel can accommodate. High frequency transmission channels have greater bandwidths than lower frequency ones, i.e. their information-carrying capacity is greater. For instance, the VHF radio band, which extends from 30 MHz to 300 MHz, has 'space' for 2700 signals 10 kHz wide. The medium waveband, 300 kHz to 3 MHz, can carry only 270 such signals.

Cables also have different bandwidths.

◆ Multiplexing

Multiplexing involves sending several different information signals along the same communication channel so that they do not interfere. In the *frequency division* method, signals (e.g. speech in analogue form) modulate carriers of different frequencies which are then transmitted, a greater bandwidth being required.

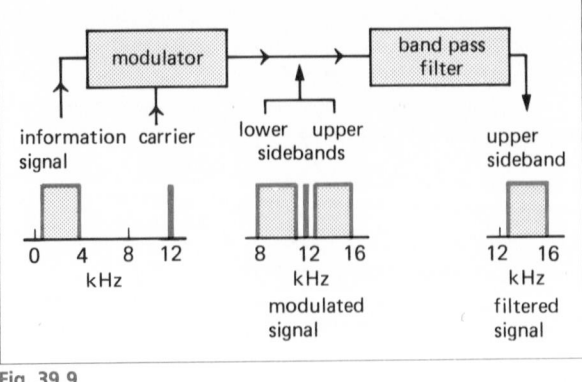

Fig. 39.9

The principle is shown in Fig. 39.9 for cable transmission. The information signal contains frequencies up to 4 kHz and the carrier frequency is 12 kHz. *Each* sideband contains *all* the modulating frequencies, i.e. all the information and so only one is really necessary. Here, a 'bandpass filter' allows just the upper sideband to pass.

The multiplexing of three 4 kHz wide information signals, 1, 2 and 3, using carriers of 12, 16 and 20 kHz is shown in Fig. 39.10.

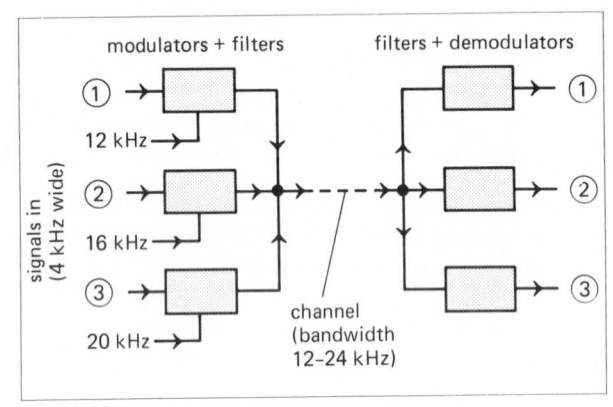

Fig. 39.10

◇ Questions

Q1
(a) Draw an example of an analogue waveform.
(b) Draw an example of a digital waveform.
(c) Name a device which produces an analogue signal.
(d) Name a device which produces a digital signal.

Q2
What is the bandwidth when frequencies in the range 500 Hz to 3500 Hz amplitude modulate a carrier?

Q3
A carrier of frequency 800 kHz is amplitude modulated by frequencies ranging from 1 kHz to 10 kHz. What frequency range does each sideband cover?

40 Telephone system

◆ Simple telephone circuits

(a) Basic circuit. This consists of a microphone connected by wires (the 'line') to an earpiece and a battery of a few volts which drives a current (d.c.) round the circuit, Fig. 40.1. When someone speaks into the microphone, its resistance varies in response to the sound and causes corresponding changes in the current. These changes reproduce the sound in the earpiece.

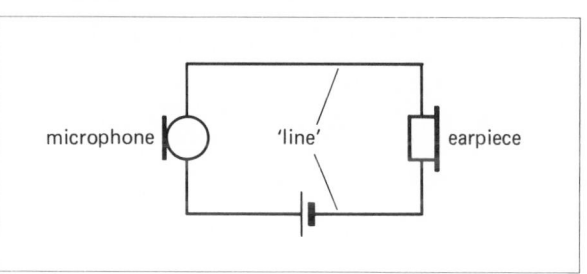

Fig. 40.1

If the line is long, the total resistance of the circuit is high and it changes only slightly when the microphone resistance varies. The current changes are therefore small and the sound in the earpiece is very faint.

(b) Two-way circuit. Speech between two telephones many miles apart is possible with the circuit of Fig. 40.2, in which the battery current does not flow in the line but only in the microphone and the primary of a transformer. When the resistance of the microphone in this low resistance local circuit varies, it causes large current changes (varying d.c.). These induce, in the secondary winding of the transformer, a current varying in the same way (but a.c.), which flows in the line and

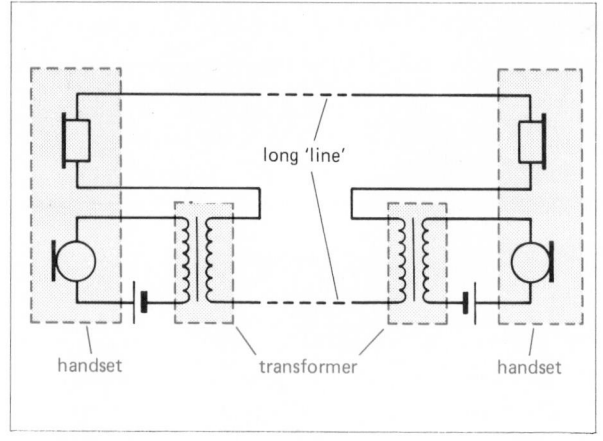

Fig. 40.2

through the earpiece at the distant end, Fig. 40.3. Communication can occur in both directions. The microphone and earpiece at each end are combined in a single unit, the handset.

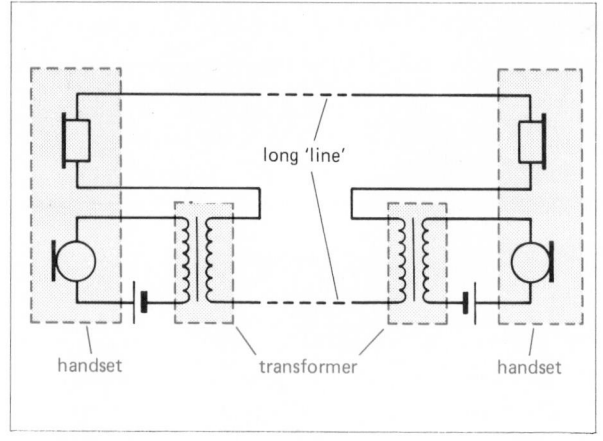

Fig. 40.3

Today most telephones are connected to an exchange with a central battery (of higher voltage, e.g. 50 V) which replaces the local battery at each telephone.

◆ Telephone exchanges

(a) The exchange network. Communication between just two telephones can be achieved quite satisfactorily by simple circuits like those in Figs. 40.1 and 40.2. In a telephone system involving many subscribers, connection of each one directly to every other subscriber would be extremely complex and costly. The number of connections can be greatly reduced if the subscribers in one area are each connected to a *local exchange*, located centrally. Any subscriber in that area can then be connected to any other subscriber in the area or to subscribers in other areas via other exchanges. Power supplies, other essential equipment and staff can also be conveniently based at the exchange.

In the same way, and for similar reasons, local exchanges are connected to *group switching centres* which in turn are linked to *main* or *trunk switching centres*, Fig. 40.4. In the UK at present there are several thousand local exchanges and a few hundred trunk centres. Subscribers can also be connected via one of six *international switching centres* for calls abroad. In future, modernization will mean many fewer exchanges. For example, the trunk network with be served by just over fifty.

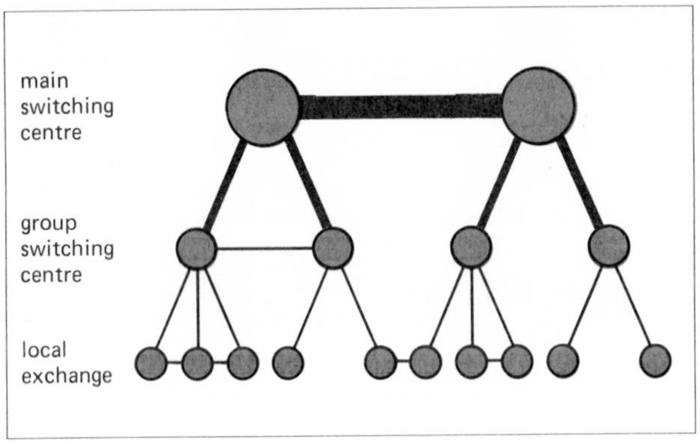

Fig. 40.4

(b) Switching. To reach its destination a telephone call must be directed or *routed*. This involves switching at the exchange to ensure the correct lines are connected.

For an automatic exchange, the destination is indicated by the number dialled or in the case of a press button telephone, by the keys pushed on the keypad. The switching, up to the late 1970s, would usually be done by electromechanical *selectors* or in some exchanges by *reed switches*.Since then, increasingly in the UK as the telephone system goes 'digital', *electronic logic gates* have been used.

(c) System X. System X is a family of electronic exchanges ranging in size from small local exchanges to large international exchanges that is more compact and cheaper than existing exchanges. It uses pulse code modulated (PCM) *digital signals, electronic switching and computers* to control the routing of calls.

The first System X exchange (Fig. 40.5) was opened in the City of London in 1980 and by the mid 1990s about half of all telephones in the UK will be connected to this type of exchange.

In addition to clearer speech, less noise, faster connection and fewer wrong numbers, System X will offer new facilities to subscribers, including the following.
(i) *Code calling*. Frequently used numbers can be stored and called quickly using a short code.
(ii) *Call diversion*. Incoming calls can be transferred to another number when required.
(iii) *Three-way calling*. While holding one call, another can be made, then a three-way conversation held.
(iv) *Reminder call*. The exchange can be programmed by the subscriber to ring back at a certain time.
(v) *Charge advice*. At the end of a call the exchange calls back giving the cost.

Eventually, by the early years of the 21st century, System X and other electronic exchanges will provide a multi-purpose, *Integrated Digital Network* (IDN) handling, in digital form, all communications whether they be speech, text, photographs, drawings, music, television or computer data.

◆ Copper cables

The earliest telephone links were copper wires carried overhead on wooden poles. Today most cables are underground and a typical one may contain hundreds of pairs of wires, each covered with plastic insulation and all bunched together inside a thicker plastic covering called the cable sheath, Fig. 40.6. The sheath provides protection and excludes moisture. The cables are laid in earthenware or plastic pipes, called 'ducts', and are joined either in 'joint boxes' just under footpaths or in 'manholes' (as large as small rooms) often under the roadway.

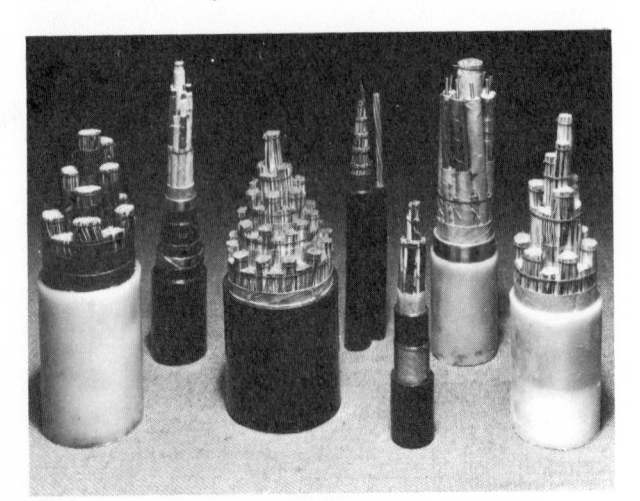

Fig. 40.5

Fig. 40.6

On local links, the cables carry AF currents; on trunk lines amplifiers, called *repeaters*, are required to boost the signals which may be multiplexed. That is, the AF speech currents are modulated on different high frequency carriers, enabling many telephone calls to be carried by one circuit.

Multiplexing requires cables to transmit RF currents with minimum loss, i.e. to have a wide bandwidth. Low-loss coaxial cables, Fig. 40.7, can handle frequencies in the ultra high frequency (UHF) range, i.e. 300 MHz to 3000 MHz. The inner conductor is solid copper and the outer one is copper braid which also acts as a screen against stray signals and 'noise'.

Fig. 40.7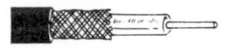

◆ Optical fibres

(a) Principle. The suggestion that information could be carried on light, and sent over long distances in thin fibres of very pure (optical) glass, was first made in 1966. Eleven years later, the world's first fibre optic telephone link was working in Britain and it is expected that eventually trunk circuits and submarine cables to other countries, as well as local lines from homes and offices, will change over from copper to glass cables. The first transatlantic one, called TAT 8, should be operating when this book is published. At present, more than 150 000 miles of optical fibre cable has been installed in the UK.

Light, like radio waves, is electromagnetic radiation but because of its much higher frequency (typically 10^{14} Hz $= 10^5$ GHz), it has a considerably greater information-carrying capacity, i.e. it has a very wide bandwidth. When modulated and guided by glass fibre cables installed in (existing) cable ducts, it escapes the severe attenuation (weakening) it would suffer from rain and fog if sent through the air. It is also free from 'noise' due to electrical interference and greater distances can be worked with fewer *signal boosters* than with coaxial cables.

Compared with copper cables, optical fibre cables are lighter, smaller and easier to handle; they can carry the same number of calls as copper cables nearly ten times as thick, Fig. 40.8.

(b) Lasers. The 'light' used is infrared radiation in the region just beyond the red end of the visible spectrum; for the earliest fibres the wavelength was 850 nm (0.85 μm). Later fibres employ 1300 or 1500 nm since the longer the wavelength, the less is the attenuation of the radiation by the glass, which is why infrared is preferred to 'visible' light.

Fig. 40.8

The infrared is generated by a tiny semiconductor *laser* made from gallium, aluminium and arsenic. A laser (standing for *l*ight *a*mplification by the *s*timulated *e*mission of *r*adiation) produces a very narrow *coherent* beam of electromagnetic radiation of one particular frequency. Coherent light, in contrast to light from other

Fig. 40.9

sources (e.g. a lamp), consists of waves vibrating in phase with each other, rather like the radiation, at much lower frequencies, from a radio transmitter. The detector at the receiving end is a *photodiode* which converts the optical signal into an electrical one.

(c) Modulation. The infrared is *pulse code modulated* by the speech or other data to be transmitted, i.e. digital signals are sent in the form of pulses of radiation, being on for a '1' and off for a '0'. An optical fibre communications system is shown in Fig. 40.9.

(d) Optics. The optical fibres (which are about 0.1 mm in diameter) have a glass core of higher refractive index than the glass cladding around it. As a result, the infrared beam is trapped in the core by *total internal reflection* at the core–cladding boundary (just as light is in the prisms of binoculars when it strikes the back surface of the prism where the refractive index is high in the glass but low in the air), Fig. 40.10*a,b*. The glass in optical fibres is so pure that a 2 km length absorbs less 'light' than a sheet of window glass.

Fig. 40.11

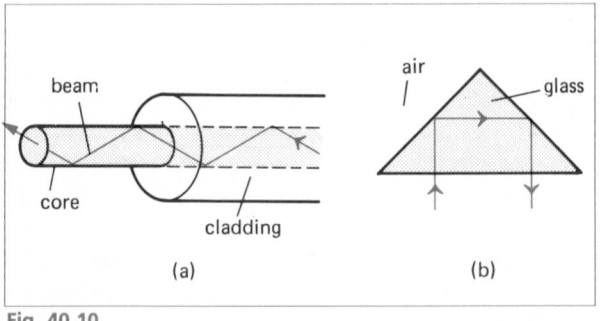

Fig. 40.10

(about 30 miles apart), like that in Fig. 40.11, containing equipment for boosting the signals before they are re-transmitted on their next hop. The nerve centre of the system is the British Telecom Tower in London which is connected to sixteen Network Switching Centres (NSCs) throughout the country.

Television programmes are also carried by the microwave system between studios and transmitters, the NSCs rerouting the programmes as required, Fig. 40.12. Microwave transmissions across the English Channel link the UK and European TV networks.

(e) Capacity. The information-carrying capacity of an optical fibre system today is 8 000 telephone calls at once over a pair of fibres and further developments will increase this to 16 000 calls and later to 30 000 or more.

◆ Microwave links

Microwaves are radio waves with frequencies of the order of 1000 MHz (and wavelengths less than 10 cm or so); their information-carrying capacity is therefore quite high (about 70 Mbit/s). They are easily focused into a narrow beam by a dish aerial 2 or 3 metres in diameter. This makes better use of the power from the transmitter and reduces the risk of interference from other transmitters on the same frequency.

About 20% of the trunk telephone calls in the UK go by microwave links which cross the country in line-of-sight hops between dish aerials mounted on tall towers

Fig. 40.12

◆ Communication satellites

Two-thirds of all intercontinental telephone calls now pass via the satellite network. A typical satellite call goes from the caller to a local exchange, to an international exchange and then by either cable or terrestrial microwave link to an earth station. There it is beamed up to the satellite by microwaves, Fig. 40.13, and retransmitted down to another country.

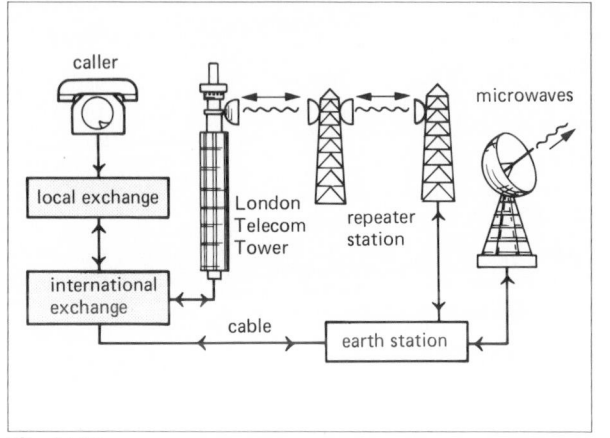

Fig. 40.13

Another important development (*SatStream*) offers businesses a small-dish satellite service in which they can communicate within Britain and with Europe directly, through rooftop aerials placed at or near their offices in cities, Fig. 40.14. Using digital techniques the system offers flexibility and diversity in that many different services such as speech, telex or computer data can be sent over the same transmission path. An A4 page of type or a colour photograph can be transmitted in 1 second, the contents of the *Concise Oxford Dictionary* in 32 seconds and of the entire *Encyclopaedia Britannica* in 30 minutes.

INMARSAT (International Maritime Satellite Organization) uses satellites to provide direct communication with ships at sea.

◆ Other telephone services

Apart from providing person-to-person communication, the telephone system has other uses.

(a) Viewdata. This uses digital techniques to display, on the screen of a modified domestic TV receiver, up-to-the-minute information on a wide range of topics. It uses the telephone network and is called *Prestel*. The information (text and diagrams) is presented a screenful (page) at a time, as in a newspaper or magazine. From the index page(s) the viewer selects the page required on a remote control keypad, Fig. 40.15.

Viewdata signals are sent serially, i.e. one after the other, from a central computer which is the database. Units called *modems* (*mo*dulator–*dem*odulator) are needed at each end of the telephone line to convert analogue to digital signals and vice versa for transmission and reception. The modem encodes digital data by representing a '1' as a low audio tone and a '0' by a high tone. Telephone lines are designed to carry AF currents not d.c. pulses.

Fig. 40.14

Fig. 40.15

Viewdata information is more detailed and comprehensive than that of Teletext (Chapter 43) because of the large number of 'pages' (⅓ million and increasing) of data the computer can store. It is an *interactive* system, allowing the subscriber to communicate with the database. Instant and easy access is given to almost unlimited information and so it provides the 'information society' with facilities such as 24-hour banking, teleshopping and paying bills, all at the touch of a button from an armchair at home. While teletext is 'free' and available to all simultaneously, viewdata has to be paid for and the number of subscribers that can be connected at any one time is limited.

(b) Telex. This is of interest mainly to firms, especially those with overseas connections. The message to be transmitted is typed by an operator at the sender's end on the typewriter-style keyboard of a teleprinter which translates letters, figures, signs and punctuation marks into code. In the modern telex terminal in Fig. 40.16, the VDU (visual display unit) permits editing and a printer gives a permanent copy of the message if it is required.

The receiving teleprinter decodes the message and types it automatically on to a sheet of paper without anyone needing to be present.

Connection between telex subscribers is by a network of teleprinter exchanges.

(c) Facsimile. Facsimile (meaning 'exact copy') allows a document to be sent over the telephone system and is a kind of electronic mail. When the document is inserted in the sender's facsimile machine, the 'optical eye' scans it and produces a string of electrical pulses which, on reaching the receiver's machine, makes it print out the same document which is then available for disucssion by both parties if required. An A4 page of text can be transmitted and printed in 1 minute.

Fig. 40.16

Fig. 40.17

(d) Mobile telephone system. In this recently developed system, called *cellular radio*, Fig. 40.17, the country is divided into small areas or 'cells'. Each cell has its own low-powered radio transmitter and is linked to a regional mobile exchange. These exchanges are in turn linked to the existing telephone system. When a caller travels from one cell to another, a computer automatically switches the caller to another cell so that the call can be continued wherever he or she travels. Calls can be made from cars, trains, ferries and hand-held portable telephones.

◇ Questions

Q1
Draw the circuit diagram of the equipment needed at one end of a simple telephone circuit which allows a two-way conversation.

Q2
Write brief notes on the use of the following in telecommunications: **(a)** coaxial cables, **(b)** optical fibres, **(c)** microwaves and **(d)** satellites.

Q3
Describe briefly how the following telephone services are useful to business organizations: **(a)** viewdata, **(b)** telex, **(c)** facsimile, and **(d)** mobile telephone system.

41 Audio systems

◆ Block diagram

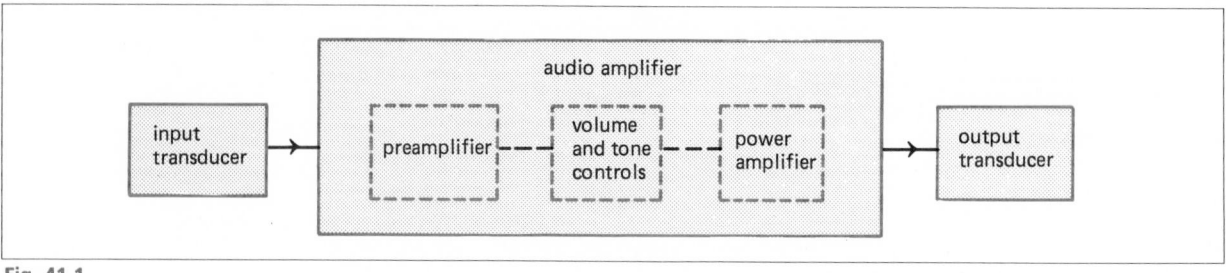

Fig. 41.1

An audio system reproduces and amplifies sound. It processes alternating voltages and currents which have frequencies from about 20 Hz to 20 kHz or so, that is, in the audio frequency (AF) range. Electrical signals with these frequencies produce sound when fed to a loudspeaker.

The block diagram for an audio system is shown in Fig. 41.1; it has three main parts.

(a) Input transducer. This may be a microphone, the pick-up of a record player or the play-back head of a cassette recorder. All change sound, produced in the first place by a source of speech or music, into electrical energy in the form of alternating AF voltages and currents.

Sound is received directly from the source in a microphone. In a record player it is stored on the wavy groove of the record. In a cassette recorder it is stored as variations in the magnetization of the tape.

(b) Audio amplifier. The electrical signals from the input transducer are too weak to operate the output transducer satisfactorily and have to be boosted by the audio amplifier. For example, the output voltage from a *magnetic pick-up* is in the range 5 to 10 mV and it should supply an amplifier with an input impedance of 50 to 100 kΩ for maximum voltage transfer. The corresponding values for a *crystal pick-up* are 100 mV and 1 to 2 MΩ. For a *cassette play-back head* the output voltage is about 300 mV.

An audio amplifier consists of a voltage amplifier, called a *preamplifier*, incorporating a potentiometer as a *volume control* to adjust the level of the sound from the whole system. It also contains *tone controls* to enable high (treble) and low (bass) notes to be emphasized more or less.

The output from the preamplifier feeds the *power amplifier* which ensures that enough power is supplied to the output transducer.

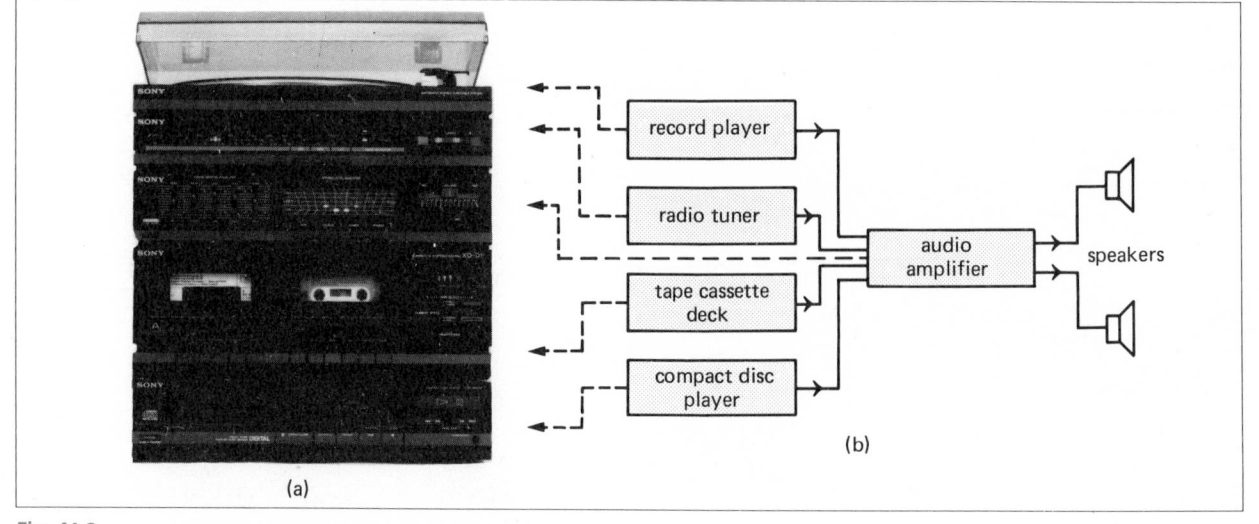

(a)

(b)

Fig. 41.2

(c) Output transducer. This is usually a loudspeaker but may also be headphones or an earpiece. It converts electrical energy into sound when AF currents and voltages are received from the audio amplifier.

To stop the system picking up interference from mains hum, cross-talk, etc., certain cables are shielded by having a wire-mesh screen surrounding them.

A typical hi-fi (high fidelity) audio system and its block diagram are shown in Fig. 41.2. It comprises
(i) a record player,
(ii) a 3-band FM/long wave/medium wave radio tuner (Chapter 42),
(iii) a tape cassette deck,
(iv) a compact disc player,
(v) an audio amplifier (pre- and power) into which the outputs from **(i)**, **(ii)**, **(iii)** and **(iv)** can be switched separately,
(vi) a loudspeaker system.

◆ Power amplifier

To obtain the power it needs, typically several watts, to produce the volume of sound required, a loudspeaker must be supplied with sufficient current by the power amplifier. In addition, for maximum power transfer, the output impedance of the amplifier should *equal* the input impedance of the loudspeaker, e.g. 8 Ω (Chapter 24). A power amplifier is therefore a *current-amplifying buffer* between the preamplifier and the speaker it has to drive.

(a) Push-pull follower. The push-pull follower circuit of Fig. 41.3 meets the above requirements for a power amplifier. It consists of two low output impedance emitter-followers (Chapter 35), one an *n-p-n* type and the other a *p-n-p* type, which employ the push-pull principle. In this, positive half-cycles of the input forward bias Tr1, which conducts and 'pushes' a series of positive half-cycles of amplified output current through the speaker. During this time Tr2 is cut off, so point E is the output for Tr1. Negative half-cycles of the input reverse bias Tr1 and cut if off but forward bias Tr2. Tr2

conducts and 'pulls' a series of negative half-cycles of amplified output current through the speaker, with E still the output point.

As a result, the two halves of the input are amplified by different transistors, but the output from both is fed to the speaker, which is the emitter 'load' for both.

(b) Crossover distortion. In practice, crossover distortion occurs because there is a 'dead zone' in the output

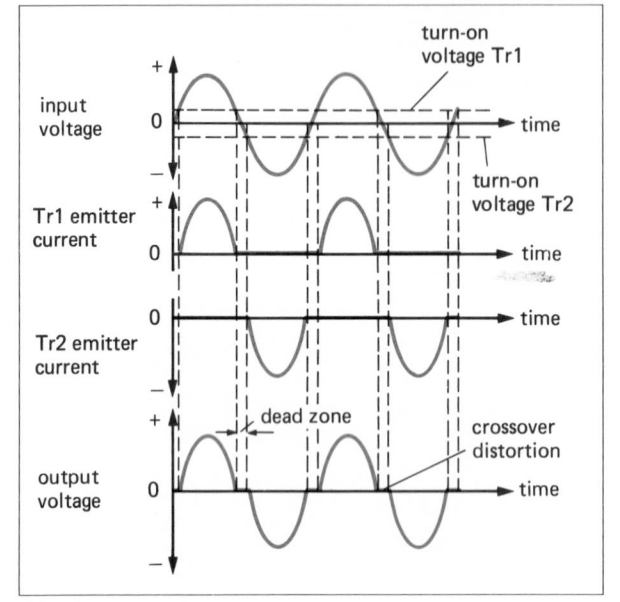

Fig. 41.4

waveform, as shown in Fig. 41.4. This is due to each transistor not turning on until the input exceeds 0.6 V or so. It can be eliminated by applying negative feedback to an op amp feeding the input to the push-pull output stage as in Fig. 41.5.

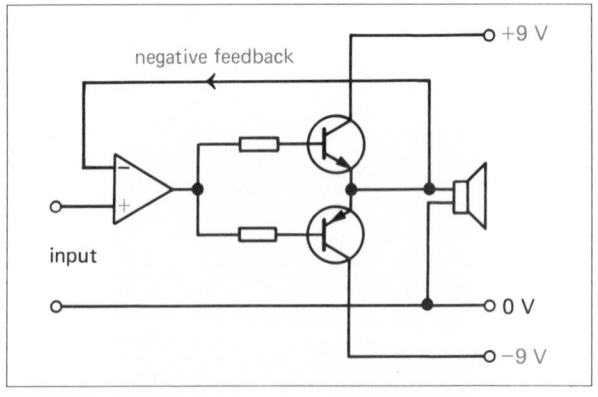

Fig. 41.5

(c) Heat sinks. When large currents are carried by the transistors in a power amplifier, they must have heat sinks (Chapter 13, Fig. 13.10.*b*) to get rid of the resulting waste heat.

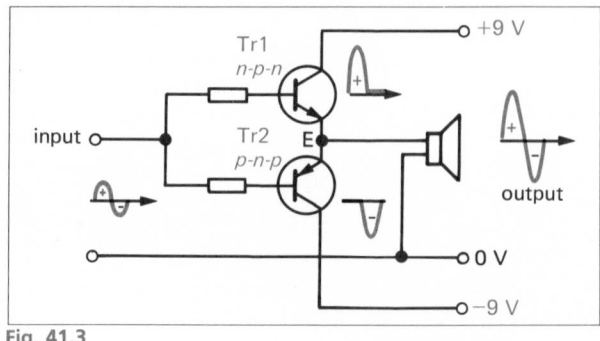

Fig. 41.3

◆ Loudspeaker systems

(a) Woofers and tweeters. More than one loud-speaker is needed to handle the full range of audio frequencies efficiently; in practice there are often two or three in the same cabinet. A large one, the *woofer*, deals with low (bass) frequencies, while a small one, the *tweeter*, handles high (treble) frequencies. Middle frequencies may also be catered for by a third speaker.

(b) Crossover circuit. The correct range of frequencies is fed to each speaker from the power amplifier by a crossover circuit. This may consist of two *filters* connected as in Fig. 41.6.

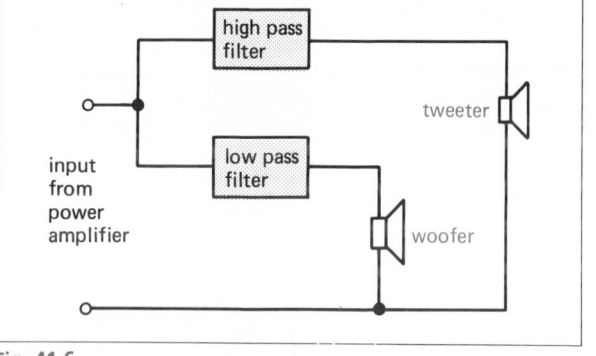

Fig. 41.6

The *high pass* one passes high frequencies and blocks low frequencies, while the *low pass* one does the opposite. A common crossover frequency is 3 kHz, i.e. frequencies above this go mostly to the tweeter, those below mostly to the woofer. Typical output voltage–frequency graphs for both types of filter are given

in Fig. 41.7*a*,*b*. Filters are circuits containing resistors and capacitors.

In the basic low pass filter of Fig. 41.7*c*, high frequencies in the input are short-circuited by *C* and do not reach the output. (*R* and *C* act as a potential divider across the input with *C* offering a much lower impedance to high frequencies than to low ones and so there is very little high frequency voltage across *C*, i.e. in the output.)

In the basic high pass filter of Fig. 41.7*d*, *C* blocks low frequencies but allows high frequencies to pass to the output.

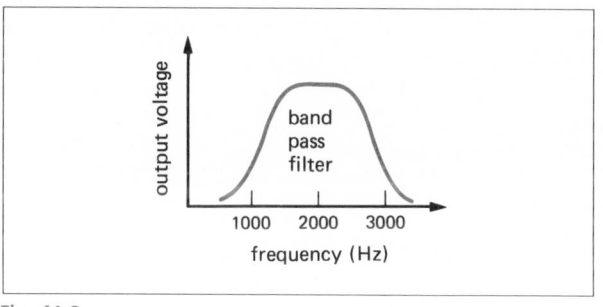

Fig. 41.8

For a middle frequency speaker a *band pass* filter would be used. It blocks all frequencies except those between certain values and has an output voltage–frequency graph like that in Fig. 41.8.

◇ Questions

Q1
Why is a.c. in the frequency range 20 Hz to 20 kHz called *audio frequency*?

Q2
In an audio system what is the function of
(a) the input transducer,
(b) the preamplifier,
(c) the volume control,
(d) the power amplifier,
(e) the loudspeaker?

Q3
(a) Why should the output impedance of a power amplifier be low (e.g. 8 Ω)?
(b) Name a circuit which can be used as a power amplifier.
(c) What kind of distortion does it cause in the output?
(d) How can the distortion in **(c)** be eliminated?

Q4
(a) What is **(i)** a woofer, **(ii)** a tweeter?
(b) What is the function of a crossover circuit?
(c) Name the components of a crossover circuit.

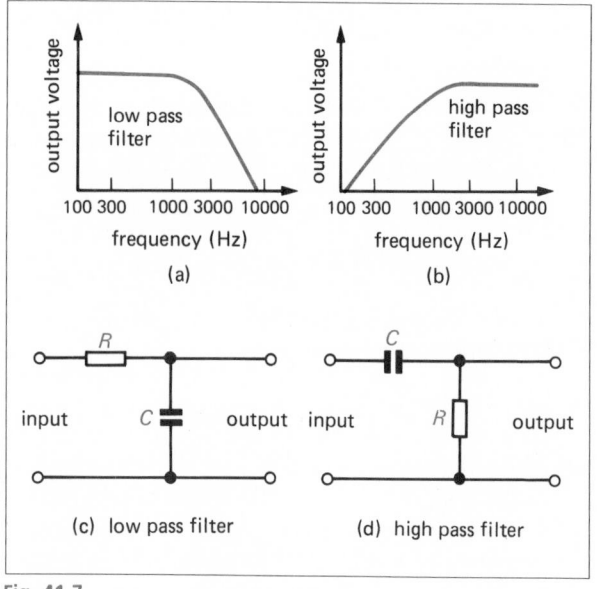

Fig. 41.7

42 Radio

◆ Radio waves

Radio waves belong to the family of electromagnetic waves that includes light, X-rays, ultraviolet and infrared. All these waves travel in space at a speed of 300 million metres per second, i.e. 3×10^8 m/s.

Like other waves, radio waves are classified according to either their *wavelength* or to their *frequency*; if one is high, the other is low. The frequencies extend from about 30 kHz upwards and are grouped in bands as in the table below, which also gives, for each band, a typical wavelength and some uses.

Frequency band	Typical wavelength	Some uses
Low (LF) 30 kHz–300 kHz	Long 1500 m	Long wave radio and communication over large distances
Medium (MF) 300 kHz–3 MHz	Medium 300 m	Medium wave local and distant radio
High (HF) 3 MHz–30 MHz	Short 30 m	Short wave radio and communication, amateur and CB radio
Very high (VHF) 30 MHz–300 MHz	Very short 3 m	FM radio, police, emergency services
Ultrahigh (UHF) 300 MHz–3 GHz	Ultra short 30 cm	TV (bands 4, 5)
Super high (SHF) Above 3 GHz	Microwaves 3 cm	Radar, communication satellites, telephone and TV links

(1 GHz = 1000 MHz)

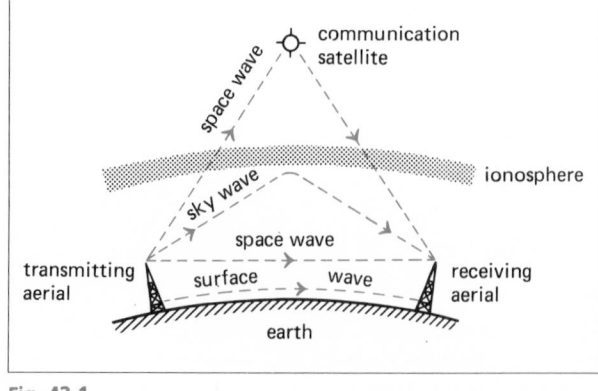

Fig. 42.1

Radio waves can travel in one or more different ways, Fig. 42.1. *Surface waves* follow the earth's surface and have a limited range, being greatest (1500 km) for long waves but much less for VHF. *Sky waves* are bounced back from the ionosphere and are used in long-distance communication by long, medium and short waves. *Space waves* travel in straight lines and can penetrate the ionosphere. VHF, UHF and microwaves travel in this way.

The ionosphere consists of layers of air molecules stretching from about 80 km above the earth to 500 km, which have become positively charged due to the removal of electrons by ultraviolet radiation from the sun.

◆ Radio transmitter

(a) Aerials. A transmitting aerial radiates radio waves. Any conductor can act as an aerial but proper design (a subject in itself) is necessary for maximum efficiency.

When a.c. from a transmitter flows in a transmitting aerial, radio waves of the same frequency f as the a.c. are emitted *if the length of the aerial is comparable with the wavelength* λ *of the waves*. For example, if

$f = 100$ MHz then $\lambda = 3$ m

but if

$f = 1$ kHz then $\lambda = 300\,000$ m.

Therefore if aerials are not to be too long, they must be supplied with radio frequency (RF) currents from the transmitter.

(b) Modulation. Speech and music generate audio frequency (AF) currents and so some way of combining AF with RF is required if they are to be sent over a distance. The transmission of sound by radio therefore involves modifying or *modulating* RF so that it 'carries' the AF information, as we saw earlier (Chapter 39).

Amplitude modulation (AM) is used in medium, long and short wave broadcasting. A block diagram showing the sub-systems of an AM transmitter is given in Fig. 42.2.

(c) Block diagram. The *oscillator* produces a sine wave RF current of constant amplitude, called the RF *carrier*, which is fed to the *mixer* or *modulator*. In the modulator the amplitude of the RF carrier is varied at the frequency of the AF signal from the *microphone* and the *AF* *amplifier*. The resulting amplitude modulated RF carrier (which has the 'shape' of the AF) is amplified by the *RF power amplifier* before it is fed to the *aerial*.

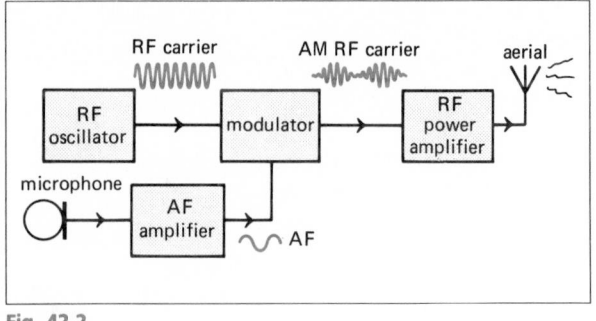

Fig. 42.2

(d) Bandwidth. The modulated signal consists of the carrier and the upper and lower sidebands (Chapter 39). The bandwidth it requires to transmit AFs up to 5 kHz is 10 kHz. In practice, in the medium waveband, which extends from about 500 kHz to 1.5 MHz, 'space' is limited if interference between stations is to be avoided and the bandwidth is restricted to 9 kHz.

◆ Simple radio receivers

(a) Block diagram. The various sub-systems of a simple AM receiver are shown in the block diagram of Fig. 42.3.

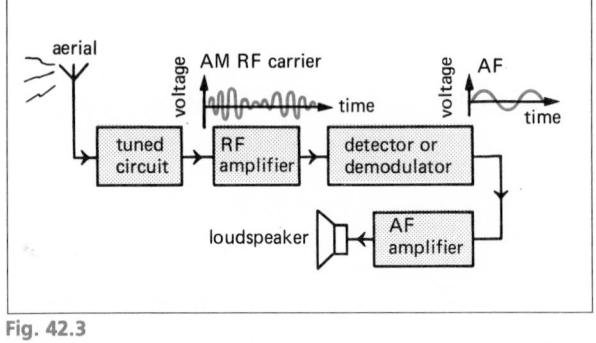

Fig. 42.3

The *aerial* picks up radio waves and converts them into alternating currents. The *tuned circuit* selects the current with the desired frequency from those received from the aerial and changes it into an alternating voltage which is amplified by the *RF amplifier*. The *detector* or *demodulator* recovers the AF signal which was modulated onto the RF carrier. After amplification by the *AF amplifier*, the audio signal is fed to the *loudspeaker* which uses it to produce sound.

Voltage–time graphs for the AM carrier and the de-modulated AF are also shown in Fig. 42.3.

ICs which are almost complete radio receivers in themselves are now available. For example the ZN414Z is a three-lead device which looks like a transistor and acts as an RF amplifier and detector. It contains 10 transistors, 15 resistors and 4 capacitors and its output can drive a sensitive earpiece. The ZN416E is a similar device.

(b) Basic action and circuit, Fig. 42.4. The inductor L (a coil of wire), in parallel with the variable capacitor C, is the *tuned circuit*. It responds most strongly to a.c. signals of one particular frequency, called its *resonant frequency*, which depends on the values of L and C. By varying C (or L or both), the resonant frequency can be changed and a different radio station tuned.

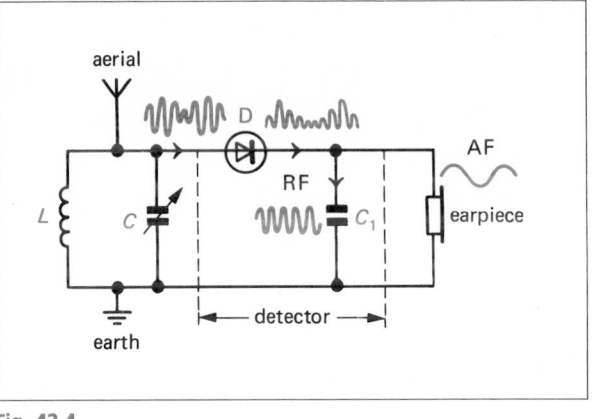

Fig. 42.4

Detection is brought about by the diode D and capacitor C_1. D rectifies the AM RF current received from the tuned circuit by 'removing' the negative half-cycles. The rectified pulses contain the now unwanted RF and the wanted AF. The small capacitor C_1 in parallel with the earpiece filters off the RF part to earth (because of the low impedance of C_1 at high frequencies). The AF (because of its much lower frequency) finds it easier to go through the earpiece where it is used to produce the original sound.

This circuit can be used to receive strong radio signals if a good aerial and earth connection are used and if the earpiece is sensitive.

◆ Superheterodyne receiver

The 'superhet' is used in commercial AM radios because of its superior performance. Fig. 42.5 shows a typical block diagram.

(a) Action. The AM RF signal of frequency f_c from the wanted station is selected by the *RF tuned circuit* and fed to the *mixer* along with an RF signal from the *local oscillator* which has a higher frequency f_o. The output

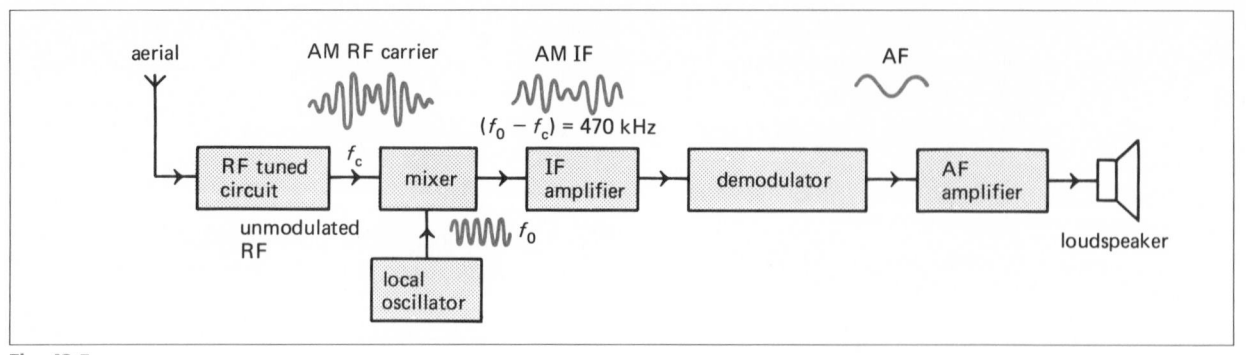

Fig. 42.5

from the mixer contains an RF oscillation of frequency $(f_0 - f_c)$, called the *intermediate frequency* (IF), having the AF modulation. Whatever the value of f_c, f_0 is always greater than it by the same amount, i.e. the IF $= f_0 - f_c$. In an AM radio this is usually 470 kHz.

The IF amplifiers are, in effect, RF amplifiers which always have to amplify AM signals of the same frequency (470 kHz). The *demodulator* and *AF amplifier* act as in a simple receiver.

(b) Advantages. As a result of changing every incoming RF signal to one lower, fixed frequency (the IF), the superhet is more
(i) *sensitive*, i.e. it picks up weaker signals,
(ii) *selective*, i.e. it tunes stations having frequencies that are near each other without getting interference.

◆ Frequency modulated (FM) radio

FM is used in VHF radio.

An FM transmitter is similar to an AM one but the *frequency* of the RF carrier is changed by the AF signal (see Chapter 39, Fig. 39.7).

Each AF modulating frequency produces a large number of side frequencies (not two as in AM) but their amplitudes decrease the more they differ from the carrier. In theory therefore, the bandwidth of an FM system should be very wide, but in practice the 'outside' frequencies can be omitted without introducing noticeable distortion.

A 250 kHz bandwidth is readily accommodated in the VHF radio broadcasting band (covering 88 MHz to 97.6 MHz, i.e. 9.6 MHz or about 40 bandwidths). This allows the full range of audio frequencies needed for 'high quality' music.

A further advantage of FM is that, compared with AM, it is relatively free from interference which makes for quiet (i.e. 'noise' free) reception.

◆ Use of radio

Apart from its use in broadcasting news, in advertising and providing entertainment to mass audiences, where one-way communication takes place, radio is important in other spheres of life. These include the police, fire, ambulance and rescue services where it may be necessary for two-way communication to be established between headquarters and those at the scene of the emergency. In such cases, radio allows a certain amount of mobility to the users. A disadvantage, however, may be the lack of security of the information transmitted, and for long-distance communication it can be unreliable under adverse weather conditions.

◇ Questions

Q1
(a) Name the *six* frequency bands for radio waves and state their frequency ranges.
(b) State the *three* ways in which radio waves can travel.

Q2
(a) What happens in the process of modulation?
(b) Why is modulation necessary?
(c) What type of modulation is represented by the voltage–time graph in **(i)** Fig. 42.6a, **(ii)** Fig. 42.6b?
(d) What happens in the process of demodulation?

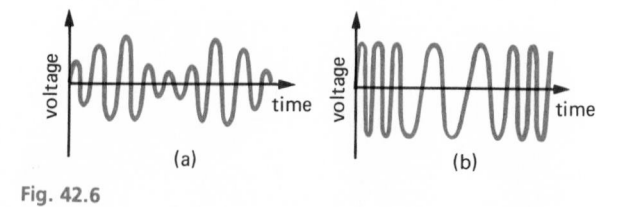

Fig. 42.6

Q3

(a) The block diagram in Fig. 42.7 is a simple radio receiver but it is not labelled. By choosing from the following terms, identify each block in the system:

microphone, loudspeaker, astable, AF amplifier, resistor, tuned circuit, op amp, RF amplifier, aerial, potentiometer, demodulator.

(b) State the function of each of the blocks you have chosen.

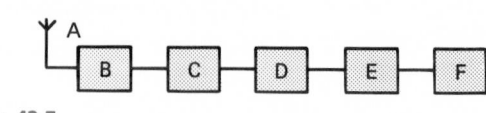

Fig. 42.7

Q4

State *two* advantages which FM has over AM for radio broadcasting.

Q5

Give *three* examples of two-way radio communication being useful in the emergency services.

43 Television

The principles involved in the transmission and reception of pictures are the same as those for sound.

◆ Black-and-white TV camera

A black-and-white (monochrome) TV camera changes light into electrical signals.

(a) Action. The *plumbicon* tube, shown simplified in Fig. 43.1, consists of an electron gun, which emits a narrow beam of electrons, and a target of photoconductive material (lead monoxide) on which a lens system focuses an optical image.

The target behaves as if the resistance between any point on its back surface and a transparent aluminium film at the front depends on the brightness of the image at the point. The brighter it is, the lower is the resistance. The electron beam is made to scan across the target and the resulting beam current (i.e. the electron flow in the circuit consisting of the beam, the target, the load resistor R, the power supply and the gun) varies with the resistance at the spot where it hits the target. The beam current thus follows the brightness of the image and R turns its variations into identical variations of voltage shown in Fig. 43.2, for subsequent transmission as the video signal.

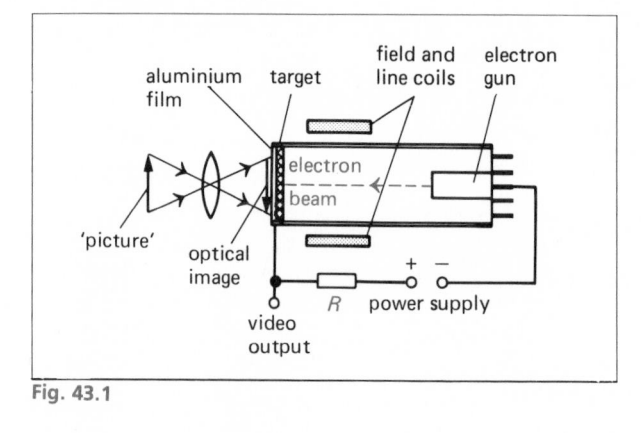

Fig. 43.1

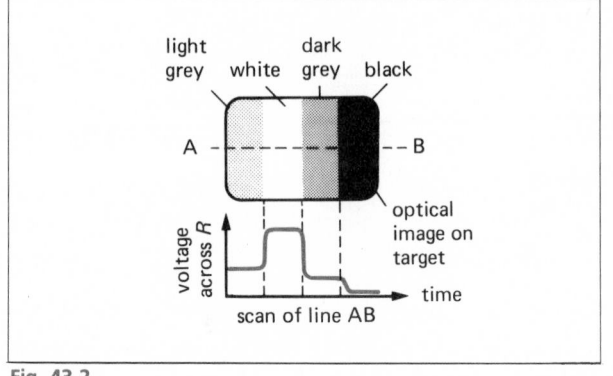

Fig. 43.2

(b) Scanning. The scanning of the target by the electron beam is similar to the way we read a page of print, i.e. from left to right and top to bottom. In effect the picture is changed into a set of parallel lines, called a *raster*.

Two systems are needed to deflect the beam horizontally and vertically. The one which moves it steadily from left to right and makes it 'flyback' rapidly, ready for the next line, is the *line scan*. The other, the *field scan*, operates simultaneously and draws the beam at a much slower rate down to the bottom of the target and then restores it suddenly to the top. Magnetic deflection is used in which ramp generators (Chapter 37) act as *time bases* and generate currents with saw-tooth waveforms, Fig. 43.3*a*, at the line and field frequencies. These are passed through two pairs of coils mounted round the camera tube.

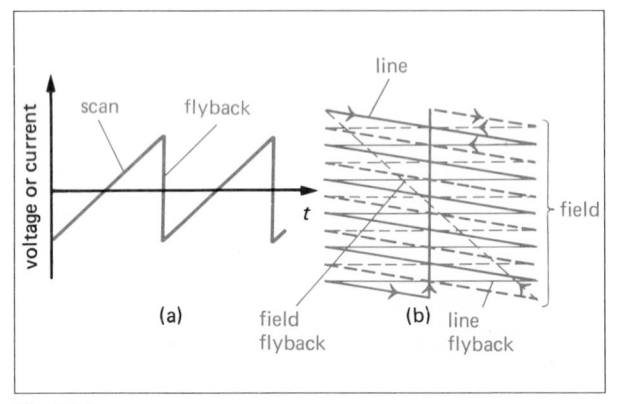

Fig. 43.3

For the video signal to produce an acceptable picture at the receiver, the raster must have at least 500 scanning lines (or it will seem 'grainy') and the total scan should occur at least 40 times a second (or the impression of continuity between successive scans due to persistence of vision of the eye will cause 'flicker'). The European TV system has 625 lines and a scan rate of 50 Hz.

It can be shown that for such a system, the video signal would need a bandwidth of about 11 MHz, owing to the large amount of information that has to be gathered in a short time. This high value would make extreme demands on circuit design and for a broadcasting system would require too much radio wave 'space'.

However, it can be halved by using *interlaced* scanning in which the beam scans alternate lines, producing half a picture (312.5 lines) every 1/50 s, and then returns to scan the intervening lines, Fig. 43.3*b*. The complete 625 lines or *frame* is formed in 1/25 s, a time well inside that allowed by persistence of vision to prevent 'flicker'.

◆ Transmission of signals

(a) Synchronization. To ensure that the scanning of a particular line and field starts at the same time in the TV receiver as in the camera, synchronizing pulses are also sent. These are added to the video signal during the flyback times when the beam is blanked out. The field pulses are longer and less frequent than the line pulses (50 Hz compared with $312.5 \times 50 = 15\,625$ Hz). Fig. 43.4 shows a simplified video waveform with line and field sync. pulses.

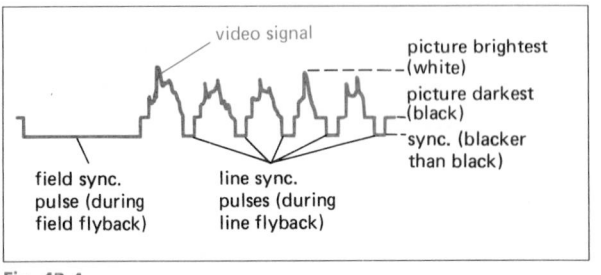

Fig. 43.4

(b) Bandwidth. In broadcast television the video signal is transmitted by amplitude modulation of a carrier in the UHF band. Since the video signal has a bandwidth of 5.5 MHz, the bandwidth required for the transmission would be at least 11 MHz owing to the two sidebands on either side of the carrier.

In practice a satisfactory picture is received if only one sideband and a part (a vestige) of the other is transmitted. This is called *vestigial sideband* transmission. The part used contains the lowest modulating frequencies closest to the carrier frequency, for it is the video information they carry that is most essential. The video signal is therefore given 5.5 MHz for one sideband and 1.25 MHz for the other, Fig. 43.5.

The accompanying audio signal is frequency modulated on another carrier, spaced 6 MHz away from the video carrier. The audio carrier bandwidth is about 250 kHz and is adequate for good quality FM sound. The complete video and sound signal lies within an 8 MHz wide channel.

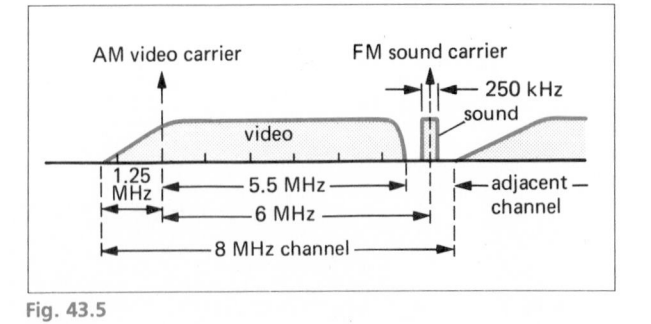

Fig. 43.5

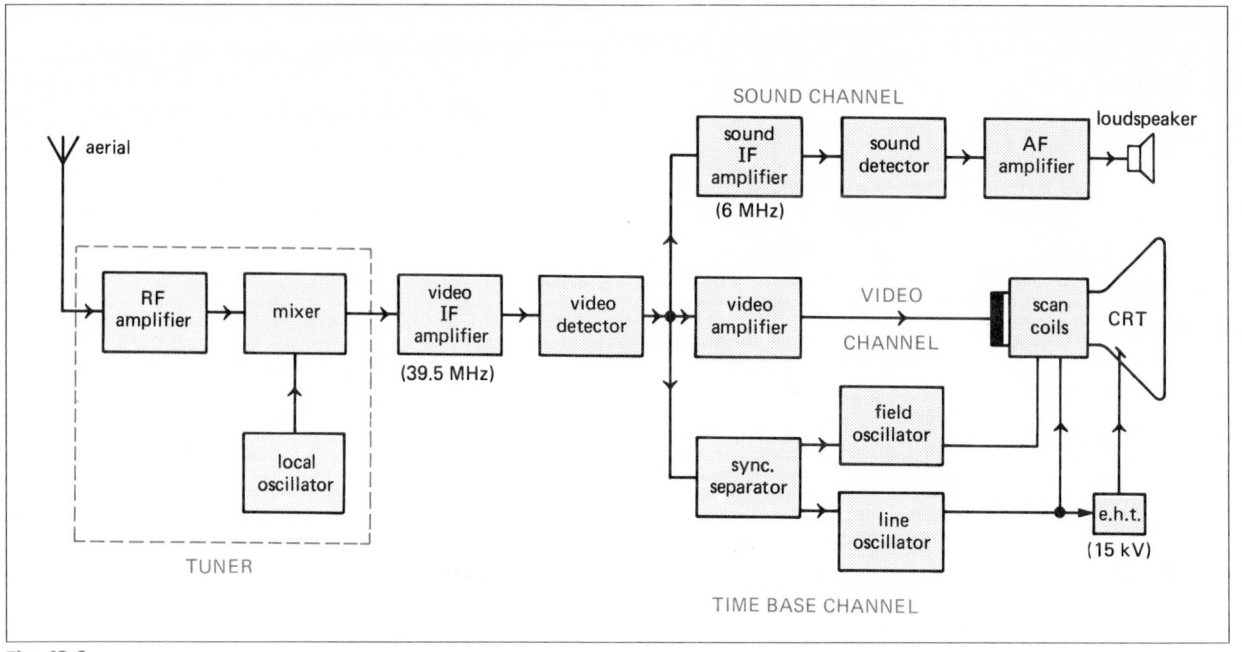

Fig. 43.6

◆ Black-and-white TV receiver

In a black-and-white TV receiver, the incoming video signal controls the number of electrons travelling from the electron gun of a cathode ray tube to its screen. The greater the number, the brighter the picture produced by interlaced scanning as in the camera.

The block diagram in Fig. 43.6. for a broadcast receiver shows that early stages are similar to those in a radio superhet, but bandwidths and frequencies are higher (e.g. the IF is 39.5. MHz). The later stages have to demodulate the video and audio signals as well as separate them from each other and from the line and sync. pulses.

Separation occurs at the output of the *video detector*. There, the now demodulated AM video signal is amplified by the *video amplifier* and applied to the CRT to control the electron beam. The still-modulated FM sound signal, having been mixed in the *video detector* with the video signal to produce a sound IF of 6 MHz (i.e. the frequency difference between the sound and video carriers, shown in Fig. 43.5), is fed into the sound channel where, after amplification and FM detection, it drives the *loudspeaker*.

The mixed sync. pulses are processed in the time base channel by the *sync. separator* which produces two sets of different pulses at its two outputs. One set is derived from the line pulses and triggers the *line oscillator*. The other set is obtained from the field pulses and synchronizes the *field oscillator*. The oscillators produce the

deflecting sawtooth waveforms for the *scan coils*. The *line oscillator* also generates the extra high voltage or tension (e.h.t.) of about 15 kV required by the *CRT*.

◆ Colour TV

(a) Camera. Colour TV uses the fact that any other colour of light can be obtained by mixing the three primary colours (for light) of red, green and blue in the correct proportions. For example, all three together give white light; red and green give yellow light.

The principles of transmission (and reception) are similar to those for black-and-white TV but the circuits are more complex. A practical requirement is that the colour signal must produce a black-and-white picture on a monochrome receiver; this is called *compatibility*. Therefore in a broadcast system the bandwidth must not exceed 8 MHz despite the extra information to be carried.

A monochrome picture has only brightness or *luminance* variations ranging from black through grey to white. In a colour picture there are also variations of colour or *chrominance*. The signals for both are combined without affecting each other or requiring extra bandwidth.

In a colour TV camera, three plumbicon tubes are required, each viewing the picture through a different primary colour filter. The 'red', 'green' and 'blue' signals so obtained provide the chrominance information, which is modulated by encoding circuits on a carrier. If added together correctly, they give the luminance as well, Fig. 43.7.

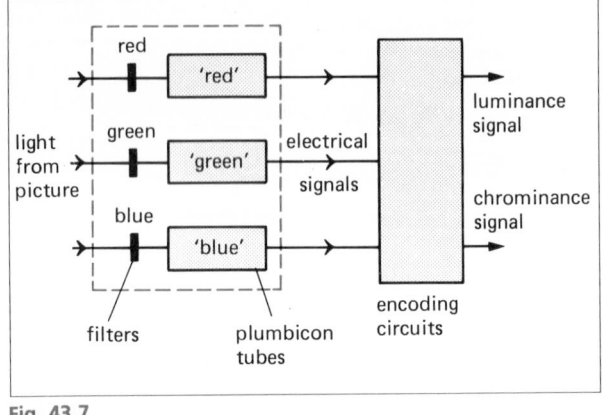

Fig. 43.7

(b) Receiver. In a colour TV receiver, decoding circuits are needed to convert the luminance and chrominance signals back into 'red', 'green' and 'blue' signals and a special CRT is required for the display.

One common type of display is the *shadow mask tube* which has three electron guns, each producing an electron beam controlled by one of the primary colour signals. The principle of its operation is shown in Fig. 43.8. The inside of the screen is coated with many thousands of tiny dots of red, green and blue phosphors, arranged in triangles containing a dot of each colour. Between the guns and the screen is the shadow mask consisting of a metal sheet with about half a million holes (for a 26 inch diagonal tube).

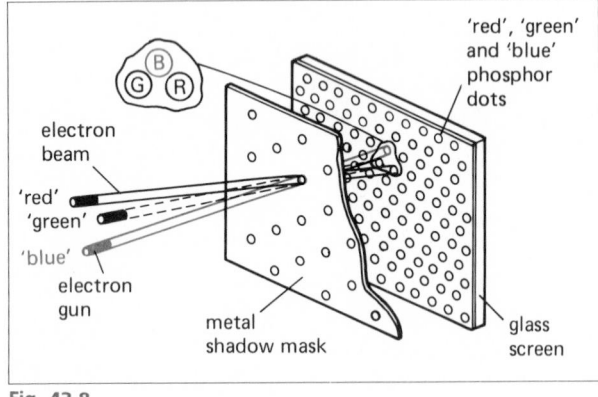

Fig. 43.8

As the three electron beams scan the screen under the action of the same deflection coils, the shadow mask ensures that each beam strikes only dots of one phosphor, e.g. electrons from the 'red' gun strike only red dots. When a particular triangle of dots is struck, it may be that the red and green electron beams are

intense but not so the blue. In this case the triangle would emit red and green light strongly and so appear yellowish. The triangles of dots are excited in turn and since the dots are so small and the scanning so fast, we see a continuous colour picture.

The holes in the mask occupy only 15 per cent of the total mask area; 85 per cent of the electrons emitted by the three guns are stopped by the mask. The beam current in a colour tube therefore has to be much greater than in a monochrome tube for a similar picture brightness. Also, the voltage required by the tube is greater, about 25 kV.

◆ Teletext

This is a system which, aided by digital techniques, displays on the screen of a modified domestic TV receiver, up-to-the-minute facts and figures on news, weather, sport, travel, entertainment and many other topics. It is transmitted along with ordinary broadcast TV signals, being called CEEFAX ('see facts') by the BBC and ORACLE by ITV.

During scanning, at the end of each field (i.e. 312.5 lines), the electron beam has to return to the top of the screen. Some TV lines have to be left to allow time for this and it is on two or three of these previously blank lines in each field (i.e. four or six per frame of 625 lines) that teletext signals are transmitted in digital form.

One line can carry enough digital signals for a row of up to 40 characters in a teletext page. Each page can have up to 24 rows and takes about ¼ second (i.e. $12 \times 1/50\,\text{s}$) to transmit. The pages are sent one after the other until, after about 25 seconds, a complete magazine of 400 pages has been transmitted before the whole process starts again.

The teletext decoder in the TV receiver picks out the page you asked for (by pressing numbered switches on the remote control keypad) and stores it in a memory. It then translates the digital signals into the sharp, brightly coloured words, figures and symbols that are displayed a page at a time on the screen.

◆ Cable television (CATV)

In cable television, pictures are sent to the homes of viewers via a cable, as distinct from over-the-air transmissions picked up by roof-top aerials.

In the *star distrubution system*, Fig. 43.9, every home is linked directly to a local cable station from which many channels could be available to choose from. Each home

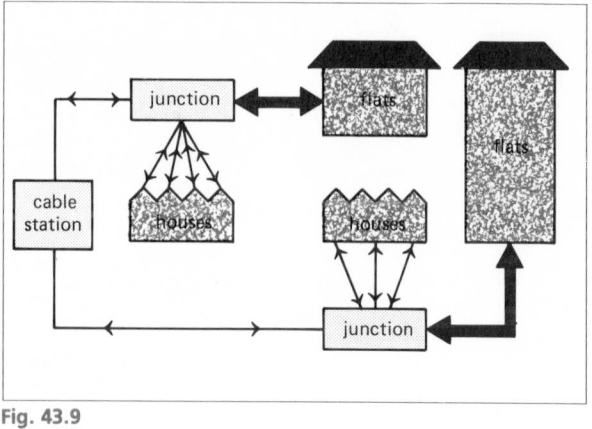

Fig. 43.9

Fig. 43.10

has its own junction box and control which would enable the subscriber to send information back to the cable station. This is called an *interactive system* and opens the way for the television set to provide additional facilities such as:

(i) shopping by ordering directly from home after the shop shelves have been viewed on the TV screen,

(ii) home banking in which bank accounts could be debited automatically at the push of a button,

(iii) two-way teaching.

(iv) booking holidays via the 'box' at home, after browsing through travel brochures seen on it,

(v) advertising articles for sale electronically,

(vi) taking public opinion poll samples very quickly and even replacing the polling booth by the TV set,

(vii) providing a burglar or fire alarm system if linked to detection sensors in the home and the police or fire station,

(viii) reading of domestic meters (e.g. electricity) remotely,

(ix) viewing TV programmes beamed live via satellites from across the world.

These developments form the basis of what is known as the *information* or *wired society*.

Cable systems using modern coaxial cables or optical fibres can carry simultaneously several TV channels, ordinary telephone links and other telecommunication services because of their wide bandwidth. The cables are laid in ducts (pipes) under the street. For economic reasons, CATV is likely to develop only in major population centres.

◆ Satellite television

British television viewers saw their first live broadcast from America on 11 June 1962. The microwave signals were beamed from a large steerable dish aerial on the east coast of the USA to the satellite *Telstar* which amplified and retransmitted them back down to a 26 m diameter dish at Goonhilly Downs earth station in Cornwall, Fig. 43.10. *Telstar* orbited the earth in 2½ hours at a height varying from 320 to 480 km (200 to 300 miles) but signals were received for only about 20 minutes when it could be 'seen' by the aerials on both sides of the Atlantic.

(a) Geostationary (synchronous) satellites. Today, the idea proposed by the space science writer Arthur C. Clarke in 1945 has been realized because rockets are powerful enough to place communication satellites in geostationary orbit 36 000 km (22 500 miles) above the equator where they circle the earth in 24 hours and appear at rest.

Early Bird, launched in 1965 over the Atlantic, was the first geostationary satellite to give round-the-clock use. At present, throughout the world there are over 200 earth stations like the one at Goonhilly (in the UK there is a second one at Madley, near Hereford and a third in London which is the world's first urban earth station, providing satellite distribution facilities for TV programmes to cable systems in the UK and Europe and to viewers with their own receiving equipment). The system is managed by the 114-nation International Telecommunications Satellite Organization (INTELSAT). Satellites are launched for different countries either by

Fig. 43.11

UHF. Existing terrestrial TV transmissions are AM but satellite transmitters use FM to carry the programme (because of the limited power available). The conversion circuits in the receiver must therefore change the signal from FM to AM. Finally, as the sound signals accompanying the TV signals are digitally encoded, conversion to analogue form is also required.

◆ Other uses of television

While the broadcasting of news, commercial advertising and the provision of entertainment to mass audiences, as in radio, are the uses of television which have the greatest public impact, it has other applications. These include

(i) education through programmes for schools; documentary films on travel and wild life; coverage of recent developments in science, technology and medicine; Open University lectures,

(ii) monitoring and surveillance in connection with closed circuit television (CCTV) security systems in banks, shops, factories, prisons and of crowds at football matches.

the American *Space Shuttle* or by the European rocket *Ariane*. The first INTELSAT V satellite, shown in Fig. 43.11 with its power-generating solar panels, was launched into geostationary orbit in 1980 with an expected life of seven years. It can handle two TV channels plus 12 000 telephone circuits using microwave frequencies of 4, 6, 11 and 14 GHz. The new generation of satellites, INTELSAT VI (launch 1989) has even greater capacity.

(b) Direct broadcasting by satellite (DBS). This development will enable homes in any part of a country to become low-cost 'earth stations' and receive TV programmes from the national geostationary satellite if they have a small roof-top dish aerial (0.9 m in diameter), pointing towards the satellite. In this way, one satellite, having had its programme beamed from an earth station, will give countrywide coverage. The dish will need to be steerable to obtain reception from the satellites of other countries although some overlap is likely. Alternatively the programmes might be received via cable from a cable station with dish aerials. .

To receive satellite signals on one of today's domestic TV receivers extra circuits are needed as well as a dish aerial. First a frequency converter in the base of the aerial has to convert the 12 GHz signals from the satellite down to around 1 GHz before they go indoors to the receiver. Here a second converter must reduce the frequency to

◇ Questions

Q1
Explain the following terms in connection with TV with the help of a diagram: line, field, raster, frame.

Q2
Name the *four* different kinds of signal that make up a colour TV signal.

Q3
In TV what type of modulation is used for **(a)** sound signals, **(b)** video signals?

Q4
What is the value of the video bandwidth in a TV signal?

Q5
How are colours reproduced on the screen of a colour TV receiver?

Q6
How does Teletext differ from Prestel?

44 Additional questions

◇ Core level

Q1
What are the consequences of portable telephones, connected by radio to the local telephone exchange, now being available?

Q2
The block diagram in Fig. 44.1 is for a record player system. The first block is a magnetic pick-up and the last is a loudspeaker.
(a) What are blocks X, Y and Z?
(b) What is the approximate output voltage from the magnetic pick-up?
(c) What is the approximate output power used to drive the loudspeaker?

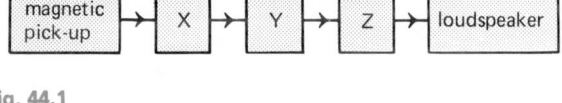

Fig. 44.1

Q3
The block diagram of a simple radio transmitter is shown in Fig. 44.2 but the sub-systems have been given letters not labels.

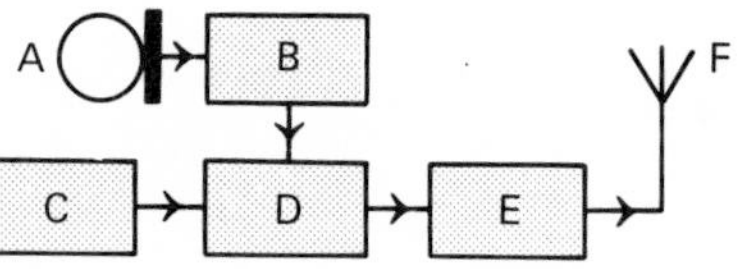

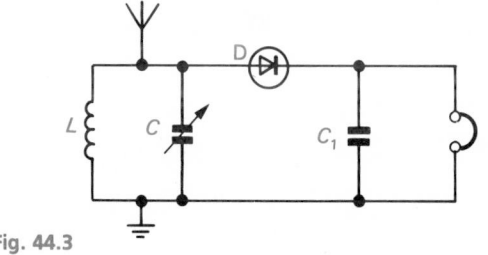

Fig. 44.2

(a) Identify each sub-system using the following terms:

modulator, AF amplifier, aerial, RF power amplifier, RF oscillator, microphone.

(b) State *one* reason why high frequencies are used as carrier waves.

Q4
In a simple radio receiver which part
(a) is the input transducer,
(b) is the output transducer,
(c) selects the required signal,
(d) separates AF from the modulated RF carrier?

◇ Further level

Q5
(a) What is a filter called which blocks **(i)** low frequencies, **(ii)** high frequencies, and **(iii)** all frequencies except those between certain limits?
(b) Draw the block diagram for the crossover circuit of an audio system which has to feed a woofer and a tweeter.

Q6
A circuit for a very simple diode radio receiver is shown in Fig. 44.3.
(a) Name the components L and C.
(b) What kind of circuit do L and C form?
(c) What is the function of that circuit?
(d) What is the function of D and C_1?

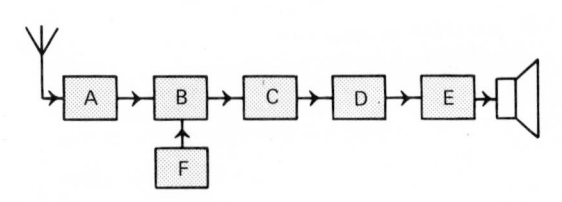

Fig. 44.3

Q7
The block diagram of a superheterodyne radio receiver is given in Fig. 44.4.
(a) Name each block.
(b) State and explain *two* advantages of this type of receiver.

Fig. 44.4

Q8
A television picture with 625 lines uses interlaced scanning in which half the lines are scanned every 1/50th of a second. What is **(a)** the line frequency, **(b)** the field frequency?

Q9
If a TV picture is made up of 350 000 dots (picture elements or pixels) and an eight-bit binary code is needed to describe their many different colours and brightness levels, how many bits per second must be sent when digital transmission is used? (*Note.* 25 complete pictures occur on the screen per second.)

Check list
Communication systems

After studying *Chapter 39: Information and electronics*, you should be able to

◊ state that information can be represented electrically by digital and analogue methods,

◊ state the relative merits of each method,

◊ explain the process of pulse code modulation for converting analogue to digital signals,

◊ draw the block diagram of a communication system,

◊ explain the processes of amplitude modulation and frequency modulation and draw voltage–time graphs for them,

◊ explain the term bandwidth and state for speech it is 300 Hz to 4 kHz, for hi-fi music it is 20 Hz to 20 kHz, and for television signals it is about 8 MHz, and

◊ state what is meant by multiplexing and explain how it is done by frequency division.

After studying *Chapter 40: Telephone system*, you should be able to

◊ describe the functions of the transmitter and receiver of a telephone handset,

◊ describe what a telephone exchange does,

◊ describe how telephone links may be made by copper cables, optical fibres, microwaves and communication satellites,

◊ state the advantages and disadvantages of copper cables and optical fibres,

◊ discuss the main uses of telephone services such as viewdata, telex and car telephone systems, and

◊ describe the use of a modem as a computer–telephone interface.

After studying *Chapter 41: Audio systems*, you should be able to

◊ draw the block diagram for an audio system containing an input transducer, a preamplifier, volume and tone controls, a power amplifier and an output transducer,

◊ state the functions of the various parts of an audio system,

◊ draw a block diagram for a hi-fi system consisting of a record player, a radio tuner, a tape cassette deck, an audio amplifier and loudspeaker,

◊ state that a power amplifier is a current-amplifying buffer which produces the power needed to drive a low impedance loudspeaker,

◊ recognize the circuit of a push-pull follower and state why it can be used as a power amplifier,

◊ explain, using graphs, what is meant by crossover distortion,

◊ state that crossover distortion can be eliminated by using negative feedback with an op amp feeding a push-pull follower,

◊ state that a crossover circuit uses high and low pass filters to supply a loudspeaker system and draw a circuit for one, and

◊ state what high, low and band pass filters do and sketch graphs of output voltage against frequency for them.

After studying *Chapter 42: Radio* **you should be able to**

◇ recall the grouping of radio waves into the various frequency bands,

◇ state the three different ways in which radio waves can travel,

◇ state that radio frequencies are radiated more efficiently from an aerial and are used as carrier waves,

◇ draw the block diagram of a simple radio transmitter and explain what each block does,

◇ draw the block diagram of a simple radio receiver,

◇ state that the function of **(a)** the aerial is to change radio waves into alternating currents, **(b)** the tuned circuit is to select the desired signal frequency, and **(c)** the demodulator or detector is to recover the audio frequency from the signal,

◇ sketch voltage–time graphs for **(a)** the AM carrier wave and **(b)** the demodulated audio signal,

◇ draw the block diagram of a superheterodyne receiver and explain how it works in terms of the sub-systems,

◇ state the advantages of the superheterodyne receiver over the simple radio receiver,

◇ state two advantages of FM over AM, and

◇ discuss uses of radio.

After studying *Chapter 43: Television*, **you should be able to**

◇ explain with the help of a suitably labelled raster pattern how a two-dimensional scene can be transmitted as a stream of information,

◇ state that a television signal contains a video signal, an audio signal, synchronizing signals and colour signals,

◇ state that the video bandwidth is 6.75 MHz and the audio bandwidth is 0.25 MHz,

◇ describe how all colours can be reproduced on the screen of a colour TV receiver from only three primary colours,

◇ outline how Teletext works and compare it with Prestel,

◇ discuss uses of television including developments in cable television relating to the information (or wired) society, and

◇ describe geostationary communication satellites and direct broadcasting.

Computers and microprocessors

45 Digital computers

◆ Computer building blocks

All computers, whatever their size and power, are basically similar. They contain the building blocks, called *hardware*, shown in Fig. 45.1.

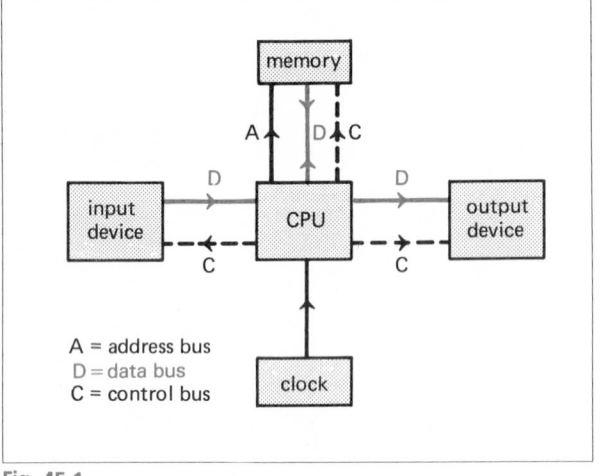

A = address bus
D = data bus
C = control bus

Fig. 45.1

(a) Central processing unit (CPU). The CPU performs, organizes and controls all the arithmetic and logical operations the computer can carry out. It is sometimes called the 'brain' of the computer and consists of a complex combination of logic gates. It interprets and obeys a sequence of instructions called the *program*.

(b) Memory. The memory stores **(i)** the *program* (called *software*), which tells the CPU what to do, and **(ii)** the *data* (coded information) processed during the running of the program.

A ROM or Read Only Memory IC is used to store the program because its contents have only to be 'read' by the CPU and are not lost when the computer is switched off. It is a permanent store (Chapter 32).

A RAM or Random Access Memory IC is used to store data. It not only allows data to be 'read' but can also have new data 'written' in. Its contents are lost when the computer is switched off, i.e. it is a temporary store (Chapter 32).

In addition to these *internal* semiconductor memories, there is usually provision for storage of programs and data not in current use in *external* or *back-up*, magnetic-type memories (Chapter 46).

(c) Clock. This generates timing pulses at a frequency of several megahertz to synchronize the computer's operations and ensure that they all occur at the correct time. It is usually a crystal-controlled oscillator.

(d) Input and output devices. The CPU accepts digital signals, in the form of four- or sixteen-bit words, from the input device, e.g. a keyboard, via its input port. After processing these are fed out via its output port to the output device, e.g. a visual display unit (VDU) or printer, Fig. 45.2, in a form that we can understand.

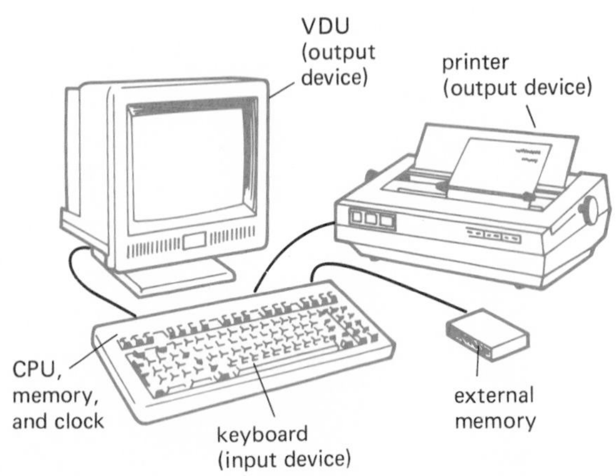

Fig. 45.2

(e) Buses. The CPU is connected to other parts by three sets of wires, called *buses* because they 'transport' information in the form of digital signals. The *one-way address bus* carries signals from the CPU which enable it to find data stored in a particular location of the memory. The *data bus* allows the *two-way* passage of data between the CPU and other parts. The *control bus* transmits timing and control signals which keep the various parts in step.

In diagrams each bus is represented by one line; in practice it may consist of 8, 16 or 32 separate lines. The arrows in Fig. 45.1 show the directions in which signals pass in the different buses.

To stop interference between parts that are not sending signals to a bus and parts that are, all parts have in their output a circuit called a *tristate gate*. Each gate is enabled or disabled by the control unit. When enabled, the output is 'high' or 'low' and pulses can be sent to the bus or received from it. When disabled, the output has such a high impedance that it is in effect disconnected. Then it can neither send nor receive signals and does not upset those passing along the bus between other parts.

◆ Types of computer

The power of a computer depends on its speed of working and the amount of data it can handle at the same time. There are three very broad classes.

(a) Mainframe computers. These are usually the most powerful and contain several large units, housed in an air-conditioned room and operated by a team of people. They are used by large organizations in, for example, data processing (see opposite).

(b) Minicomputers. These are made from smaller units, require only one or two operators and are used by, among others, government departments and hospitals for keeping records.

(c) Microcomputers. These are the personal computers found today in homes, schools and small offices. They have been made possible by the development of microprocessors (Chapter 49).

◆ Uses of computers

The impact on society of electronics in general was considered in Chapter 26. Here we shall discuss very briefly some of the vast number of ever-increasing applications of, in particular, computers.

(a) Data processing. This accounts for about three-quarters of all computer use today. It includes
(i) *payroll preparation* for firms with a large number of employees and requires a knowledge of the hours worked, rate of pay and income tax code,
(ii) *stock control* in large shops, supermarkets and factories so that an up-to-date record of present stock is kept and orders are placed for new stock when it runs low. Fig. 45.3 shows a bar code reader (Chapter 26) and data recorder in use for stock control in a supermarket. Subsequently the data recorder sends the data collected directly to a central computer (via a modem and a telephone link) where it is processed and an order sent to the stock depot or warehouse,

Fig. 45.3

(iii) *airline ticket booking* for travel agents giving details of flights and seats available,
(iv) *preparation of invoices* (bills) to accompany goods that will not be paid for until after delivery, and
(v) *production of gas and electricity bills* from quarterly meter readings.

(b) Process control (automation). Large-scale control applications using mainframe or minicomputers are common in process industries where raw materials are converted into useful goods. Some examples are
(i) steel making,
(ii) oil refining,
(iii) brick making,
(iv) chemical manufacture,
(v) paper making, and
(vi) float-glass production.

Hundreds of *sensors* are needed to control temperatures, pressures, flow-rates and other factors and *activators* (switches, valves, motors) are also needed to keep the process going. Apart from achieving automation, the aim is to maintain quality of the end-product with maximum economy and output. By monitoring the process at all stages, warnings can be given when things go wrong and if necessary, the operation can be shut down.

(c) Robotics. An industrial robot is like a human arm with several separately controllable joints. In small arms the joints are worked by *stepper motors*. These rotate through exact angles when an electrical pulse is received from a computer that has the required movement program stored, often in a ROM chip. The 'hand' at the end of the arm may be a claw-like device which grips things or a special tool such as a paint sprayer or a spot welder.

Sometimes the control program is worked out by monitoring and recording the actions of a human operator taking the robot arm through the job.

Larger arms use hydraulic or pneumatic systems to operate the joints. In some factories many assembly jobs are done entirely by robots, Fig. 45.4.

Fig. 45.4

(d) Computer integrated manufacture (CIM). At present this is being researched and hailed as the next great leap forward for industry. It is attempting to bring under computer control all the various stages of manufacturing, from ordering the materials, to making the product, to quality control and to issuing invoices.

Traditional technologies such as production, mechanical and electrical engineering will be married with computer and information technology in the hope of creating a single completely integrated operation. Warehousing, accounting procedures and management information will be computerized and by using robots, automation will be introduced into the actual manufacturing process itself.

The potential for progress through CIM appears to be enormous and many industrialized nations are now involved in the race to achieve what will undoubtedly be another technological revolution. It is a development that countries which rely on exporting manufactured goods for their livelihood cannot afford to ignore.

(e) Other users. These include
(i) *The police* for storing details of criminals, fingerprints, lists of missing persons and information about major crime investigations that would otherwise be stored in a card index system,
(ii) *Banks* for handling cheques, keeping customers' accounts, dealing with standing orders and direct debits, processing cash dispenser transactions and in the future for 'cashless shopping' or Electronic Funds Transfer at Point of Sale (EFT-POS) in which the cost of the shoppers' purchases is automatically deducted from their bank account and credited to the shop's account by a computer,
(iii) *Driver and Vehicle Licensing Centre* (DVLC), Swansea, for storing information (registration number, make, model, colour, engine size, owner's name and address) about every vehicle in the country,
(iv) *Newspaper publishers* to speed up the production (with fewer employees) of their papers and enable some or all of them to be transmitted as digital signals to regional centres for printing,
(v) *Scientists, engineers, geologists and weather forecasters* who can make models or simulations of real life situations using a computer and predict likely outcomes, e.g. engineers can predict how structures they design will behave without building prototypes so saving time and money and allowing other alternatives to be studied,
(vi) *Doctors and dentists* for storing patients' records,
(vii) *Solicitors and estate agents* for whom computers with word processing facilities can be more efficient than typewriters,
(viii) *Farmers* for planning the use of agricultural chemicals and recording production of meat, milk, cereals etc.

◆ Data protection and the public

In Britain most law-abiding adults have data stored about them in computers operated by
(i) their employer,
(ii) their bank,
(iii) a local authority,
(iv) the Department of Health and Social Security,
(v) the National Health Service,
(vi) the DVLC,
(vii) the Inland Revenue, and
(viii) a building society.

Many see this as an unwelcome and menacing intrusion of their pivate lives because the data may neither be accurate nor up to date and could be passed to others without their consent and be misused.

To help to allay public fears the government passed the *Data Protection Act* in 1984 and created a Data Protection Registrar
(i) to enforce the provisions of the Act which included 'obligations for data users', and
(ii) to set up a public register of all data users that was available to anyone who wished to know who held data about him or her.

Exemptions are allowed for matters involving some police work, tax collection and national security.

◇ Questions

Q1
(a) Name the unit in which the electronic processing occurs in a computer.
(b) What is the device called which changes physical quantities we can understand into electrical signals a computer can process? Give an example of one.
(c) Name the device that reverses the process described in **(b)**. Give an example.

Q2
(a) Name *two* types of memory used in computers.
(b) State *two* ways in which they differ.
(c) Which type stores **(i)** the program, **(ii)** the data?

Q3
Give *three* examples in each case of a computer being used for
(a) data processing, **(b)** process control.

Q4
Investigate *one* job in which the use of computers has changed the way people work and state
(a) what the job is,
(b) how it has changed,
(c) whether the number of people employed has been affected, and
(d) whether you think the changes have been for the better.

Q5
(a) Why are many people concerned about the increasing amount of personal data stored by computers?
(b) Explain briefly the ways in which the Data Protection Act attempts to allay these concerns.

Q6
There are many points of view about how computers will affect our working lives in the future.
(a) List the possible views of an *extreme optimist*.
(b) List the possible views of an *extreme pessimist*.

46 Computer peripherals

The input and output devices of a computer and the external memories are called *peripherals*.

◆ Input and output devices

These enable the computer to communicate with the outside world. Their form depends on the role of the computer. They are also called *terminals*.

(a) Visual display unit (VDU). In *data processing* the VDU is commonly used as both the input and output device. It consists of a keyboard on which data can be entered manually as the input and a television-type screen to display the input as well as the output. The keyboard is similar to that on a typewriter and contains the usual range of alphanumeric characters (A to Z and 0 to 9) as well as some 'command' keys for giving instructions to the computer. A typical screen has 25 lines of up to 80 characters and printing occurs at about 1000 characters per second. A VDU is shown in Fig. 26.1c.

(b) Teletype. This also has a keyboard as the input device but a printer for the output (and input) and looks like an electric typewriter. Data or instructions typed in at the keyboard are copied automatically on the printer for checking. They are then entered into the computer which takes over the printer to print the output at a relatively low speed, e.g. 10 to 50 characters per second.

A teletype is noisier than a VDU, requires more maintenance as well as paper and ink ribbons but a permanent record ('hard copy') is obtained.

(c) Graphics display unit (GDU). This third type of *interactive input–output* device also allows the user to have two-way communication with the computer. It looks like a VDU but can display pictures and diagrams. In one system the screen is divided up into an array of picture elements or *pixels* which can be switched on or off individually by the computer. A graphics display is built up by switching on the correct pixels and a *light pen*, which sends back signals to the computer, allows lines to be 'drawn' on the screen (see Fig. 26.1*f*).

The use of GDUs by engineers for computer aided design (CAD) enables them to produce plans in about one-third of the time required by pencil and paper methods. Fig. 46.1 shows a GDU being used for CAD in the car industry.

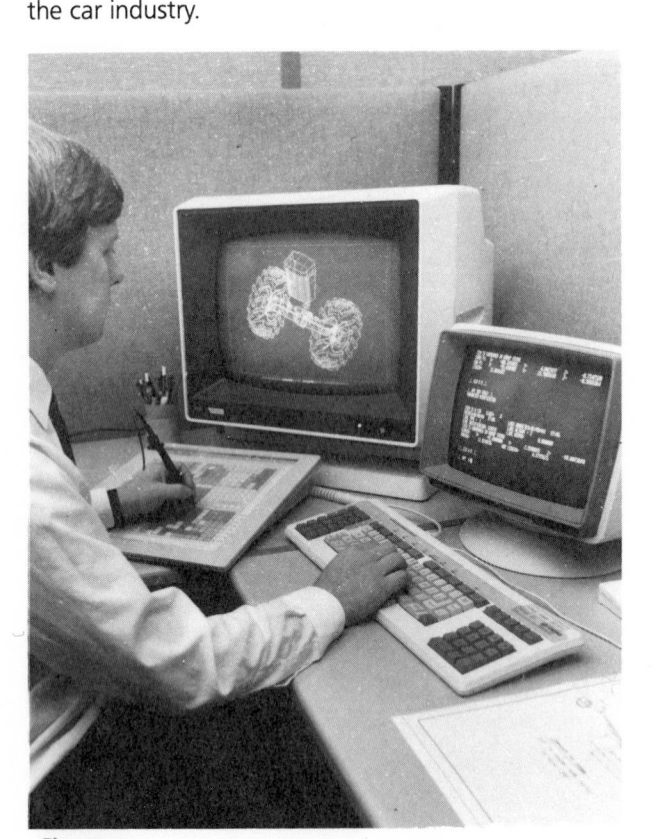

Fig. 46.1

(d) Optical readers. These are *input* devices used in data processing which read the data directly from the source of information.

The *bar code reader* (which may be a laser) used in supermarkets for stock control was described earlier (Chapters 26 and 45). It works on the principle that a narrow beam of light from the reader is reflected back from the pattern of black lines of various widths on the bar code, and changed into a series of electrical pulses. These enable the computer to identify the item.

An *optical mark reader* (OMR) works on the same principle and detects marks on specially prepared documents, e.g. answer sheets for multiple choice questions in an examination!

An *optical character reader* (OCR) reads letters and figures and is used in the preparation of gas and electricity bills.

Magnetic ink character readers (MICR) are used by banks for handling cheques. Some of the characters on cheques are printed in a special magnetic ink.

(e) Printers. When a printed output ('hard copy') is required from a computer, a printer is necessary. These are of three main types.
(i) *Dot-matrix* printers form letters and numbers from tiny dots, at speeds from 30 to 300 characters per second.
(ii) *Daisy-wheel* printers print one character after the other using a daisy-wheel mechanism (the characters are arranged on it like the petals of a daisy). They are slower but the printing is of a high quality.
(iii) *Laser printers* are now available which have the speed of a dot-matrix printer and the quality of a daisy-wheel printer, but they are expensive at present.

(f) Sensors and activators. In *industrial process control*, in science, in medicine and in other areas; inputs come from transducers or *sensors* that produce *analogue voltages*. These may represent continuously varying quantities such as temperature, light intensity, sound level, pressure, fluid flow rate or movement and must be changed to *digital signals* by an analogue-to-digital converter before being input to the computer (Chapter 47).

Outputs from the computer may be used to control *activators*, often electric motors, which in turn operate the switches, gears, valves, etc. that in turn control the machine or an industrial process. If an activator requires an *analogue voltage* to operate, the digital output from the computer has to be converted by a digital-to-analogue converter (Chapter 47).

◆ External memories

The *internal* memory of a computer is limited in size and the RAM type loses the material stored when the power is switched off. It is used mainly to give access to material that is to be processed immediately. For data and programs not in current use, an *external* back-up store is required with a large storage capacity. External memories generally use some form of magnetic storage

(a)

(b)

Fig. 46.2

on tapes and on 'floppy' or 'rigid' plastic discs coated with magnetic material.

Magnetic tape is the simplest and cheapest backing store, the data being stored serially as 1s and 0s by magnetizing small areas of the tape in either of two directions, Fig. 46.2*a*. Data transfer is slow. *'Floppy' discs*, Fig. 46.2*b*, are common for small computers; they have limited storage (less than 4 million bits) and resemble small audio records; data transfer is quite fast. They are inserted one at a time into a disc drive with a read and write device in a magnetic head. The high cost of a disc drive makes floppy disc storage about four times greater than cassette tape storage. *'Rigid' discs* are used in larger systems and several are stacked permanently on a spindle. They have capacities of up to 8000 million bits. Compared with semiconductor memories, access to such devices is slow, especially with tape, but storage is 'permanent', i.e. they are non-volatile.

Bubble memories offer storage of high capacity (greater than 1 million bits) and high bit-packing density with much faster access times than magnetic tapes or discs. Their action is complex but they are made of crystals in

which the bits are stored as minute magnetic regions, called 'bubbles', which can be moved around by a magnetic field. They are mounted in a d.i.l. package like an IC and at present are used mostly for computers in military aircraft and ships where discs would be affected by dust and gunfire.

In *optical disc* storage systems the data is stored in binary form in 'pits' in a disc with a transparent coating. It is 'read' by a laser beam reflected from the disc's surface, Fig. 46.3. A 'pit' reflects the beam back to the detector to give a '1'; the absence of a 'pit' results in no reflection and hence a '0'. The technology is the same as that used in compact discs for music. The spiral of 'pits' in the disc is 3 miles long.

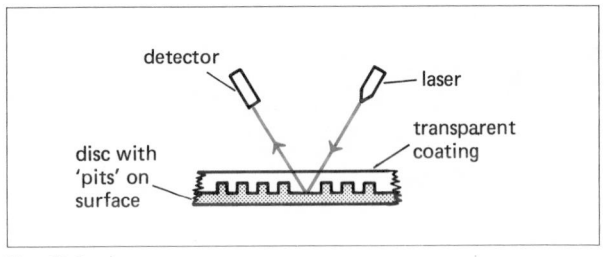

Fig. 46.3

Very large amounts of data can be stored on one disc, the same as 1500 floppy discs, but at present once stored it cannot be changed. In the future, optical discs might replace magnetic discs for large systems if current research is successful in producing read/write versions. At present WORM discs (write once, read many times) can be written on once.

◆ Interfacing chips

Data in its original form cannot usually be fed directly from an input device into the CPU. It must be presented in digital form. Similarly digital signals from the CPU may not be acceptable to an output device. Very often *interfacing chips* are required between the CPU and its peripherals. They may also have to compensate for differences of, for example, voltage levels (Chapter 24), operating speeds and codes.

(a) Analogue-to-digital (A/D) and digital-to-analogue (D/A) converters. The need for chips to perform these operations for certain input and output devices has been mentioned. Their action will be considered in the next chapter.

(b) Encoders and decoders. To interface a teletype or VDU to a computer, an encoder is required to produce a different pattern of binary bits, according to the ASCII code (Chapter 39), for every key operated. The action of one kind of decoder was considered earlier (Chapter 31).

(c) Modems. A computer connected to a telephone line requires a modem at each end to convert digital signals to and from analogue signals, since the line is designed to handle the latter only. A '1' is encoded as a low audio tone and a '0' as a high tone (Chapter 40).

(d) PIO and SIO chips. A peripheral may be a *serial* or a *parallel* device. Teletypes and VDUs are serial types which produce and must receive a string of bits following one after the other. A seven-segment LED display requires parallel interfacing so that the bits of the output are supplied together, i.e. in parallel.

Input and output devices are connected to the input and output *ports* of the computer which usually consist of eight lines, for handling eight-bit words. Interfacing a serial device therefore requires a serial input/output (SIO) chip; a parallel input/output (PIO) chip would enable a parallel device to communicate with a computer.

◇ Questions

Q1
(a) Name **(i)** the input device, and **(ii)** the output device in a teletype.
(b) Repeat **(a)** for a VDU.

Q2
State **(a)** *two* advantages, and **(b)** *two* disadvantages of a VDU compared with a teletype.

Q3
(a) Give one example of **(i)** a sensor and **(ii)** an activator.
(b) What are sensors and activators used for in industry?

Q4
(a) Why does a computer require an external memory?
(b) Name *three* types of external memory.
(c) Compare *two* microcomputer external storage systems in respect of cost, data transfer rate, and time to locate data.

Q5
What is a modem and what is its function?

47 A/D and D/A converters

◆ Digital-to-analogue (D/A) conversion

There are many occasions when digital signals have to be converted to analogue ones. For example, a digital computer is often required to produce a graphical display on the screen of a VDU. This involves using a D/A converter to change the two-level digital output voltage from the computer into a continuously varying analogue voltage for the input to the CRT, so that it can deflect the electron beam and make it 'draw pictures' at high speed.

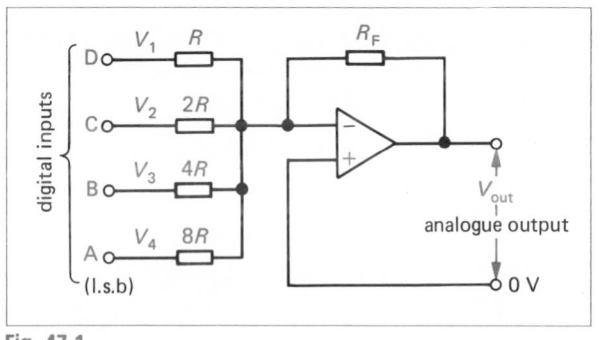

Fig. 47.1

The principle of the *binary weighted resistor* D/A converter is shown in Fig. 47.1 for a four-bit input (DCBA). It is so called because the values of the resistors, R, $2R$, $4R$ and $8R$ in this case, increase according to the binary scale, the l.s.b. of the digital input (A) having the largest value resistor. The circuit uses an op amp as a *summing amplifier* (Chapter 36) with a feedback resistor R_F.

When an input is '1' it is connected to a fixed reference voltage V_{REF} and when it is '0' it is connected to 0 V. The input voltages V_1, V_2, V_3 and V_4 applied to the op amp by the four-bit input (via the resistors) therefore have one of two values, either V_{REF} or 0 V.

Using the summing amplifier formula, the analogue output voltage V_{out} from the op amp is numerically given by

$$V_{out} = R_F \left(\frac{V_1}{R} + \frac{V_2}{2R} + \frac{V_3}{4R} + \frac{V_4}{8R} \right)$$

If $R_F = 1\,k\Omega = R$ then

$$V_{out} = V_1 + \tfrac{1}{2}V_2 + \tfrac{1}{4}V_3 + \tfrac{1}{8}V_4$$

If the digital (binary) input is 0001 (i.e. decimal 1), then $D = C = B = '0'$ and $A = '1'$, making $V_1 = V_2 = V_3 = 0\,V$

and $V_4 = V_{REF}$. To make the arithmetic easier; supposing $V_{REF} = 8\,V$, we get

$$V_{out} = 0 + 0 + 0 + \frac{8}{8} = 1\,V$$

If the digital input is 0010 (i.e. decimal 2), then $D = C = A = '0'$ and $B = '1'$, making $V_1 = V_2 = V_4 = 0\,V$ and $V_3 = V_{REF} = 8\,V$, so

$$V_{out} = 0 + 0 + \frac{8}{4} + 0 = 2\,V$$

For an input of 0110 (i.e. decimal 6), $V_1 = V_4 = 0\,V$ and $V_2 = V_3 = V_{REF} = 8\,V$, therefore

$$V_{out} = 0 + \frac{8}{2} + \frac{8}{4} + 0 = 4 + 2 = 6\,V$$

From these three examples we see that the analogue output voltage V_{out} is directly proportional to the digital input. V_{out} has a stepped, but *varying* waveform with a shape that depends on the digital input pattern, as shown in Fig. 47.2 where the 'steps' are each 1 V.

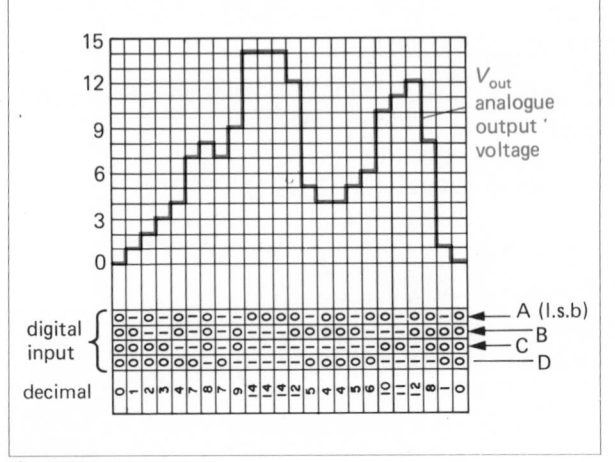

Fig. 47.2

In the ZN425E D/A converter IC $V_{REF} = 2.55\,V$ and since it has an eight-bit input (which can represent, in binary, decimal 0 to 255), each 'step' is $2.55\,V/255 = 0.01\,V$, giving V_{out} a much smoother waveform.

◆ Analogue-to-digital (A/D) conversion

In many modern measuring instruments (e.g. a digital voltmeter), the reading is frequently displayed digitally,

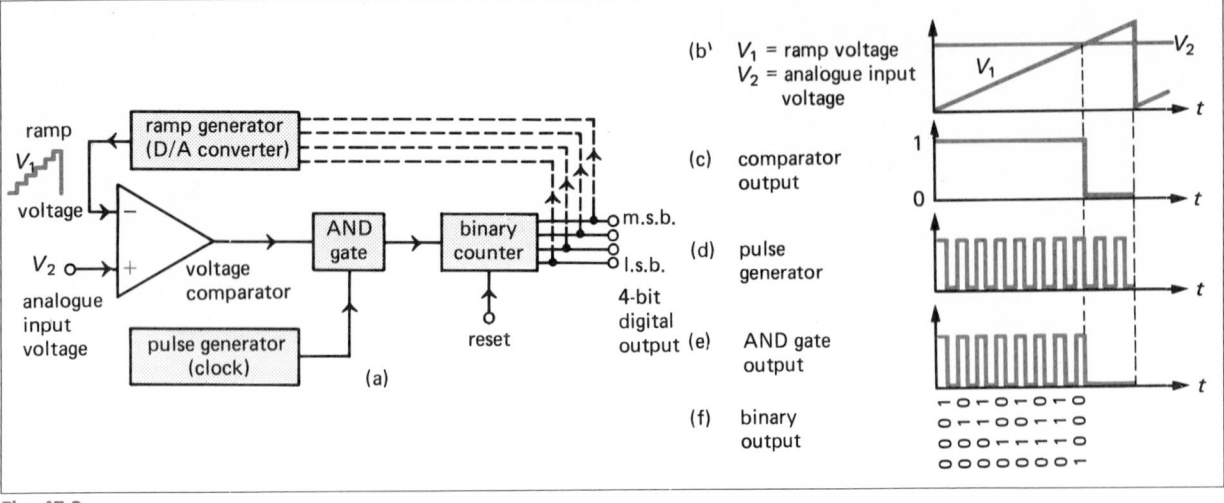

Fig. 47.3

but the input is in analogue form. An A/D converter is then needed.

The block diagram for a four-bit *counter* type A/D conversion circuit is shown in Fig. 47.3*a*, with waveforms to help explain the action. An op amp is again used but in this case as a *comparator* (Chapter 37). The analogue input voltage V_2 (shown here as a steady d.c. voltage) is applied to the non-inverting (+) input; the inverting (−) input is supplied by a ramp generator with a repeating sawtooth waveform voltage V_1, Fig. 47.3*b*.

The output from the comparator is applied to one input of an AND gate and is 'high' (a 1) until V_1 equals (or exceeds) V_2, when it goes 'low' (a 0), as in Fig. 47.3*c*. The other input of the AND gate is fed by a steady train of pulses from a pulse generator, as shown in Fig. 47.3*d*. When both these inputs are 'high', the gate 'opens' and gives a 'high' output, i.e. a pulse.

From Fig. 47.3*e*, you can see that the number of pulses so obtained from the AND gate depends on the 'length' of the comparator output pulse, i.e. on the time taken by V_1 to reach V_2. This time is proportional to the analogue voltage if the ramp is linear. The output pulses from the AND gate are recorded by a binary counter and, as shown in Fig. 47.3*f*, are the digital equivalent of the analogue input voltage V_2.

In practice the ramp generator is a D/A converter which takes its digital input from the binary counter, shown by the dashed lines in Fig. 47.3*a*. As the counter advances

through its normal binary sequence, a staircase waveform with equal steps (i.e. a ramp) is built up at the output of the D/A converter, like that shown by the first four steps in Fig. 47.2.

Similar conversion techniques are used in digital voltmeters (Chapter 24).

The ZN425E IC can also be used as an A/D converter if its 'logic select' input pin is held 'high' instead of 'low' as it is when it acts as a D/A converter.

◇ **Questions**

Q1
(a) What is a D/A converter?
(b) What does a D/A converter do?
(c) What part does an op amp play in the action of a D/A converter?

Q2
A D/A converter IC has a four-bit input and a reference voltage of 1.5 V. What will be the size of the 'steps' in the output voltage waveform?

Q3
(a) What is an A/D converter?
(b) What does an A/D converter do?
(c) What part does an op amp play in the action of an A/D converter?

48 Programs and flowcharts

◆ Program languages

A computer must be programmed so that it knows what to do. A *program*, referred to as *software* (or *firmware* if it is stored in a ROM) consists of a series of instructions (from the CPU's instruction set which shows what operations the CPU can perform), each followed by an address for data, and involves the computer in a 'fetch-and-execute' process.

Programs can be written in *machine code*, i.e. the 0s and 1s of the binary system in which the computer must work. But it is a tedious, time-consuming process, liable to error. Program 'languages' have therefore been developed to make the job easier.

(a) Low-level or assembly languages. These are close to the binary system. Programs are written in mnemonics (i.e. memory aids) and by referring to the instruction set for the CPU we might find, for example, that the mnemonic for 'load data from memory' is LD. It would also give the binary code for this operation, say 1001 1110. To enable the CPU to understand the instruction LD, i.e. to convert the input into machine code, a special program called an *assembler* is stored in a ROM.

(b) High-level languages. These are more like everyday English and are easier to understand and work with since they use terms such as LOAD, ADD, FETCH, PRINT, STOP. However they need more memory space and computer time because each statement converts into several machine code instructions, not just one as is usual in a low-level program. A *compiler* or an *interpreter* (the equivalents of an assembler and, like it, consisting of a program) does the translation into machine code. BASIC (Beginner's All-purpose Symbolic Instruction Code) is a popular high-level language. COBOL is designed for business use, while FORTRAN is suitable for scientific and mathematical work.

◆ Flowcharts

All programs, whether high- or low-level must give absolutely clear instructions to the computer. Writing a program is easier if a *flowchart* is drawn up initially to show the sequence of events required to complete the task. A flowchart consists of a number of box-like symbols joined together by arrowed lines. The shape of a symbol depends on what it is used to indicate; some are shown in Fig. 48.1.

Symbol	Used to show
 ⬭	When flow of data <u>starts</u> or <u>stops</u>
 ▱	When data is <u>input</u> or <u>output</u>
 ▭	When data is <u>processed</u>
 ◇	When a <u>decision</u> is made

Fig. 48.1

◆ Some simple examples of flowcharts

(a) Voltage calculation. The voltage V across a resistor R carrying a current I is to be calculated by a computer. This is most unlikely, but the flowchart, Fig. 48.2, shows the steps which have to be taken to perform the task, however it is done.

(b) Rain alarm. A computer is to be programmed to cause an alarm to be sounded when a rain sensor detects rain by supplying a logic 1 signal to input A of the computer. The flowchart for the system is given in Fig. 48.3. Note the *loop* to ensure processing continues until the condition 'Input A = 1' is satisfied.

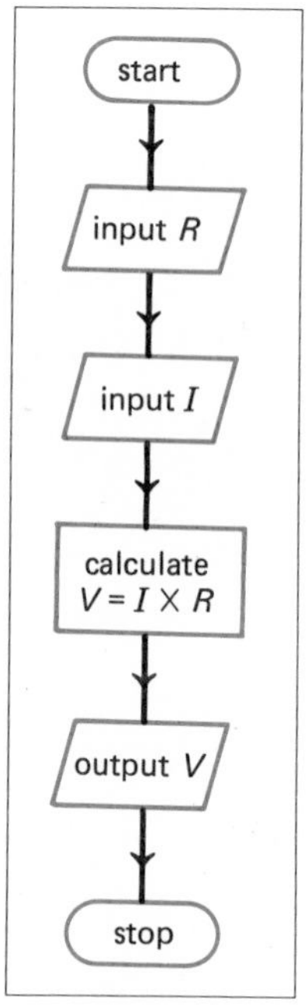

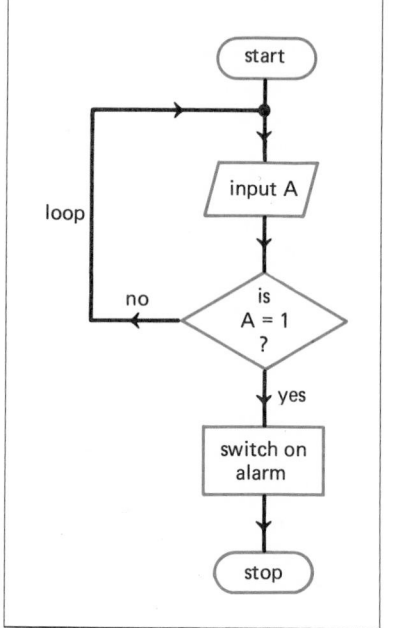

Fig. 48.2   **Fig. 48.3**

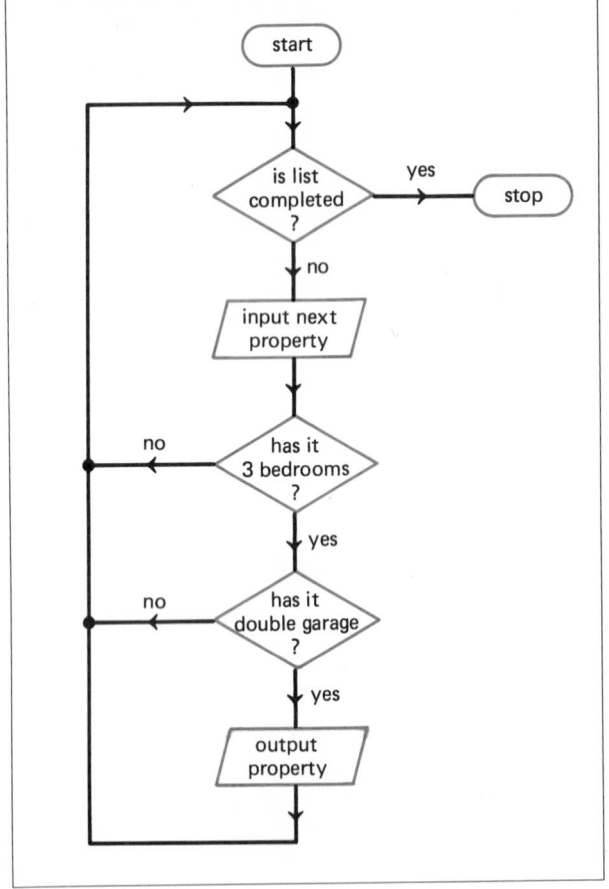

Fig. 48.4

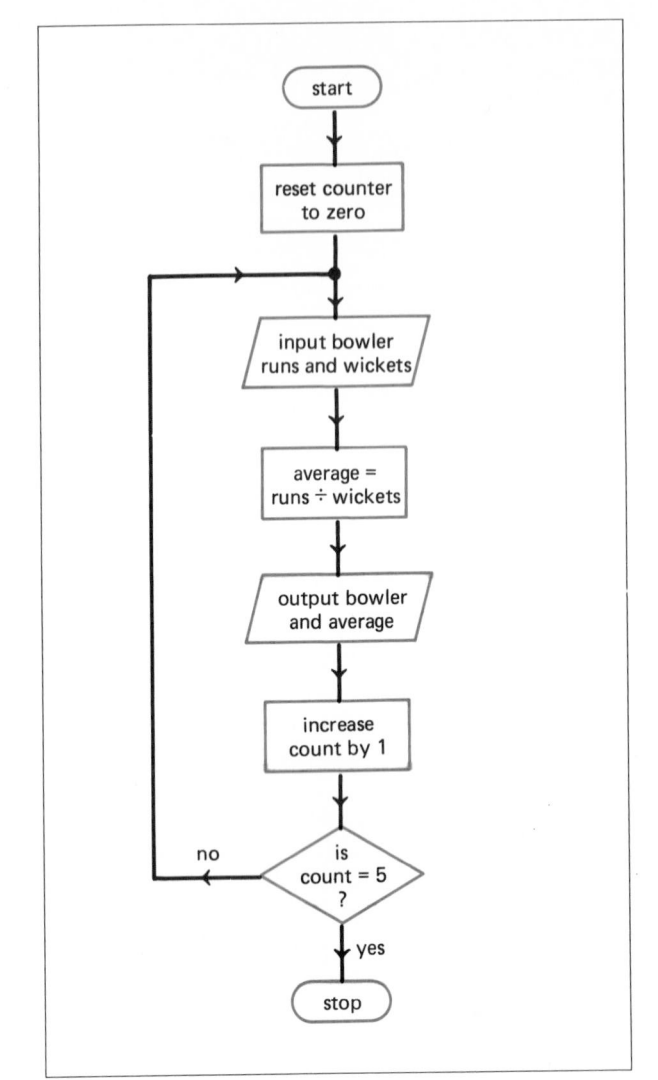

Fig. 48.5

(c) House search problem. An estate agent wishes to search a list of properties he has for sale to discover for a prospective buyer which have three bedrooms *and* a double garage. If he decided to use a computer and write his own program, he might first construct a flow-chart like that in Fig. 48.4.

◆ Counter-controlled loop

When a *fixed* number of items is to be processed in an operation, a counter-controlled loop is included in the flowchart. For example, if we wish a computer to stop when it has produced a list of the bowling averages of *five* bowlers in a cricket team, a flowchart like that in Fig. 48.5 would be constructed.

◆ Condition-controlled loop

If the number of times a loop has to be repeated is not known beforehand, the operation is stopped by in-serting a *rogue value* at the end of the data. This is cho-

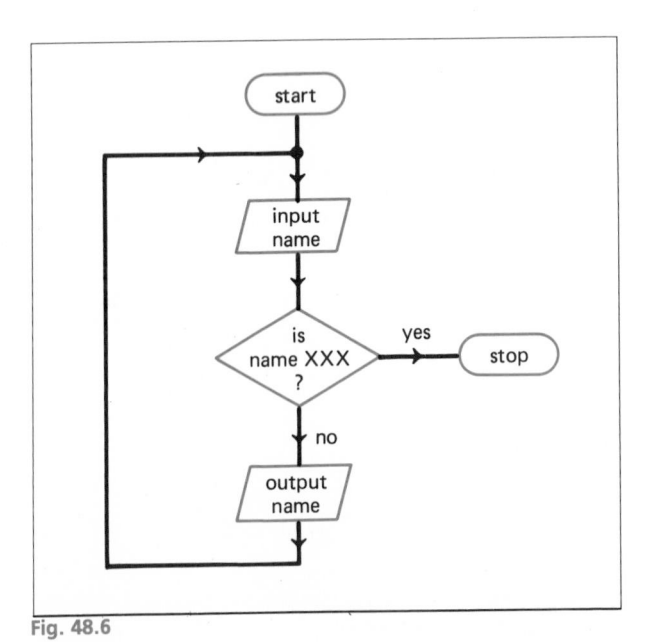

Fig. 48.6

sen to be so different from the other data that it is easily identified. The loop, called a *condition-controlled loop*, then repeats until the rogue value is met and is the signal for data entry to end.

The flowchart for a system to print a long list containing an unknown number of names is shown in Fig. 48.6. It uses the rogue value XXX.

◆ Subroutines

Sometimes instead of changing by one step at a time it is useful to 'jump' from the step-by-step sequence of the main program to what is known as a *subroutine*. For

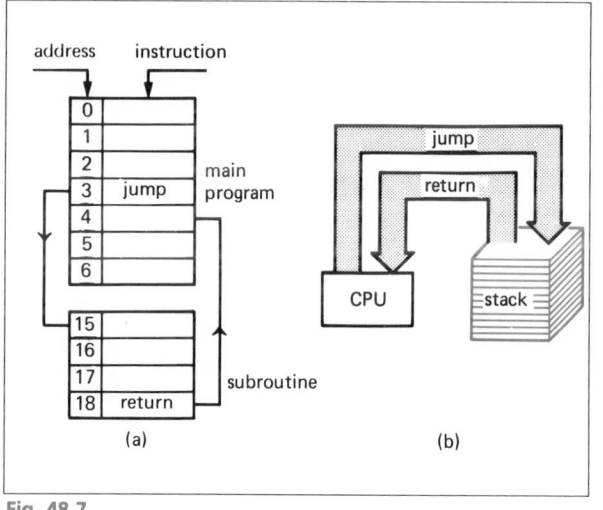

Fig. 48.7

example, the process of multiplication requires a computer to make a large number of additions. To save writing this out every time it is used in a program, it can be written just once as a subroutine, stored and recalled when needed, Fig. 48.7a.

The store is called a *register stack* because the data are 'stacked' on top of each other in order and then recovered from the top in reverse order, i.e. last in, first out, Fig. 48.6b.

◇ Questions

Q1
Flowcharts are often used for purposes other than drawing up a computer program. Construct one giving the sequence of events for the following operations:
(a) switching on a television set to watch a certain programme,
(b) making a phone call.

Q2
Construct a flowchart to switch off an electric kettle when it boils, using a microcomputer.

Q3
In an investigation the police wish to search through a list, stored in a computer, of car owners to find the names and addresses of all those with green Astras. Draw up a flowchart for the task.

49 Microprocessors

◆ About microprocessors

A microprocessor (MPU or μP) is a miniature version of the CPU of a digital computer with some memory, input and output ports and their bus connections, Fig. 49.1. It is a complex chip containing a combination of logic gates which can perform a variety of logic and arithmetic functions. Fig. 49.2 shows an enlarged microprocessor chip.

Microprocessors were developed in the early 1970s when, as ICs became more specialized, the need was

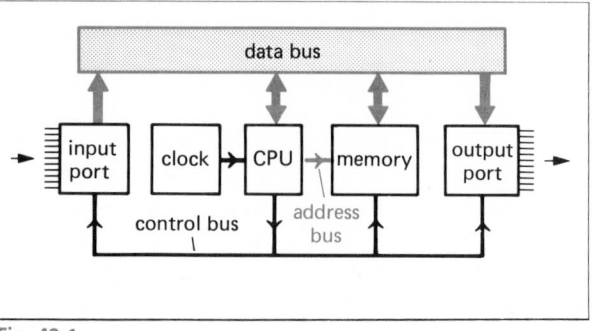

Fig. 49.1

Fig. 49.2

◆ Microprocessor controlled devices

(a) Washing machine. *Sensors* provide the inputs to the microprocessor (μP) and the *activators* receive digital signals from its outputs. The water level sensor (LS) and the temperature sensor (TS) are connected to two of the

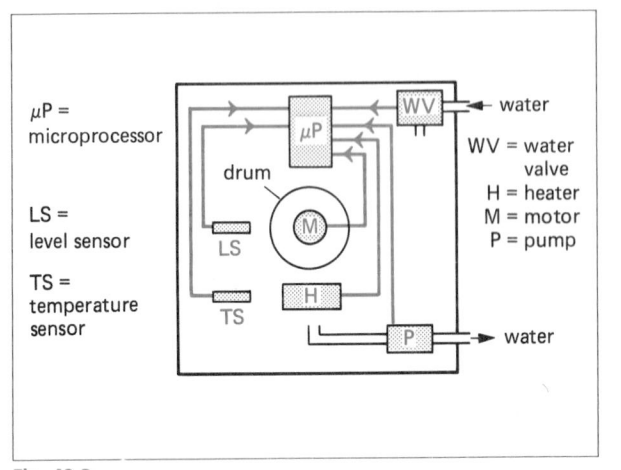

Fig. 49.3

input port lines. Activators in the form of a water valve (WV: to allow water into the drum), a heater (H: to heat the water), a motor (M: to rotate the drum) and a pump (P: to empty the drum) are connected to four lines of the output port, Fig. 49.3.

The programs for different wash cycles are stored in the microprocessor's ROM.

A simplified flowchart and washing sequence are given in Fig. 49.4.

Microprocessor controlled washing machines have replaced mechanical and electromechanical systems because they are more reliable, more flexible, cheaper, require less maintenance and use less energy.

(b) Digital watches. A microprocessor counts the very accurate pulses, with a frequency of exactly 32 768 Hz (2^{15} Hz), from a quartz crystal oscillator and converts them into hours, minutes and seconds for an LCD or LED display. As well as giving the date, alarm and stop-watch facilities may also be included.

(c) Camera. In a camera with microprocessor control, sensors measure the light level and distance of the subject. After conversion to digital form the signals are applied to the microprocessor which causes small activators to automatically set focus, shutter speed and aperture.

(d) Other devices. In addition to those mentioned earlier (Chapter 26), microprocessors are also used in

felt for a general purpose device, suitable for a wide range of jobs. Their versatility is due to the fact that they are *program-controlled*. Simply by changing the program, one can be used not only as the 'brain' of a microcomputer but as a calculator, a cash register, a washing machine, a juke box or a petrol pump. Alternatively they can be used to control traffic lights or an industrial robot. The market for such a flexible device is much greater than for a *dedicated* chip doing just one job.

There are many MPUs on the market, with instruction sets for various tasks and which operate on words of different lengths (usually four-, eight- or sixteen-bit). Some cost just a few pounds and are often the cheapest part of a system. They are often housed in 40-pin 0.6 inch wide d.i.l. packages and operate from 5 V and/or 12 V power supplies. The first useful MPU was the 8080; two popular types are the Z80A (used in the Sinclair ZX *Spectrum*) and the 6502 (used in the BBC *Acorn*).

Microprocessors can now be designed only by using computers, which probably contain microprocessors. An MPU is not a computer itself — to be a microcomputer it needs input and output devices and external memories. However, the trend is to incorporate as many as possible of the peripheral support chips into the MPU package.

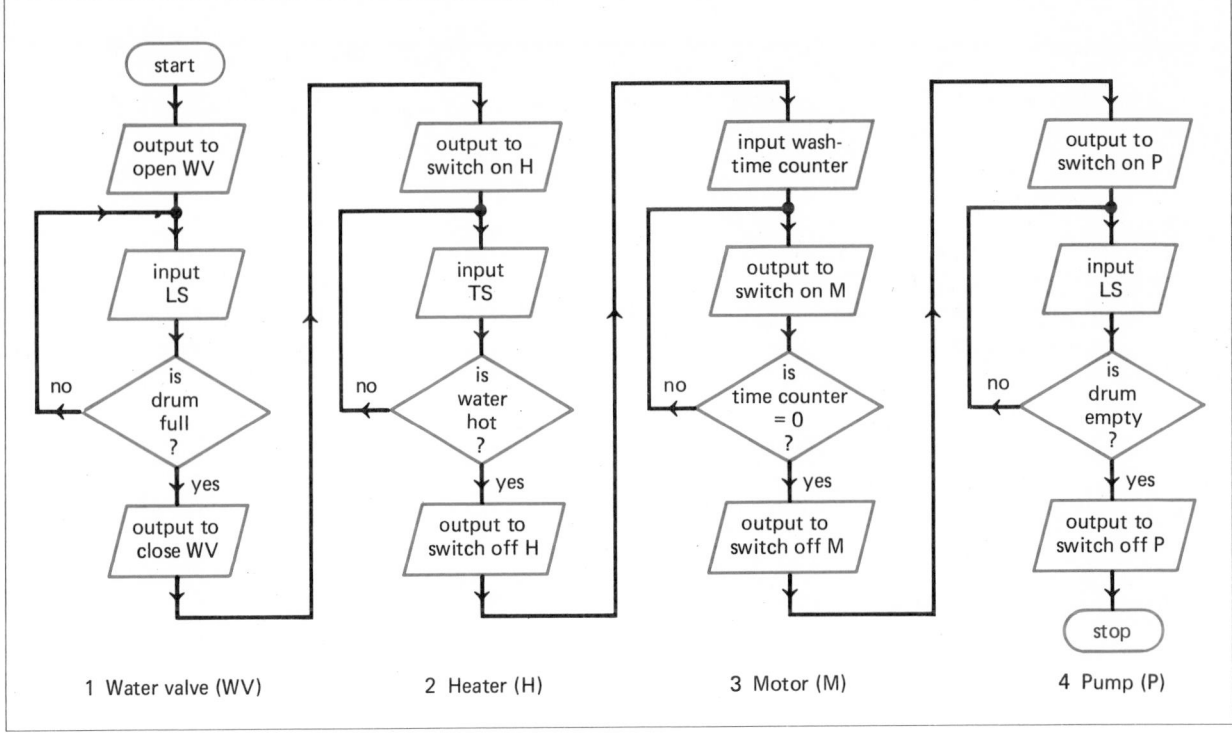

Fig. 49.4

telephones, lifts, radio tuners, TV games, security systems and 'systems' in a car where their speed, robustness, very small size and low cost offer many advantages.

(e) Integrated home system (IHS). The IHS or 'intelligent' house is under development in several countries (UK, USA, Japan). The idea is to achieve central control by a computer or microprocessor, fed by sensors, of systems that have previously been independent. These include lighting, heating, television, video recorder, alarm system, cooker, washing machine, telephone, drawing blinds and curtains, etc. A VDU, located in the kitchen, could monitor gas and electricity consumption and represent it graphically. It might also display recipes. The overall benefit would be improved economy and increased security of homes.

◇ **Questions**

Q1
State some advantages and disadvantages of *microprocessor* systems compared with *wired logic* systems that consist of dedicated chips.

Q2
Explain the advantages of a microprocessor-controlled washing machine
(a) to the manufacturer,
(b) to the user, and
(c) to the service engineer.

Q3
What are the advantages of digital watches over ordinary ones?

50 Additional questions

◇ Core level

Q1
The block diagram for the microcomputer system in Fig. 50.1 shows the direction in which data travels between the blocks by arrows.
(a) What do the letters CPU stand for?
(b) What is the function of **(i)** the CPU, **(ii)** the clock?
(c) Identify blocks A, B and C.
(d) What is meant by 'data'?
(e) In what type of memory is data stored? Explain your answer.
(f) What is meant by the term 'program'?
(g) In what type of memory is the program usually stored? Explain your answer.

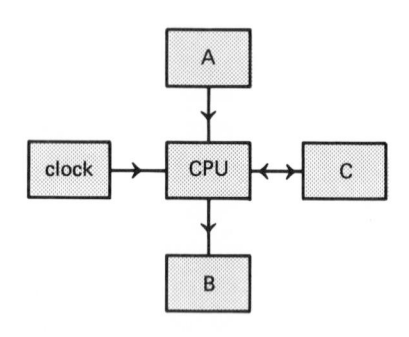

Fig. 50.1

Q2
Some people think that the increasing use of computers to store personal data threatens their privacy.
(a) State briefly why people are more worried about this now then they were before computers were used.
(b) Describe the kind of personal information that might be stored by *two* different data processing users.

Q3
(a) What is meant by the term 'interactive terminal'?
(b) Name *three* different types of interactive terminal and give *one* application for each.

Q4
Give *two* examples in each case of devices which give signals that
(a) would need analogue to digital conversion,
(b) would *not* need analogue to digital conversion.

Q5
What should be the value of the reference voltage of a five-bit D/A converter to produce 'steps' of 0.1 V in the analogue output voltage?

Q6
The A/D converter in Fig. 50.2*a* responds to the analogue input voltage V_{in} as in the table of Fig. 50.2*b*. If a logic 1 output is 4.5 V and a logic 0 output is 0.5 V, what will the voltages be at **(a)** A, **(b)** B, **(c)** C when V_{in} is 3.5 V?

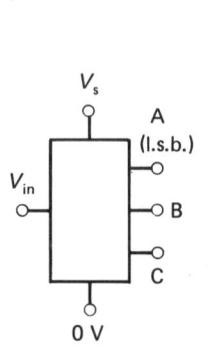

Analogue input V_{in}/V	Digital output		
	C	B	A
Below 1	0	0	0
1 to 2	0	0	1
2 to 3	0	1	0
3 to 4	0	1	1
4 to 5	1	0	0
5 to 6	1	0	1
6 to 7	1	1	0
Above 7	1	1	1

(a)   (b)

Fig. 50.2

Q7
The boiler and pump of a heating system, controlled by the program in a microcomputer, are only both switched on when the microcomputer receives logic 1 inputs from *two* thermostats A and B. Construct a flowchart for the system.

Q8
(a) What type of signal must be applied to the input of a microprocessor?
(b) Why does a microprocessor need a clock?
(c) Give *three* examples of appliances used in the home which may now contain a microprocessor rather than wired logic units.

◇ Further level

Q9
Give *four* reasons why computers are so widely used today.

Q10
What type of computer terminal would you recommend for
(a) a travel agent,
(b) a library to record the issue and return of books,
(c) a scientific experiment in which temperature has to be monitored?

Q11

The circuit in Fig. 50.3 is for a very simple type of A/D converter using op amps (which saturate at 0 V and +5 V) as comparators. It produces a four-bit output A, B, C, D from an analogue input voltage V_{in}.

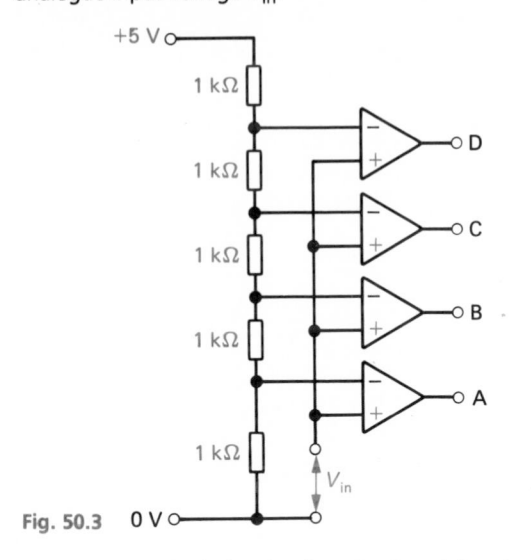

Fig. 50.3

What are the logic levels of A, B, C and D when V_{in} is between **(a)** 0 and 1 V, **(b)** 2 and 3 V and **(c)** 4 and 5 V?

Q12

A computer controls an industrial process in which the raw materials have to be kept at a certain temperature. It is programmed to bring on a heater if the temperature falls below 200°C and to turn it off if the temperature is above 210°C.

(a) Construct a flowchart describing the sequence of events in the process.

(b) Draw a circuit diagram of a temperature sensor using a thermistor which gives an increasing output voltage when the temperature rises.

(c) What kind of interfacing circuit could be required to use the voltage in **(b)** as an input to the computer?

Check list
Computers and microprocessors

After studying *Chapter 45: Digital computers*, you should be able to

◇ draw the block diagram of a computer system including a central processing unit (CPU), memory, clock, input and output devices, address, data and control buses,

◇ state the function of each part of a computer, including tristate gates,

◇ name the three broad groups of computers,

◇ give examples of computers being used for data processing,

◇ give examples of computers being used for process control,

◇ explain how industrial robots are controlled by computers,

◇ recall what is meant by 'computer integrated manufacture',

◇ describe briefly the use of computers by the police, banks, DVLC, newspaper publishers, scientists, engineers, geologists, weather forecasters, doctors, dentists, solicitors, estate agents and farmers,

◇ explain why many people feel the increasing use of computers threatens their private lives,

◇ explain how the Data Protection Act attempts to protect individuals from the misuse of data stored by computers,

◇ give reasons why computers are so widely used, and

◇ discuss how computers might affect our working lives in the future.

After studying *Chapter 46: Computer peripherals*, you should be able to

◇ state that the input and output devices of a computer and external memories are called peripherals,

◇ state that VDUs, teletypes and GDUs are interactive input–output devices and briefly describe them,

◇ state that bar code readers, OMRs, OCRs and MICRs are input devices and briefly describe their uses,

◇ recall and compare the three main types of present-day printer,

◇ outline the use of sensors and activators in industrial control processes,

◇ recall the main types of external memory,

◇ state why interfacing chips are required between the CPU and its peripherals, and

◇ give examples of the use of A/D converters, D/A converters, encoders, decoders, modems, PIO and SIO chips.

After studying *Chapter 47: A/D and D/A converters*, you should be able to

◇ state what a D/A converter does,

◇ recognize the circuit for a simple D/A converter and outline how it works,

◇ state uses for D/A converters,

◇ state what an A/D converter does,

◇ recognize the block diagram of an A/D converter and outline how it works with the help of waveforms,

◇ state uses for A/D converters, and

◇ recall that IC versions of D/A and A/D converters exist.

After studying *Chapter 48: Programs and flowcharts*, you should be able to

◇ state that a computer works in machine code,

◇ distinguish between low-level and high-level languages,

◇ state that a flowchart describes the sequence of events that has to be performed to carry out a certain task,

◇ recognize flowchart symbols and what they mean,

◇ recall that a loop in a flowchart represents an event that has to be repeated until a particular condition is fulfilled,

◇ construct and interpret flowcharts, including those with counter-controlled and condition-controlled loops, and

◇ understand the use of the instructions load, store, compare, jump to and return from a subroutine, in a program.

After studying *Chapter 49: Microprocessors*, you should be able to

◇ state that a microprocessor is a miniature version of the CPU of a computer which consists of a complex chip containing a combination of logic gates capable of performing a variety of arithmetic and logic operations,

◇ state the advantages of microprocessor systems over those using dedicated chips,

◇ explain the use of microprocessors in washing machines, digital watches and cameras, and

◇ name other devices containing microprocessors.

Appendix   List of practical books

1 *Practical Electronics for GCSE*, Bishop, O.
(John Murray, 1989)
(Contains investigations, assessment exercises and design projects using breadboards, stripboards, printed circuit and matrix boards.)

2 *Electronics Through Systems*, Geddes, M.
(Institution of Electrical Engineers, 1983)
(A systems-approach guide using commercial modules, e.g. Alpha.)

3 *Alpha Electronics—Teachers' Handbook*,
Meredith, R. (Unilab, 1987)
(Gives details of investigations and projects using a systems approach.)

4 *Microelectronics — Practical Approaches for Schools and Colleges*, Bevis, G. and Trotter, M.
(eds) (BP Education Service, 1981)
(Contains details of a large number of projects.)

5 *Practical Electronics Handbook*, Sinclair, I.R.
(Newnes Technical, 1980)
(A very useful book for all work in electronics.)

6 *Adventures with Electronics*, Duncan, T.
(John Murray, 1980)
(Contains projects using S-DeCs.)

7 *Adventures with Microelectronics*, Duncan, T.
(John Murray, 1981)
(Contains projects using one prototype board.)

8 *Adventures with Digital Electronics*, Duncan, T.
(John Murray, 1985)
(Contains projects using two prototype boards.)

9 *GCSE Electronics syllabuses*. Some examining groups, e.g. Midland (MEG) and Northern (NEA), include a list of 'Suggestions for possible projects' in the booklets containing syllabus details.

Answers

1 Electric current

1 (a) B, **(b)** C, **(c)** A
2 (a) Ⓐ₂ 0.2 A: Ⓐ₃ 0.2 A
   (b) 0.5 A
3 Ⓐ₂ 0.2 A: Ⓐ₃ 0.2 A
4 (a) Ⓐ₁ 0.3 A: Ⓐ₃ 0.3 A
   (b) See Fig. A1.

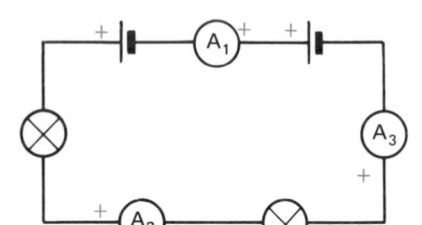

Fig. A1

5 (a) (i) 1000 mA, **(ii)** 500 mA, **(iii)** 20 mA
   (b) (i) 1.5 A, **(ii)** 0.3 A, **(iii)** 0.06 A
   (c) (i) 2000 μA, **(ii)** 400 μA, **(iii)** 5 μA

2 Potential difference

1 (a) $4 \times 1.5 = 6\,V$
   (b) $3 \times 1.5 - 1 \times 1.5 = 4.5 - 1.5 = 3\,V$
2 (a) Ⓥ₂ 3 V
   (b) See Fig. A2.

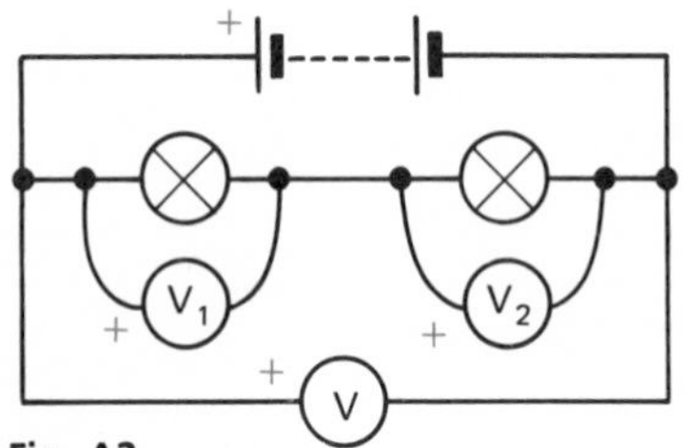

Fig. A2

3 x: 18, y: 2, z: 8
4 (a) 6 V, **(b)** 6 V
5 (a) 0 V, **(b)** 5 V
6 (a) (i) 1000 mV, **(ii)** 700 mV, **(iii)** 20 mV
   (b) (i) 1.6 V, **(ii)** 0.4 V, **(iii)** 0.05 V

3 Resistance and Ohm's law

1 (a) $12\,V/6\,\Omega = 2\,A$
   (b) 12 V
   (c) See Fig A3.
2 (a) $6\,V/1.5\,A = 4\,\Omega$
   (b) $2\,A \times 10\,\Omega = 20\,V$
3 (a) $5\,mA \times 2\,k\Omega = 10\,V$
   (b) $12\,V/3\,mA = 4\,k\Omega$
   (c) $10\,V/5\,k\Omega = 2\,mA$

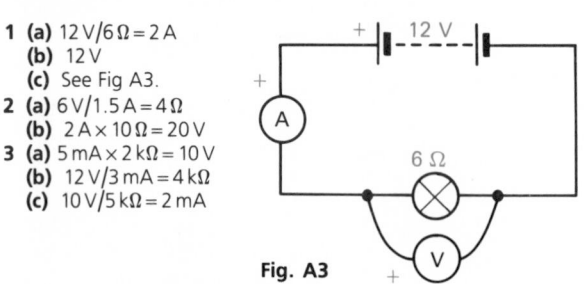

Fig. A3

4 Resistor networks

1 See Fig A4.

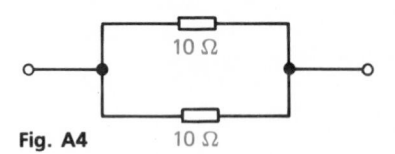

Fig. A4

2 (a) 1 A
   (b) 1 A
   (c) $1\,A \times 3\,\Omega = 3\,V$
   (d) $1\,A \times 6\,\Omega = 6\,V$
   (e) $3\,V + 6\,V = 9\,V$
3 (a) 4 A (twice as much as through 6 Ω)
   (b) 2 A (half as much as through 3 Ω)
   (c) $4\,A \times 3\,\Omega = 12\,V$
   (d) $2\,A \times 6\,\Omega = 12\,V$
   (e) 12 V
4 (a) $1\,k\Omega + 3\,k\Omega = 4\,k\Omega$
   (b) $\dfrac{4 \times 4}{4 + 4} = \dfrac{16}{8} = 2\,k\Omega$
   (c) $4\,k\Omega + 2\,k\Omega = 6\,k\Omega$

5 Potential divider

1 (a) 2 V
   (b) 4 V
   (c) 3 V
   (d) 4 V
2 6 V
3 $V_{out} = I R_2$
   $V_{in} = I(R_1 + R_2)$

Therefore $\dfrac{V_{out}}{V_{in}} = \dfrac{IR_2}{I(R_1 + R_2)} = \dfrac{R_2}{R_1 + R_2}$

Therefore $V_{out} = \left(\dfrac{R_2}{R_1 + R_2} \right) V_{in}$

6 Electric power

1 (a) 6 W
   (b) 60 W
2 $240\,V \times 13\,A = 3120\,W = 3.12\,kW$
3 $(240\,V \times 5\,A)/100 = 12$
4 Power $= I^2R = 2^2 \times 4 = 16\,W$
5 (a) $1/10\,A = 100\,mA$
   (b) $2/10\,A = 200\,mA$
   (c) $1/60\,A = 17\,mA$
6 $9\,V \times 3\,mA = 27\,mW$

7 Alternating current

1 d.c. because it never changes *direction* even though its value changes
2 (a) 0.2 s, **(b)** $1/0.2 = 5\,Hz$

3 (a) $2\,\text{ms} = 2/1000\,\text{s} = 0.002\,\text{s}$
 (b) $1/0.002 = 500\,\text{Hz}$
 (c) $3\,\text{V}$
 (d) $0.7 \times 3\,\text{V} = 2.1\,\text{V}$
4 (a) $12\,\text{V}$
 (b) $1.4 \times 12 \approx 17\,\text{V}$
 (c) $12\,\text{V} \times 2\,\text{A} = 24\,\text{W}$

8 Additional questions

1 (A) $4\,\text{V}/2\,\text{k}\Omega = 2\,\text{mA}$
 (V) $2\,\text{mA} \times 1\,\text{k}\Omega = 2\,\text{V}$
2 (a) $(6 \times 3)/(6 + 3) = 18/9 = 2\,\text{k}\Omega$
 (b) $0.5\,\text{k}\Omega$
3 (a) $5\,\text{V}$
 (b) $0\,\text{V}$
 (c) $5\,\text{V}$
4 (a) $400 + 100 = 500\,\Omega$
 (b) $10\,\text{V}/500\,\Omega = 1/50 = 0.02\,\text{A}$
 (c) $100\,\Omega \times 0.02\,\text{A} = 2\,\text{V}$
 (d) $2\,\text{V} \times 0.02\,\text{A} = 0.04\,\text{W}$
 (e) No chance since it can dissipate a maximum of $0.25\,\text{W}$
 safely
5 (a) ampere
 (b) volt
 (c) ohm
 (d) watt
 (e) hertz
6 Maximum safe $I = \sqrt{P/R} = \sqrt{\dfrac{0.1\,\text{W}}{1\,\text{k}\Omega}} = \sqrt{\dfrac{0.1\,\text{W}}{1000\,\Omega}}$

 $= \sqrt{\dfrac{0.1 \times 10}{1000 \times 10}} = \sqrt{\dfrac{1}{10\,000}} = \dfrac{1}{100}\,\text{A} = 10\,\text{mA}$

 I on a $20\,\text{V}$ supply $= 20\,\text{V}/1\,\text{k}\Omega = 20\,\text{mA}$
 therefore resistor will overheat
7 (a) $10\,\text{V}$
 (b) $0.7 \times 10 = 7\,\dot{\text{V}}$
 (c) $0.02\,\text{s}$
 (d) $1/0.02 = 50\,\text{Hz}$
8 (a) $3/1$
 (b) $1/4$

9 Resistors and potentiometers

1 $R_1 = 1\,\text{k}\Omega \pm 10\%$; $R_2 = 47\,\text{k}\Omega \pm 5\%$; $R_3 = 560\,\text{k}\Omega \pm 20\%$
2 (a) Brown green brown silver, **(b)** Brown black black gold,
 (c) Orange white red silver, **(d)** Brown black orange silver,
 (e) Orange orange yellow, **(f)** Brown black green silver
3 (a) $2.2\,\text{k}\Omega \pm 20\%$, **(b)** $270\,\text{k}\Omega \pm 5\%$,
 (c) $1\,\text{M}\Omega \pm 10\%$, **(d)** $15\,\Omega \pm 10\%$
4 (a) 100RJ, **(b)** 4K7M, **(c)** 100KK, **(d)** 56KM
5 (a) $1.2\,\text{k}\Omega$, **(b)** $4.7\,\text{k}\Omega$, **(c)** $68\,\text{k}\Omega$, **(d)** $330\,\text{k}\Omega$

10 Capacitors

1 (a) Capacitance is $0.1\,\mu\text{F}$ and voltage rating is $250\,\text{V}$.
 (b) The *peak* value of a $240\,\text{V}$ a.c. supply is $340\,\text{V}$ which exceeds
 the rated voltage.
2 $2.2\,\text{nF}$, $100\,\text{pF}$, $4.7\,\mu\text{F}$
3 Connect a capacitor in series with the component.
4 Positive terminal (coloured or marked $+$ or shown by a groove
 or arrow) must lead to $+$ of supply.

11 Transformers and inductors

1 (a) $N_s/N_p = 400/200 = 2/1$ (step-up)
 (b) $N_s/N_p = 300/600 = 1/2$ (step-down)
 (c) $N_s/N_p = V_s/V_p = 4/1$ (step-up)
 (d) $N_s/N_p = V_s/V_p = 2/10 = 1/5$ (step-down)
2 (a) $12\,\text{V}$, **(b)** $20\,\text{V}$, **(c)** 1000, **(d)** 4000
3 $100\,\text{mA}$

12 Transducers

1 (a) LDR, **(b)** Loudspeaker, **(c)** Lamp for illumination,
 (d) Thermistor, **(e)** Indicator or signal lamp, **(f)** Electric motor,
 (g) Relay, **(h)** Microphone, **(i)** Push-on switch.
2 An input transducer has a non-electrical input and an electrical
 output. An output transducer has an electrical input and a non-
 electrical output.
3 (a) Brighter, **(b)** Dimmer
4 (a) Increases, **(b)** Decreases
5 DPDT

13 Diode and power supplies

1 (a) L_1 bright, L_2 off
 (b) L_1 bright, L_2 off because the diode is forward biased and
 offers an easy path for the current to bypass L_2.
 (c) L_1 and L_2 both dim because the reverse biased diode forces
 current through L_2 and there is $4.5\,\text{V}$ across each lamp — they
 need $6\,\text{V}$ to be bright.
2 (a) $5\,\Omega$, **(b)** $1\,\text{W}$

14 Other semiconductor diodes

1 (a) $3\,\text{V}$, **(b)** $4\,\text{V}$, **(c)** $40\,\text{mA} = 0.04\,\text{A}$
 (d) $4\,\text{V}/0.04\,\text{A} = 100\,\Omega$
 (e) $3\,\text{V} \times 5\,\text{mA} = 15\,\text{mW}$
2 (a) $(8\,\text{V} - 3\,\text{V})/50\,\Omega = 5\,\text{V}/50\,\Omega = 0.1\,\text{A} = 100\,\text{mA}$
 (b) $(100 - 20)\,\text{mA} = 80\,\text{mA}$
3 $5\,\text{W}/10\,\text{V} = 0.5\,\text{A} = 500\,\text{mA}$
4 $(9\,\text{V} - 2\,\text{V})/10\,\text{mA} = 7\,\text{V}/0.01\,\text{A} = 700\,\Omega$

15 Transistors and ICs

1 (a) ABE, **(b)** ACE
2 B
3 (a) $+0.6\,\text{V}$
 (b) I_B starts to flow.
4 $200/1 = 200$
5 (a) $50 \times 0.3 = 15\,\text{mA}$
 (b) $R_B = (V_s - V_{BE})/I_B = (6\,\text{V} - 0.6\,\text{V})/0.3\,\text{mA} = 5.4\,\text{V}/0.3\,\text{mA}$
 $= 18\,\text{k}\Omega$
6 (a) Drain, gate, source
 (b) Very much greater
7 (a) A microelectronic circuit consisting mainly of transistors
 (bipolar or FET) on a silicon chip
 (b) (i) CMOS since battery operated, **(ii)** TTL because it is
 faster, **(iii)** TTL since it is more robust

16 Additional questions

1 **(a)** R_1:10 000 Ω (10 kΩ)
R_2:470 000 Ω (470 kΩ)
R_3:33 Ω
  (b) (i) Red red orange
  (ii) Blue grey red
  (iii) Brown black blue
  (c) Max.: 100 kΩ + 10 kΩ = 110 kΩ, Min.: 100 kΩ − 10 kΩ = 90 kΩ
3 **(a)** $\dfrac{100}{(100+400)} \times 5 = \dfrac{100}{500} \times 5 = \dfrac{1}{5} \times 5 = 1$ V
  (b) $\dfrac{100}{100+100} \times 5 = \dfrac{1}{2} \times 5 = 2.5$ V
4 **(a)** −5 V
  (b) (i) 5 V, **(ii)** 5 V, **(iii)** 3 V
5 **(a)** Push-on, release-off
  (b) Thyristor
  (c) (i) Lights up, **(ii)** Stays alight
6 **(a)** CMOS
  (b) TTL
  (c) TTL
  (d) CMOS
7 **(a)** and **(b)** See Fig. A5.

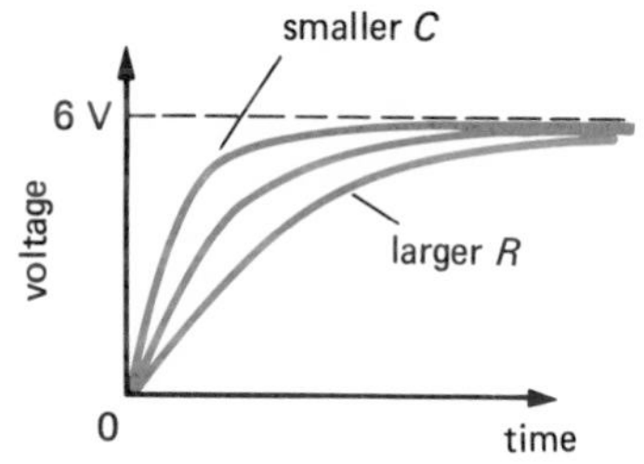

Fig. A5

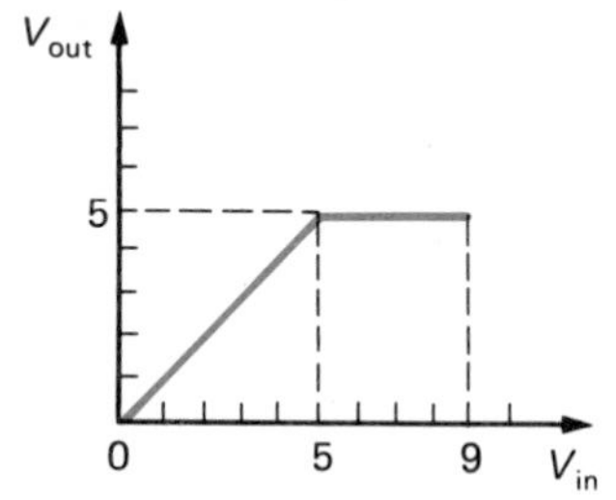

Fig. A6

8 **(a)** See Fig. A6.
  (b) (i) $I = (9 − 5)/400 = 4/400 = 1/100$ A = 10 mA
  (ii) $I_L = 5\,V/1\,kΩ = 5$ mA
  (iii) $I_Z = I − I_L = 10 − 5 = 5$ mA
  (c) $I_{max} = 0.5\,W/5\,V = 0.1$ A = 100 mA
  (d) Voltage regulation of an unstabilized power supply
9 **(a) (i)** To step down 240 V a.c. to 12 Va.c.
  (ii) Rectification of a.c. to d.c.
  (iii) Smoothing of rectified a.c.
  (b) Better smoothing, i.e. smaller ripple voltage
  (c) V_{out} decreases
10 Supplies greater average current

17 Test meters

1 B, D and F are ammeters reading 6 V/6 Ω = 1 A.
  C and E are voltmeters reading 1 A × 3 A = 3 V.
2 G is an ammeter reading 6 V/2 Ω = 3 A.
  H and J are ammeters reading 1.5 A each.
  I and K are voltmeters reading 1.5 A × 4 Ω = 6 V.

3 Yes; it is easier to read the wrong scale, also the pointer may be between marks on the scale and an estimate has to be made.
4 It should have a 'high' resistance when connected in reverse bias and a 'low' resistance in forward bias.
5 **(a)** Y is the base because when + it has a low resistance with the other connections to X or Z.
  (b) Yes, because it has a high resistance for all other pairs of connections.
6 It is connected in reverse bias.

18 Oscilloscope

1 Lower (since electrons have a negative charge and are attracted to the positively charged plate)
2 **(a)** E, **(b)** C
3 C
4 **(a) (i)** 6 vertical divs × 5 V/div = 30 V
  (ii) 3 vertical divs × 5 V/div = 15 V
  (b) (i) 8 divs × 500 mV/div = 4000 mV = 4 V
  (ii) 2 V
5 **(a) (i)** 5 horizontal divs × 200 ms/div = 1000 ms = 1 s
  (ii) 1 Hz
  (b) (i) 5 divs × 100 ms/div = 500 ms = 0.5 s
  (ii) 1/0.5 = 2 Hz

19 Signal generators

1 A CRO with a calibrated time base

20 Dangers of electricity

1 **(a)** Current
  (b) Because good contact is being made with the ground through the feet
2 They can store a large electric charge for a long time.
3 **(i)** Check that cause of the shock has been removed, e.g. switch of power supply at once, or if victim is still holding source of shock, pull him/her away using an insulator.
  (ii) Send for qualified medical help.
  (iii) Check whether heart has stopped; if it has apply cardiac massage.
  (iv) Check breathing if victim unconscious; if it has stopped apply 'kiss of life'.
4 If there is no personal danger and you think it is small enough for you to put out
  (i) raise the alarm.
  (ii) use an extinguisher (carbon dioxide or powder).
  (iii) shut all doors to slow the spread of the fire and of smoke or fumes.

21 Safety precautions

1 **(a)** Live (L), neutral (N), earth (E)
  (b) L — brown, N — blue, E — yellow/green
  (c) To stop connections being pulled loose in the plug
2 **(a)** To prevent wiring catching fire and to protect the appliance
  (b) (i) $I = P/V = 480/240 = 2$ A: a 3 A fuse would be suitable.
  (ii) $I = P/V = 3000/240 = 12.5$ A: a 13 A fuse would do.
3 **(a)** Residual current device
  (b) To protect the user from electric shock
  (c) With outside portable appliances or wherever the user is making good contact with the earth
  (d) See text
  (e) Faster acting, more sensitive, more easily reset
4 It is enclosed in an insulating case.

22 Additional questions

1 (a) 10 V, **(b)** 3 V, **(c)** 10 mA, **(d)** 500 μA
2 (a) A — green, B — blue, C — brown, D — gold
  (b) (i) 3 V, **(ii)** 5 mA, **(iii)** 3 V/5 mA = 3 V/0.005 A = 600 Ω
  (iv) 560 ± 5/100 of 560 = 560 ± 5 × 5.6 = 560 ± 28 = 588 Ω.
  Resistor is not inside required tolerance.
3 (a) Yellow/green
  (b) To provide a low resistance path to earth so that a current,
  large enough to blow the fuse, passes if a fault develops. The
  equipment is then disconnected from the mains and is safe to
  touch.
  (c) (i) Outer sheath securely clamped in cord grip (separate
  wires should not be showing)
  (ii) Insulation not worn or broken (no bare wires showing)
  (iii) A grommet where cable enters or cable securely clamped to
  case of equipment
4 (a) 4 V, **(b)** 6 ms, **(c)** 1/6 ms = 1/0.006s $\approx$ 167 Hz
5 An alternating voltage of amplitude 0.2 V, period 400 μs,
  frequency $1/(400 \times 10^{-6}) = 10^6/400 = 10^4/4 = 2500$ Hz with a
  sine waveform
6 (a) F — fuse, S — single pole switch, T — step-down
  transformer, N — neon lamp mains-on indicator, R — current
  limiting resistor to protect N
  (b) For safety reasons, F is before S and both are in the live lead.
  N is before S to show when power supply is connected to mains
  (c) To T

23 Electronic systems I

1 (a) Input: a button is pressed
  Output: electric motor moves lift cage
  Processing: electrical supply connected to motor which turns at
  a controlled rate
  (b) Input: a tap is turned
  Output: water delivered
  Processing: valve opens and controls flow of water
  (c) Input: a button is pressed
  Output: bell rings
  Processing: electrical supply connected to bell causing the
  clapper to vibrate
  (d) Input: steering wheel is turned
  Output: car moves in a certain direction
  Processing: linkage rods move and control direction of wheels
2 (a) Recording and playback head: loudspeaker or phones
  (b) Keyboard: numerical display
  (c) Pick-up: loudspeaker or phones
  (d) Television aerial: picture screen and loudspeaker
3 See Fig. A7. It is assumed that the output from the *light sensing
  unit* goes 'high' when light falls on it.

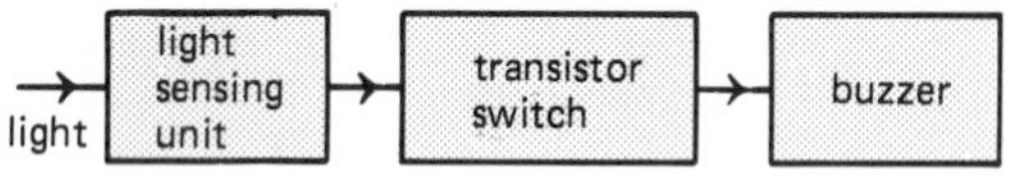

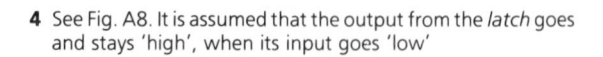

Fig. A7

4 See Fig. A8. It is assumed that the output from the *latch* goes
  and stays 'high', when its input goes 'low'

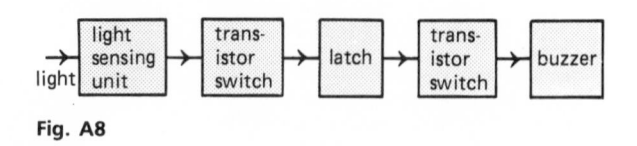

Fig. A8

5 A — OR, B — AND, C — NOR, D — NAND

24 Electronic systems II

1 (a) Non-inverting amplifier — output voltage has same waveform as input voltage but greater amplitude. Inverting amplifier
  — output voltage has same waveform as input voltage but is
  inverted and greater in amplitude.
  (b) Comparator — compares two input voltages and gives a
  digital output, i.e. a 'high' (1) or 'low' (0) voltage depending on
  which input is larger. Difference amplifier — output voltage is
  an amplification of the voltage difference between its two
  inputs (a.c. or d.c.).
2 (a) $x = 1$ V, **(b)** $y = 0$ V, **(c)** $z = 3$ V
3 For example: when the light beam is broken by someone
  passing through the doorway, the output from the *light sensing
  unit* goes from 'high' to 'low' to 'high', i.e. an inverted pulse.
  This makes the output from the *inverter* (e.g. a *transistor switch*)
  go from 'low' to 'high' to 'low', i.e. a positive pulse. Each time
  this happens the *counter* advances the total on the *display* by
  one. See Fig. A9.

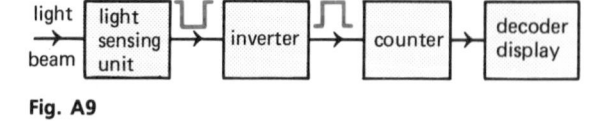

Fig. A9

4 Fig. A10 shows one arrangement.

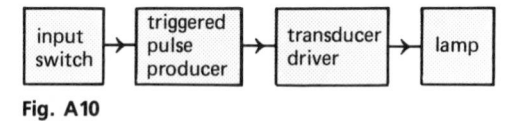

Fig. A10

5 (a) *Range selector sockets* which connect the appropriate
  circuits
  (b) Display (LED or LCD)
  (c) Comparator, ramp generator, pulse generator, AND gate
6 (a) Supply of *sufficient current* to next stage and *matching of
  voltage ranges and levels*
  (b) *Transducer driver or buffer* — a current amplifier
  Decoder — changes binary signals to decimal
  Encoder — changes decimal signals to binary
  Analogue-to-digital converter — changes analogue to digital
  signals
  Digital-to-analogue converter — changes digital to analogue
  signals
  (c) (i) Z_{in} much greater (at least ten times) than Z_{out}
  (ii) $Z_{in} = Z_{out}$

25 Electronic systems III

1 (a)

A	B	Q
0	0	0
0	1	0
1	0	0
1	1	1

(b) AND

2 (a)

A	B	Q
0	0	1
0	1	1
1	0	1
1	1	0

(b) NAND

3 A = '0', B = '0': a rain detector
4 See Fig. A11.

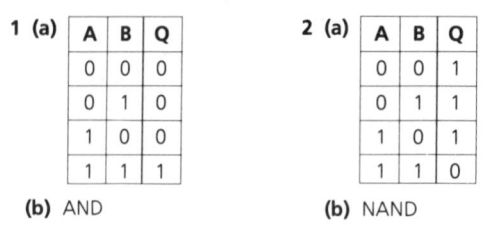

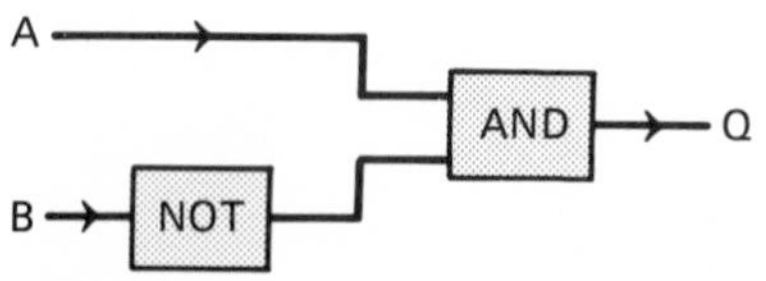

Fig. A11

5

A	B	C	D	E	Q
0	0	1	1	0	1
0	1	1	0	1	0
1	0	0	1	1	0
1	1	0	0	1	0

6

A	B	C	D	Q
0	0	0	0	0
0	0	1	0	1
0	1	0	0	0
1	0	0	0	0
0	1	1	0	1
1	1	0	1	1
1	0	1	0	1
1	1	1	1	1

7

A	B	C	D	E	F	Q
0	0	1	1	0	0	1
0	1	1	0	0	1	0
1	0	0	1	1	0	0
1	1	0	0	0	0	1

8 (a) (i) '0', **(ii)** '1'
(b) (i) '1', **(ii)** '0'
(c) NOR since it gives a '1' output only when A = '0' and B = '0'
(d) The logic gate cannot supply enough current to ring the electric bell.

26 Electronics and society

1 (a) Faster service and mistakes less likely since only one key has to be pressed per item
(b) Covers a limited number of items and does not show total if more than one bought
2 (a) Stocks replaced automatically **(b)** Stocks should always be available.
3 (a) Smaller, more reliable, longer life, could perform more complex jobs, cheaper to fit
(b) If it failed more systems in the car would fail, couldn't be repaired only replaced, fewer people might be employed to assemble car

4 (a)

A	B	C	D	E	F	G	H	J
0	0	0	1	1	1	0	0	0
0	0	1	1	1	1	0	0	0
0	1	0	0	1	0	0	1	1
1	0	0	1	0	0	1	1	1
0	1	1	0	1	0	0	0	0
1	1	0	0	1	0	0	1	1
1	0	1	1	0	0	1	0	1
1	1	1	0	1	0	0	0	0

(b) CBA (since in this order the input goes from 001 (C closed) to 011 (C and B closed) to 111 (C, B and A closed) and as can be seen from the truth table, J is '0' for all of these input combinations)

27 Transistor as a switch

1 (a) 6 V, **(b)** 0 V since current flows through R_L
2 (a) + 0.6 V approx.
(b) 5 V − 0.6 V = 4.4 V
(c) 4.4 V/22 kΩ = 0.2 mA
(d) 10 V
(e) 10 V/1 k Ω = 10 mA
(f) 10 mA/0.2 mA = 50
(g) 0 V
3 (a) (i) 0 V **(ii)** 6 V
(b) V_{in} increases since a larger fraction of the 6 V supply is dropped across it due to the ratio R_2 to R_1 increasing.
(c) (i) 6 V, **(ii)** 0 V
(d) (i) To prevent excessive base currents destroying the transistor if R_1 is made zero **(ii)** To act as a 'load' which causes the collector – emitter (output) voltage to change from 6 V to 0 V when the transistor switches fully on
4 (a) When S is closed the transistor (and L) is on since it can receive base current via S and R_B. When S is opened, initially the p.d. V_C across C is zero and the p.d. V_R across R is 6 V — the latter keeps the transistor on. As C charges up through R, V_C rises and V_R falls (see Chapter 10). Eventually V_R is too small to make the base – emitter p.d. V_{BE} equal to 0.6 V (for a silicon transistor) and the transistor switches off. Finally $V_C = 6$ V and $V_R = 0$.
(b) The lamp stays on longer since C takes longer to charge up through the larger R.
5 (a) Light
(b) V_{in} decreases because the resistance of the LDR increases in the dark.
(c) Allows light level at which switching occurs to be changed

28 Logic gates

1

A	B	C	D	P	Q
0	0	1	0	1	0
0	1	0	0	1	1
1	0	1	1	0	0
1	1	0	1	1	0

2 (a)

A	B	C	D	E
0	0	1	1	0
0	1	1	0	0
1	0	0	1	0
1	1	0	0	1

AND gate

(b)

P	Q	R	S	T
0	0	1	1	0
0	1	1	0	1
1	0	0	1	1
1	1	0	0	1

OR gate

3 (a)

A	B	C	Q
0	0	0	1
0	0	1	1
0	1	0	1
1	0	0	1
0	1	1	1
1	1	0	1
1	0	1	1
1	1	1	0

(b) See Fig. A12.

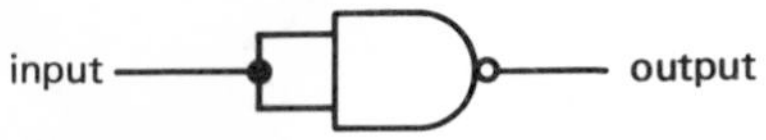

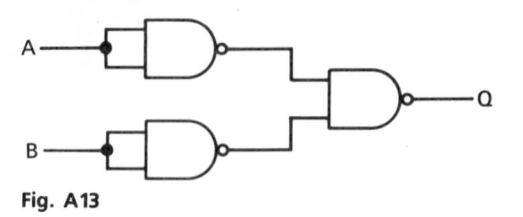

input ——— output

Fig. A12

(c) See Fig. A13

A ———

B ———

——— Q

Fig. A13

(d) Logic level 1 is a voltage near the positive of the supply voltage (e.g. + 5 V) and logic level 0 is a voltage near 0 V.

4 (a)

A	B	C	D	F
0	0	0	0	0
0	0	1	0	0
0	1	0	0	0
1	0	0	0	0
1	1	0	1	0
0	1	1	0	0
1	0	1	0	0
1	1	1	1	1

(b)

A	B	C	F
0	0	0	0
0	0	1	0
0	1	0	0
1	0	0	0
0	1	1	0
1	1	0	0
1	0	1	0
1	1	1	1

5 (a)

Decimal number	Binary		
	A	B	Q
0	0	0	0
1	0	1	1
2	1	0	0
3	1	1	0

(b) Q = $\bar{A}$.B (line 2 of truth table). See Fig. A14.

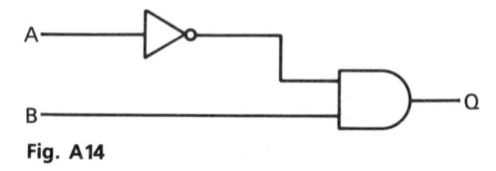

A ———
B ———
——— Q

Fig. A14

(c) See Fig. A15.

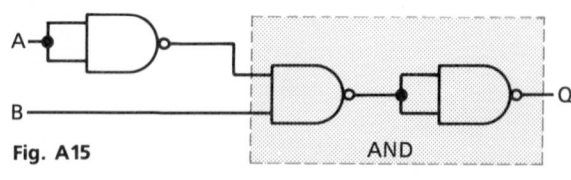

A ———
B ———
——— Q

Fig. A15   AND

29 Binary adders

1 (a) 100, 1101, 10101, 100110, 1000000
(b) 7, 25, 42, 50
(c) 6, B, F, 1F, 53, 12C
(d) 3, 10, 13, 30, 421
(e) 1001, 0001 0111, 0010 1000, 0011 0111 0000, 0110 0100 0101

30 Bistables

1 1 Hz
2 (a) To debounce a switch
(b) Rise and fall-time improver, noise eliminator, pulse generator
3 (a) D is the data input.
CK is the clock pulse input.
Q is the output.
$\bar{Q}$ is the complementary output.
(b) Its output has two possible stable states.
(c) $\bar{Q}$ = 1
(d) Q = 1
(e) Q = 1

31 Counters and decoders

1 (a) (i) $2^1 = 2$, **(ii)** $2^2 = 4$, **(iii)** $2^3 = 8$, **(iv)** $2^4 = 16$, **(v)** $2^5 = 32$
(b) (i) 1, **(ii)** 3, **(iii)** 7, **(iv)** 15, **(v)** 31
2 (a) The number of output states before it resets
(b) (i) 2, **(ii)** 3, **(iii)** 3, **(iv)** 4, **(v)** 5
(c) $f/16$
3 5

32 Memories and registers

1 (a) abcd
(b) ABCD
(c) 1101
2 (c) (i) 512 **(ii)** 64
3 (b) 8

33 Astables and monostables

1 (a) Its output retains its logic level of 1 or 0 until a clock pulse changes its state.
(b) (i) 1, **(ii)** 0, **(iii)** 2
2 (a) See Fig. A16.

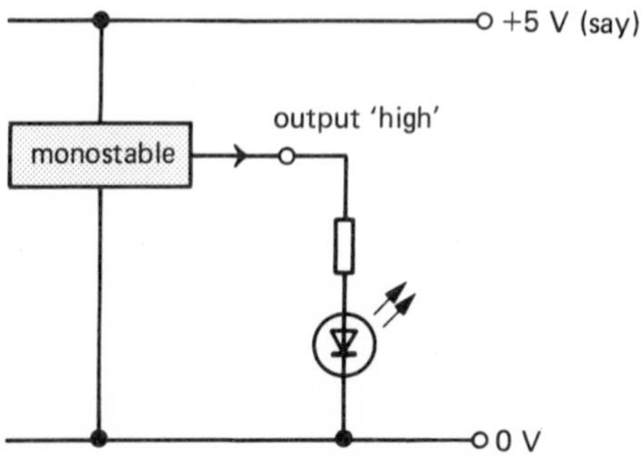

○ +5 V (say)

output 'high'

monostable

○ 0 V

Fig. A16

(b) See Fig. A17.

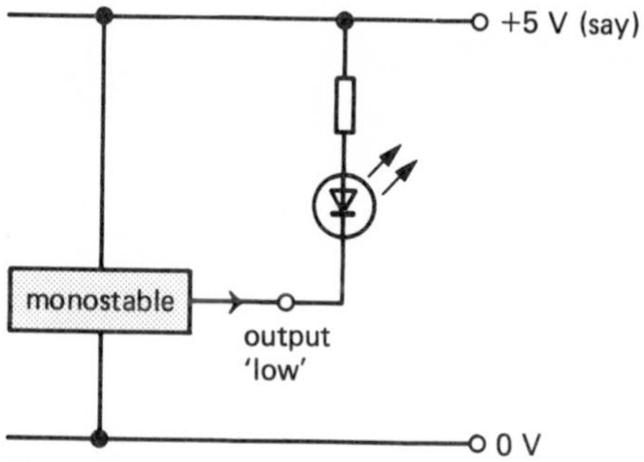

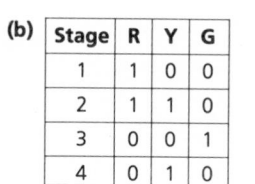

Fig. A17

3 (a) 0.2 s
   (b) 1/0.2 = 5 Hz
   (c) 0.1/0.1 = 1
4 (a) Flashing on and off once per second (on for 1/2 s, off for 1/2 s)
   (b) Flashes twice per second
   (c) Flashes once every 2 seconds

34 Additional questions

1 (a) 0 (near enough)
   (b) 10 V/100 Ω = 0.1 A = 100 mA
   (c) 0 (since Tr short-circuits the load)
   (d) 10 V/500 Ω = 0.02 A = 20 mA
2 (a) Increases
   (b) (i) Decreases, **(ii)** increases
   (c) + 0.6 V
   (d) The temperature at which L comes on can be changed.

3

A	B	C	D	Q
0	0	1	0	1
0	1	1	0	1
1	0	0	0	0
1	1	0	1	1

4 (a) Q = 0
   (b) Q = 1 (otherwise the voltage across the probe is zero)
5 See Fig. A18.

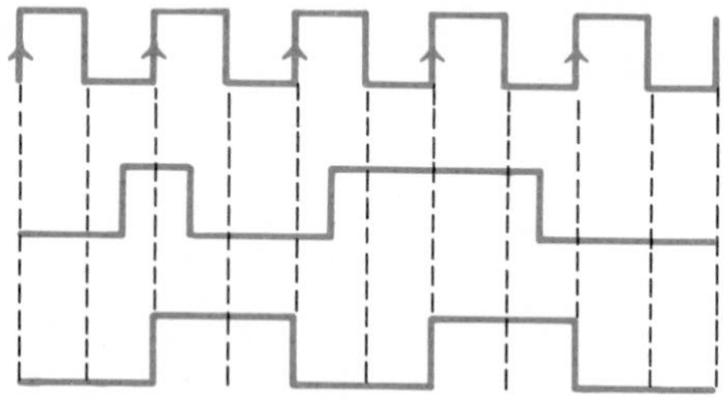

CK input

D input

Q output

Fig. A18

6 (a) See Fig. A19

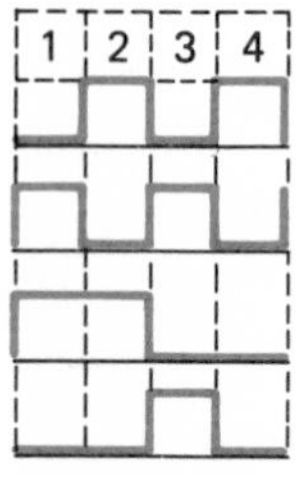

| 1 | 2 | 3 | 4 | Stage |

Output A

Output B

(i) Flip-flop output

(ii) NOR gate output

Fig. A19

(b)

Stage	R	Y	G
1	1	0	0
2	1	1	0
3	0	0	1
4	0	1	0

7 (a) Three-bit binary up-counter which counts from 0 to 7
   (b) $Q_2 = 1$, $Q_1 = 0$, $Q_0 = 1$ (101 = 5 in decimal)
   (c) (i) 80/2 = 40 Hz, **(ii)** 80/4 = 20 Hz, **(iii)** 80/8 = 10 Hz
8 (a) Advantage: very small current needed
       Disadvantage: needs to be illuminated in dark to be seen
   (b) Advantage: can be seen in dark
       Disadvantage: larger current needed than LCD
9 (a) It can store a bit (1 or 0) at its Q output indefinitely.
   (b) 16
10 (a) Increases
    (b) Decreases
11 (a) Tr_2 'on', Tr_1 'off'
    (b) Mains lamp on because Tr_2 is on and causes the relay contacts to close
    (c) C starts to charge up through R and after a certain time the p.d. across it exceeds + 0.6 V and Tr_1 is turned 'on'. The voltage at A falls to zero, switching off Tr_2, the relay and the lamp.
    (d) Change the value of R or C or both.
    (e) To protect Tr_2 from damage by the large voltage induced in the relay coil (due to its inductance) when the collector current in Tr_2 falls to zero at switch-off
    (f) To prevent excessive base currents in Tr_2 destroying it when Tr_1 is off and the voltage at A is + 6 V
    (g) Interchange R with S and C (as in Fig. 27.14).

12 (a)

Line	A	B	C	D	E	F	Q
1	0	0	0	1	1	0	1
2	0	0	1	1	1	0	1
3	0	1	0	1	1	0	1
4	1	0	0	1	1	0	1
5	0	1	1	1	0	1	0
6	1	1	0	0	1	1	0
7	1	0	1	1	1	0	1
8	1	1	1	0	0	1	0

(b) Logic level 0
(c) (i) + 5 V i.e. '1' **(ii)** 0 V. i.e. '0'
(d) S_1 only closed (line 5 in truth table)
     S_3 only closed (line 6)
     none closed (line 8)

13 (a)

A	B	S	C
0	0	0	0
0	1	1	0
1	0	1	0
1	1	1	1

(b) Adds two bits at a time
14 (a) R–S bistable
    (b) (i) R and S **(ii)** Q and $\bar{Q}$
    (c) (i) Q = 1 **(ii)** $\bar{Q}$ = 0
    (d) (i) Q = 1 **(ii)** $\bar{Q}$ = 0

15 See Fig. A20.

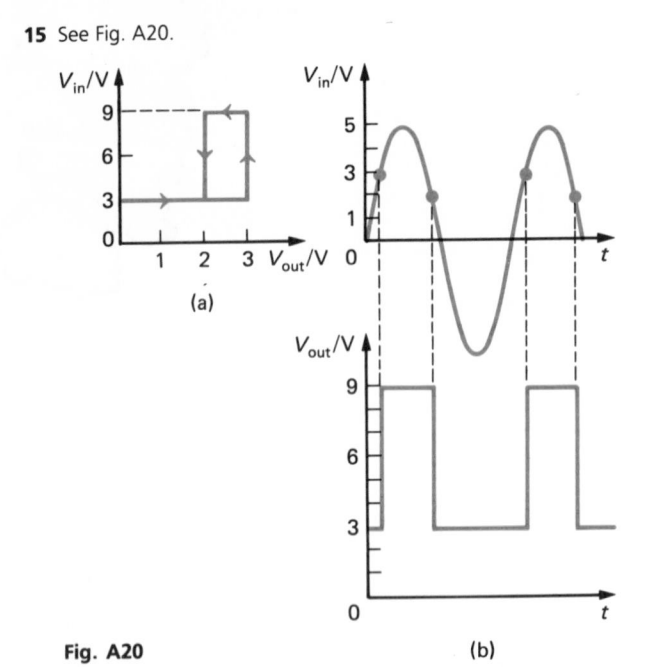

Fig. A20

(a)

(b)

16 See Fig. A21.

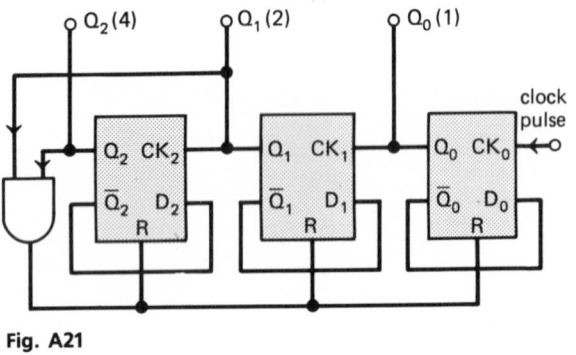

Fig. A21

17 (a) ME = memory enable
WE = write enable
(b) Memory cannot 'read' or 'write' and its outputs are tri-stated, i.e. electrically isolated from the data bus
(c) Set **(i)** address inputs DCBA to 0010,
(ii) $\overline{\text{ME}}$ to 1,
(iii) $\overline{\text{WE}}$ to 0,
(iv) data inputs $I_3 I_2 I_1 I_0$ to 1100,
(v) $\overline{\text{ME}}$ to 0 briefly.
(d) Set **(i)** address inputs DCBA to 1010,
(ii) $\overline{\text{WE}}$ to 1,
(iii) $\overline{\text{ME}}$ to 0 and the stored word should be fed to the data outputs.

18 (a)

R_1 (kΩ)	R_2 (kΩ)	t_1 (s)	t_2 (s)	T (s)	t_1/t_2
0	100	0.7	0.7	1.4	1
50	100	1.05	0.7	1.75	1.5/1
100 Ω	100	1.4	0.7	2.1	2/1

(b) Period of waves
(c) Duty cycle or mark-to-space ratio
(d) $t_1/t_2 = 1$

(e) See Fig. A22.

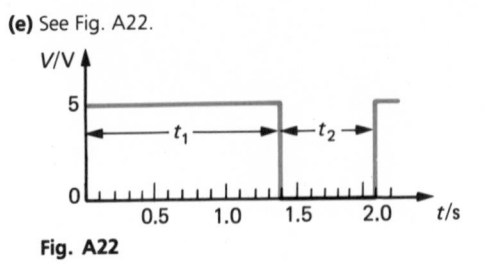

Fig. A22

35 Transistor as an amplifier

1 (a) *npn*
(b) + to A, − to D
(c) E and F
2 (a) To hold the voltage of the collector at about *half* that of the supply voltage so that V_{out} can vary over its maximum possible range (in theory from 0 V to V_s) without distortion, when there is an a.c. input
(b) Supply-to-base, collector-to-base, potential divider
3 (a) $I_B = 2\,\text{mA}/100 = 0.02/\text{mA}$
(b) $R_B = (V_s - V_{\text{BE}})/I_B = (9\,\text{V} - 0.6\,\text{V})/0.02\,\text{mA} = 8.4\,\text{V}/0.02\,\text{mA}$
$= 840/2 = 420\,\text{k}\Omega$

36 Operational amplifiers I

1 (a) (i) $G_V = -20\,\text{k}\Omega/10\,\text{k}\Omega = -2$, **(ii)** $V_{\text{out}} = G_V \times V_{\text{in}} = -2 \times 1\,\text{V} = -2\,\text{V}$
(b) $V_{\text{out}} = -8\,\text{V}$ approx. since op amp will be saturated and cannot exceed maximum of supply negative, i.e. −9 V but is less in practice.
2 (a) +1 V to −1 V
(b) $G_V = +4\,\text{V}/-1\,\text{V} = -4\,\text{V}$
(c) $G_V = -R_F/R_{\text{in}}$, ∴ $R_{\text{in}} = -R_F/G_V = -20\,\text{k}\Omega/(-4) = 5\,\text{k}\Omega$
(d) $4 \times 0.5\,\text{V} = 2\,\text{V}$
(e) See Fig. A23.

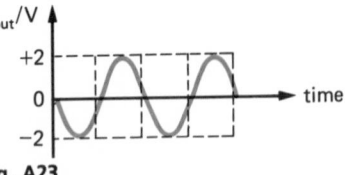

Fig. A23

(f) See Fig. A24.

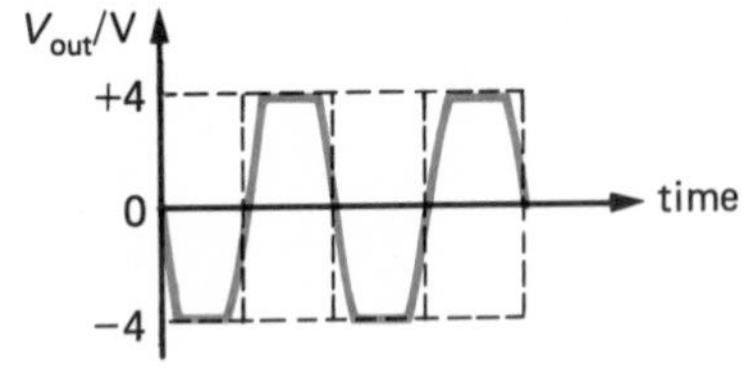

Fig. A24

3 (a) (i) $G_V = 1 + \dfrac{20\,\text{k}\Omega}{10\,\text{k}\Omega} = 1 + 2 = 3$

(ii) +3 V
(b) $V_{\text{out}} = +8\,\text{V}$ approx. since op amp will be saturated and cannot exceed maximum of supply positive, i.e. +9 V.
4 (a)

$$V_{\text{out}} = -R_F\left(\frac{V_1}{R_1} + \frac{V_2}{R_2}\right) = -30\left(\frac{1}{15} + \frac{4}{15}\right) = -30 \times \frac{5}{15} = -10$$

(b)

$$V_{\text{out}} = -30\left(\frac{1}{15} - \frac{4}{15}\right) = -30\left(\frac{-3}{15}\right) = +6\,\text{V}$$

37 Operational amplifiers II

1 (a) $V_1 > V_2$
  (b) (i) Resistance large **(ii)** $V_2 > V_1$ **(iii)** Goes positive
  (iv) Switches on **(v)** Switches on
  (c) Interchange R_1 and LDR.
2 (a) (i) $V_1 = +5\,V$, $\therefore V_1 > V_2$, V_{out} negative **(ii)** C charges up
  through R until $V_1 = -5\,V$, $\therefore V_2 > V_1$, V_{out} positive
  (b) C charges more slowly.
3 (a) Falls, $-5\,V/s$
  (b) Near $-15\,V$ after about 3 s

38 Additional questions

1 (a) (i) B, **(ii)** D, **(iii)** A
  (b) C
2 (a) (i) A is inverting input, **(ii)** B is non-inverting input, **(iii)** C is
  output.
  (b) Dual power supply connections
3 (a) Output voltage is of opposite polarity to the input voltage.
  (b) $G_V = 33\,k\Omega/10\,k\Omega = 3.3$
  (c) $p = 0$, $q = -3.3 \times 2 = -6.6$, $r = +9.9/3.3 = +3$, $s = +13$
  (approx: op amp saturated)
  (d) See Fig. A25

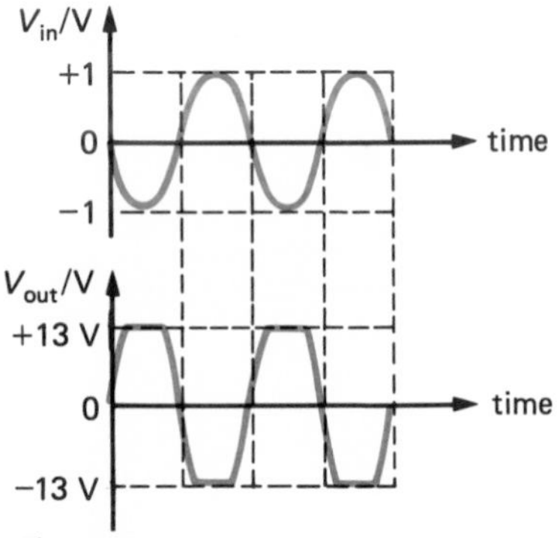

Fig. A25

4 (a) $20\,k\Omega$
  (b) $10\,k\Omega$
  (c) $20\,k\Omega$
5 (a) Non-inverting
  (b) $1 + \dfrac{47\,k\Omega}{10\,k\Omega} = 1 + 4.7 = 5.7$
  (c) $\pm 5.7 \times 100\,mV = 570\,mV$
6 At temperatures *above* $0\,°C$, the resistance of TH is low enough
to make V_1 less than V_2, i.e. $V_2 > V_1$, therefore V_{out} is positive,
e.g. $+13\,V$. D is thus reverse biased, so no current passes in the
relay coil.

At temperatures *below* $0\,°C$, the resistance of TH increases, V_1
becomes greater than V_2, i.e. $V_1 > V_2$, therefore V_{out} becomes
negative, e.g. $-13\,V$. D is now forward biased and current
passes through the relay coil, causing the contact to close and
switch on the heater.

Altering the setting of the potential divider R_2 changes the
temperature at which the heater is switched on.
7 (a) Summing amplifier
  (b) Both have $G_V = 20\,k\Omega/10\,k\Omega = 2$.
  (c) $2 \times (\pm 1\,V) + 2 \times (\pm 3\,V) = \pm 8\,V$
  (d) Potential dividers controlling the inputs to each channel
  (e) To block d.c. but pass a.c.

8 (a) $V_2 = +9\,V\,(24\,k\Omega/36\,k\Omega) = 2/3 \times 9 = +6\,V$
  (b) (i) 0 V since C is short-circuited and 9 V are dropped across R
  due to the current passing through it
  (ii) C starts to charge up through R and the voltage across it, i.e.
  V_1, rises from 0 to $+9\,V$ when it is fully charged. (Voltage across
  R is then 0 V.)
  (c) (i) $V_1 = 0$, $V_2 = +6\,V$, $\therefore V_2 > V_1$ making $V_{out} \approx +8\,V$
  (ii) When $V_1 > 6\,V$, $V_1 > V_2$, making $V_{out} \approx -8\,V$
  (d) When $V_1 < 6\,V$ since then $V_{out} \approx +8\,V$, i.e. after S is released
  and C is charging up from 0 to 6 V
  (e) 10 s, since here $T = CR = 10\,\mu F \times 1\,M\Omega = 10\,s$ = time for
  voltage across C (i.e. V_1) to rise from 0 to 2/3 of 9 V, i.e. to 6 V

39 Information and electronics

1 (a) See Fig. 15.7*a*.
  (b) See Fig. 15.7*b*.
  (c) Microphone, LDR, thermistor
  (d) Switch, keyboard
2 7000 Hz
3 Lower sideband 790–799 kHz
  Upper sideband 801–810 kHz

40 Telephone system

1 See text.
2 See text.
3 See text.

41 Audio systems

1 It causes sound to be produced by a loudspeaker.
2 (a) Changes sound into electrical energy
  (b) Amplifies the small voltage produced by the input voltage
  (c) Adjusts the level of sound from the whole system by
  controlling the input voltage to the power amplifier
  (d) Supplies power to the loudspeaker
  (e) Changes electrical energy into sound
3 (a) To transfer maximum *power* to the loudspeaker
  (b) Push-pull follower
  (c) Crossover distortion
  (d) By applying negative feedback from the push-pull follower
  output to an op amp feeding the push-pull follower
4 (a) (i) A speaker handling low frequencies, **(ii)** A speaker
  handling high frequencies
  (b) To direct low frequencies to the woofer and high
  frequencies to the tweeter
  (c) High and low pass filters

42 Radio

1 (a) See Table 42.1.
  (b) Surface waves, sky waves, space waves
2 (a) RF signals are modified to carry AF signals.
  (b) Sound produces AF signals but only RF signals are radiated
  effectively over a distance by an aerial.
  (c) (i) amplitude modulation (AM), **(ii)** frequency modulation
  (FM)
  (d) AF is separated from RF in the modulated carrier.

3 **(a)** A — aerial, B — tuned circuit, C — RF amplifier, D — demodulator, E — AF amplifier, F — loudspeaker
(b) See text.

4 FM is relatively free of interference and because it is transmitted on VHF, there is room for a wide modulation bandwidth so giving better 'quality' sound.

5 **(i)** Lifeboat service — to direct other craft to scene of rescue if more help needed
(ii) Police — to enable reinforcements to be called to a trouble spot
(iii) Ambulance — to obtain specialist advice at an accident.

43 Television

1 See text and Fig. 43.3*b*.
2 Audio, video, synchronizing, colour
3 **(a)** FM **(b)** AM
4 6.75 MHz
5 By mixing the three primary colours (red, green, blue) in the correct proportions
6 See Chapters 40 and 43

44 Additional questions

1 In emergencies doctors and others can be called even when they are not near a public telephone. Disabled people and those in remote areas can have a telephone. Conversations could be overheard and tapped.
2 **(a)** X — preamplifier
    Y — volume and tone controls
    Z — power amplifier
(b) 5 to 10 mV
(c) Several watts
3 **(a)** A — microphone, B — AF amplifier, C — RF oscillator D — modulator, E — RF power amplifier, F — aerial
(b) They are radiated more efficiently by an aerial and travel further.
4 **(a)** Aerial
(b) Loudspeaker
(c) Tuned circuit
(d) Detector
5 **(a)** **(i)** High pass, **(ii)** low pass, **(iii)** band pass
(b) See Fig. 41.6.
6 **(a)** *L* — inductor (coil), *C* — variable capacitor
(b) Tuned circuit
(c) Select required frequency
(d) To rectify the AM modulated RF carriers so that, with the help of *C*, the AF can be separated from the modulated RF
7 **(a)** A — tuned circuit, B — mixer, C — IF amplifier, D — demodulator, E — AF amplifier, F — local oscillator
(b) Greater sensitivity, i.e. picks up weak signals from more distant stations.
Greater selectivity, i.e. enables stations that are close together to be separated without overlapping.
8 **(a)** $312.5 \times 50 = 15\,625$ Hz **(b)** 50 Hz
9 $25 \times 8 \times 350\,000 = 70\,000\,000 = 70$ Mbits/s

45 Digital computers

1 **(a)** Central processing unit (CPU)
(b) Input device: keyboard
(c) Output device: printer

2 **(a)** RAM and ROM
(b) RAM — read and write, temporary
ROM — read only, permanent
(c) **(i)** ROM **(ii)** RAM
3 **(a)** Payroll, stock control, invoicing
(b) Steel making, oil refining, float-glass production
4 Office work and banking are two areas that are not too difficult to investigate.
5 **(a)** They feel it intrudes on their private lives.
(b) See text.
6 **(a)** **(i)** Greater productivity, **(ii)** Higher profits, **(iii)** More employment and shorter hours due to **(i)** and **(ii)**, **(iv)** Boring and unpleasant work done by computer-controlled machines, **(v)** More people doing socially useful jobs, e.g. health care, teaching, **(iv)** More time and resources for leisure activities
(b) **(i)** Much greater unemployment, **(ii)** Sharper social division between the jobless and the employed leading to antagonism, **(iii)** Devaluation of human work

46 Computer peripherals

1 **(a)** **(i)** Keyboard **(ii)** printer
(b) **(i)** Keyboard **(ii)** screen
2 **(a)** Faster at printing out and more reliable since fewer moving parts
(b) No 'hard copy' and can display only a limited amount of information at one time
3 **(a)** **(i)** Thermistor for temperature measurement, **(ii)** Electric motor to operate a machine
(b) Process control, e.g. steel production
4 **(a)** Its internal memory (RAM and/or ROM) has limited storage capacity; only enough to deal with data being currently processed.
(b) Magnetic tape, floppy disc, rigid disc
(c) Consider magnetic tape and floppy disc. Tape costs much less but has slower data transfer rate and a longer data location time.
5 An interfacing device which allows digital signals from a computer to be sent along telephone lines designed for AF currents. At the sending end it modulates '1s' by converting them into a low audio tone and '0s' into a high audio tone. At the receiving end demodulation occurs and the tones become digital signals again.

47 A/D and D/A converters

1 See text.
2 A four-bit input can take any value from 0 to 15, therefore size of steps = 1.5 V/15 = 0.1 V.
3 See text.

48 Programs and flowcharts

1 **(a)** For example, see Fig. A26.
(b) For example, see Fig. A.27.
2 Similar to Fig. 48.2.
3 Similar to Fig. 48.3.

49 Microprocessors

1 Advantages: more flexible since easily reprogrammed, more easily designed and require less time.
Disadvantages: all facilities may not be used for a particular job.

2 **(a)** Cheaper and fewer parts to assemble, therefore reduced labour and material costs giving more competitive product or greater profits
More reliable, giving better reputation
(b) More flexible and reliable, less frequent repair bills
(c) Servicing quicker and simpler because complete modules are replaced by new ones

3 Fewer parts, therefore assembled more easily and cheaply
More facilities, e.g. date, stop watch and alarm facilities easier to incorporate

50 Additional questions

1 **(a)** Central processing unit
(b) **(i)** To perform, organize and control all the operations of the computer, **(ii)** To synchronize those operations so that they occur in step at the correct time
(c) A — input device, B — output device, C — memory
(d) Coded information

(e) RAM because it may have to be changed, i.e. 'read' and 'write' facilities are required
(f) The sequence of instructions obeyed by the computer
(g) ROM because its contents are only 'read'

2 **(a)** Computers can store much more data which is quickly retrieved and easily transferred to other computers where it might be used for unauthorized purposes to damage the person concerned.
(b) See Chapter 45 'Uses of computers'.

3 **(a)** It allows the user to have two-way communication with the computer and acts as both an input and an output device.
(b) Teletype — to produce 'hard' copy in an office
VDU — travel agent for showing flight and seat availabilities for booking holidays etc.
GDU — CAD by draughtsmen or engineers

4 **(a)** Microphone, thermistor, LDR
(b) Switch, keyboard

5 A five-bit input can have 2^5 values (i.e. 32 values), i.e. from 0 to 31, therefore for steps of 0.1 V, ref. voltage $= 31 \times 0.1\,V = 3.1\,V$.

6 **(a)** A — 4.5 V **(b)** B — 4.5 V **(c)** C — 0.5 V

7 For example, see Fig. A28.

8 **(a)** Digital
(b) To synchronize all operations
(c) Washing machine, cooker, sewing machine, telephone

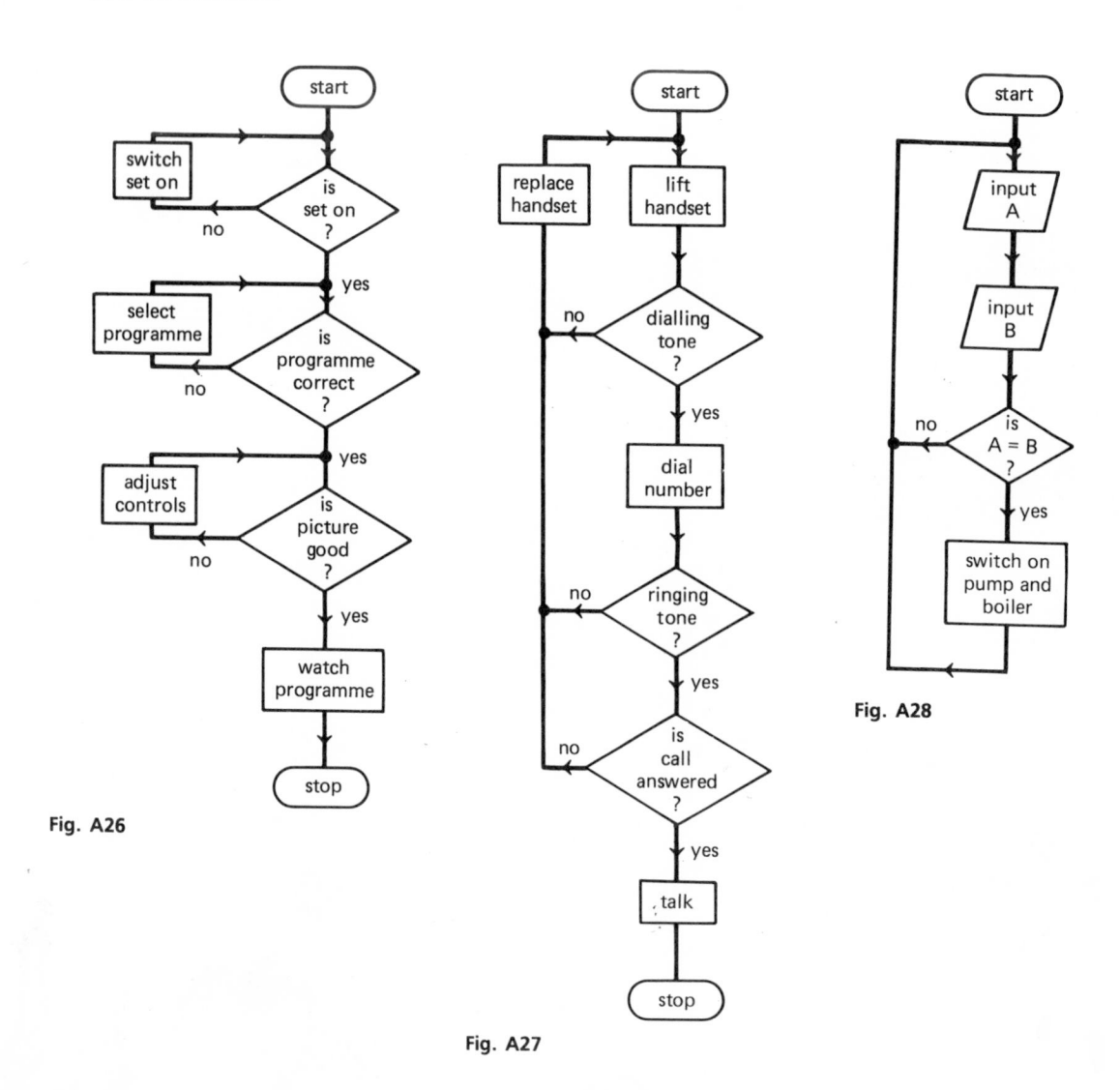

Fig. A26

Fig. A27

Fig. A28

9 (i) Speed — perform millions of operations per second
   (ii) Storage capacity — huge amounts of data can be stored and speedily retrieved
   (iii) Reliability — don't tire or make mistakes if programmed correctly
   (iv) Control — runs automatically and can control other machines and processes

10 (a) VDU
   (b) Bar code reader
   (c) Temperature (thermistor) sensor

11 (a) A = 0, B = 0, C = 0, D = 0
   (b) A = 1, B = 1, C = 0, D = 0
   (c) A = 1, B = 1, C = 1, D = 1

12 (a) For example, see Fig. A29.
   (b) For example, see Fig. A30.
   (c) A/D converter

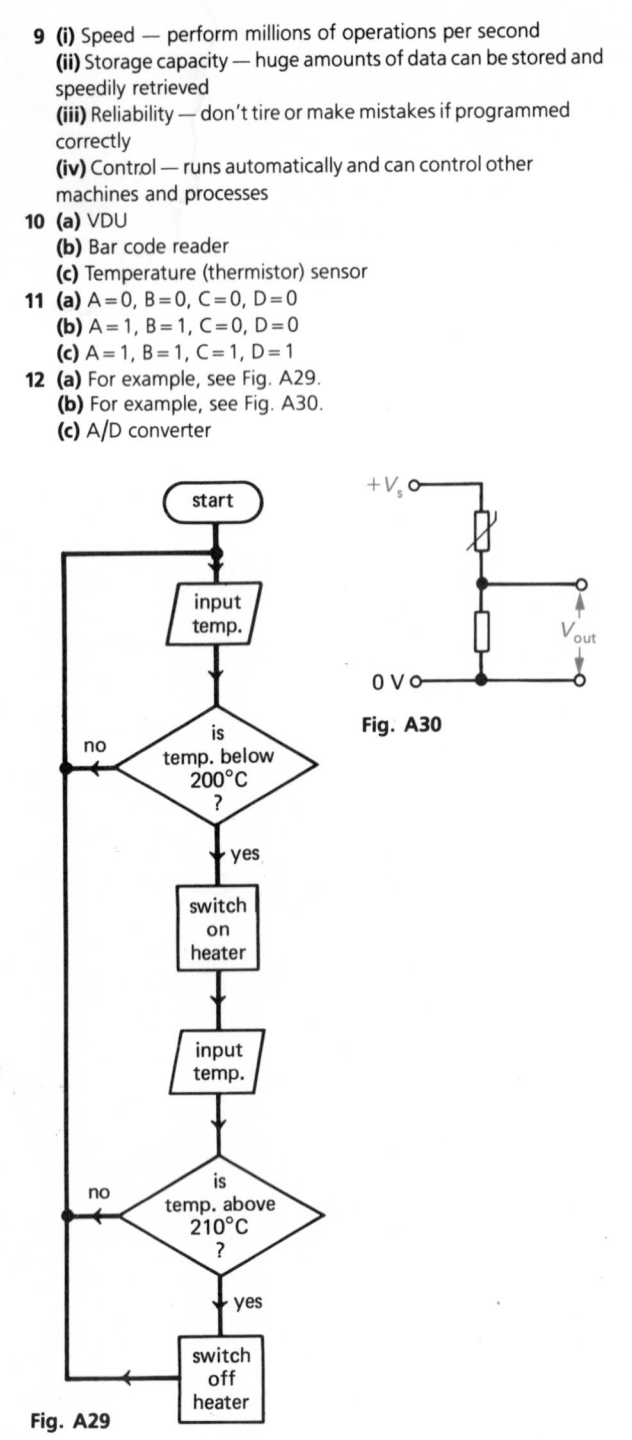

Fig. A29

Fig. A30

Index

Acknowledgements

Thanks are due to the following for permission to reproduce copyright photographs:
Figs. 1.5a, 2.2a. 12.12a, 18.1, 19.1, 23.3b, 23.8b, 24.6b, 24.10b, 24.11b Unilab Ltd.; 2.1a
Ever Ready Ltd.; 3.3a, 3.4a, 9.3a, b, 12.1a, 12.2a, 12.3a, 12.5a, 12.6a, b, c, 12.7a, 12.8a,
12.10a, 13.10a, b, 14.1a, 14.8a, 15.1a, 17.3, 19.3, 19.4, 19.5, 21.6a, 21.7 RS Components
Ltd.; 10.5a Maplin Electronics Ltd.; 17.1 Avo Ltd.; 26.1a SDL Ltd.; 26.1c, 46.2b IBM UK Ltd.;
26.1d, e University of St Andrews; 26.1f, 40.5, 40.8, 40.11, 40.12, 40.14, 40.15, 40.16,
43.10, 43.11 British Telecommunications plc; 40.6 BICC plc; 40.17 Racal-Vodafone Ltd.;
41.2a Sony (UK) Ltd.; 45.3 NCR Ltd.; 45.4 Austin Rover Group Ltd.; 46.1 Ford Motor
Company Ltd.; 46.2a 3M UK plc; 49.2 Texas Instruments Incorporated.

Design by Colin Reed

Technical artwork by RDL Artset

Cover photograph is of a computer graphic taken by Nicholas Foster (Image Bank)

Cover design by Peter Theodosiou